Manual
of
Seamanship

Volume I

B.R. 67(1)

Amendment Nos. 1—4
and other minor revisions have been
incorporated in this reprint.

LONDON
HER MAJESTY'S STATIONERY OFFICE
1951 : Reprinted 1957

1951 *edition published July* 1951
Fourth impression (incorporating
Amendments Nos. 1 *to* 4) . . . 1957

Published by
HER MAJESTY'S STATIONERY OFFICE

To be purchased from
York House, Kingsway, London w.c.2
423 Oxford Street, London w.1
P.O. Box 569, London s.e.1
13A Castle Street, Edinburgh 2
109 St. Mary Street, Cardiff
39 King Street, Manchester 2
Tower Lane, Bristol 1
2 Edmund Street, Birmingham 3
80 Chichester Street, Belfast
or through any bookseller

Price 10s. 0d. net

ADMIRALTY, S.W.1.

1st *January*, 1951

B.R. 67(1), *Manual of Seamanship, Volume I*, 1951, having been approved by My Lords Commissioners of the Admiralty, is hereby promulgated.

By Command of Their Lordships,

J. G. Lang

Preface

The *Manual of Seamanship* is divided into three volumes.

Volume I, herewith, is intended to be used as a text-book for Naval Cadets and Seaman Boys who are under training at shore establishments, and Volume II by junior officers, and by Petty Officers and men desiring to qualify for advancement.

Both these volumes will also serve as books of reference for junior officers and senior ratings, and it is hoped that they will also prove useful and instructive to other professional seamen, yachtsmen, and all instructors of seamanship.

Lists of questions on the information given in each chapter have been included as an appendix to each of Volumes I and II, to give candidates for examination some idea of what they are expected to know and of the type of question they may be asked.

Volume III comprises information on the more advanced aspects of seamanship, and is intended as a book of reference for seamen of experience.

Contents

CHAPTER I

GENERAL SEA TERMS

CHAPTER II

TYPES OF SHIP

CHAPTER III

DESIGN AND CONSTRUCTION OF WARSHIPS: ELEMENTARY SHIP CONSTRUCTION

CONTENTS

CHAPTER IV

ROUTINE, PASSING ORDERS, AND ORGANISATION

CHAPTER V

ROPE AND ITS USAGE

CHAPTER VI

RIGGING

CONTENTS

CONTENTS

CHAPTER XII

CHARTS: BUOYAGE: LIGHTS

CHAPTER I

General Sea Terms

EVERY profession and trade uses its own technical terms to describe the more specialised parts of its work, and nowhere is this more evident than in the language of the seaman.

Many of those used by the British seaman have, in the course of time, become part of the English language. This is because so many of the inhabitants of our small island Kingdom have been born and bred near the sea, and because no other country or empire has for so long been dependent for its existence and prosperity on its Royal and Merchant Navies.

To learn seamanship, the young seaman must first learn the more general nautical terms and expressions which are explained in this chapter. Others, more technical, are dealt with in the chapters on the different aspects of seamanship to which they are applied.

At the end of Volume II of this manual is a glossary which, in addition to giving the terms used by experienced seamen, includes the various phrases by which he expresses himself, and, in some cases, their origins. Such expression, rich in vigour, vividness and humour, characteristically portrays the typical British seaman.

TERMS RELATING TO A SHIP

Terms for the Parts of a Ship

PARTS OF THE HULL

The main body of a ship is called the hull.

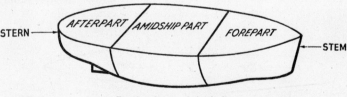

Fig. 1.—Parts of the hull

The length of the hull (see Fig. 1) is divided into three parts—the " fore " part, the " amidship " part in the centre portion of the ship, and the " after " part. The fore part ends in the " stem," and the after part in the " stern."

When standing anywhere inside the hull bear in mind that towards the stem is " forward," and towards the stern is " aft." Any line which runs lengthways in the ship is said to run " fore-and-aft "; the line which joins the stem to the stern is called the " fore-and-aft midship line," because it runs forward and aft and is midway between each side (see Fig. 2). In ships' plans and drawings this line is called the " middle line " or the " centre line."

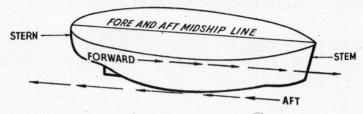

Fig. 2.—Parts of the hull

The fore-and-aft midship line divides the ship into two equal parts. When looking towards the stem, the right hand part is the " starboard " half of the ship, and the left hand part is the " port " half (see Fig. 3). It will be found that objects lying in the port half of a ship are given even numbers while those in the starboard half are given odd numbers.

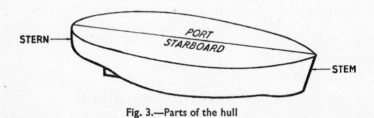

Fig. 3.—Parts of the hull

HULL SURFACES

The hull has a port side and a starboard side. These sides meet at the keel below, and at the stem forward and the stern aft.

When the ship is afloat that part of each side above the water-line is called the " ship's side," and the part below the water-line is called the " bottom."

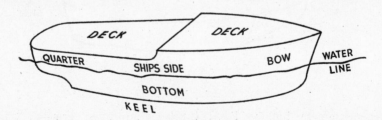

Fig. 4.—Hull surfaces

The hull surface each side of the fore part which curves to meet the stem is called the " bow " (port bow and starboard bow), and the corresponding surface each side of the after part is called the " quarter " (port quarter and starboard quarter).

The continuous horizontal surfaces in ships are called " decks," and those which are not continuous are called " flats " or " platforms." Decks which are exposed to the weather are called " weather decks."

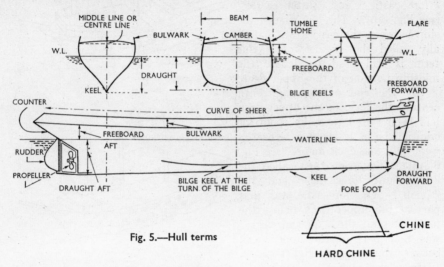

Fig. 5.—Hull terms

HARD CHINE

Terms Applied to the Hull (Fig. 5)

Freeboard is the height above the water-line of the highest continuous water-tight deck (usually known as the upper deck).

Draught is the depth from the waterline to the bottom of the keel at any point along the hull.

The Beam of a ship is the greatest width of her hull.

Sheer is the upward curve in the fore-and-aft line of the surface of the upper deck at the sides of a vessel.

Camber is the curve given to the surface of a deck from side to side so that water will drain off it.

The Bilge of a ship is that part of the bottom each side of the keel which meets the sides. In a normally designed ship the bilge meets the sides in a curve, and this part of the hull is known as " the turn of the bilge." Fast motor craft are built with flat bottoms (for planeing on the surface of the water) ; the bottom meets the sides at an angle known as the " chine," and such craft are said to be " hard-chined."

The sides are said to " tumble home " when they slope or curve inward above the water-line.

When a ship's sides curve outward above the water-line they are said to be " flared."

A ship is said to be " flush-decked " when the uppermost deck of her hull runs in a continuous line from stem to stern, unbroken by any raised or sunken portion (except for upper works or superstructure).

Decks (Figs. 6 and 7)

Whatever the arrangement of decks in different ships may be, it is useful and instructive to know their origin.

At the time of the Armada the ends of the upper deck were built up in two tiers of decks, to form the " fore castle " and " after castle " (see Fig. 6 (i)). The low part of the ship between the castles was naturally called the " waist," and this term is still used to denote the midship portion of the upper deck.

By the end of the eighteenth century the level of the upper deck had been raised to make room for additional gun decks, and the castles were only one deck higher (see Fig. 6 (ii)). They were then called the " topgallant forecastle," and the " poop." The forecastle was that part of the upper deck before the foremast, and the " quarter deck " was that part of the upper deck between the mainmast and the poop.

In a large ship of Nelson's days the waist between topgallant forecastle and poop was filled in by an extra deck, which thus became the upper deck, and the poop was stepped up to make room for the Admiral's quarters. The upper deck was the uppermost of a tier of decks ; those below it were then known as the " main," " middle," " lower " and " orlop " decks, and the space below the orlop deck was known as the " hold " (see Fig. 6 (iii)).

On the upper deck were the " booms," situated amidships over the " main hatch " ; as the name implies, they constituted the stowage for spare spars and also the ship's boats (see Fig. 6 (iv)). Right aft on the main deck (next below the upper deck) were the admiral's cabin and the cabins of his staff, and the space between them and the mainmast was called the " half deck " ; the space between the mainmast and the foremast was the waist, and the space between the foremast and the bows, which housed the kitchens, was known as the " galley " (see Fig. 6 (v)).

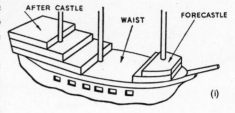

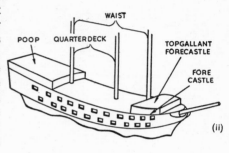

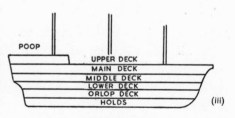

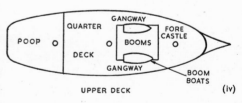

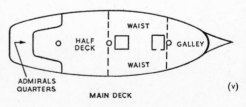

Fig. 6.—Arrangement of decks in a sailing man-of-war

Most of these terms have been retained in naming the decks of a modern warship, and adapted to suit the changes in construction and design.

The decks in the main tier of a large modern ship are named as shown in Fig. 7.

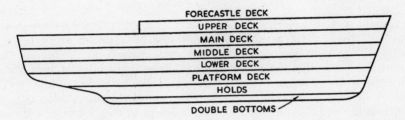

Fig. 7.—Arrangement of decks in a modern battleship

The highest complete deck is known as the upper deck and the lowest space is known as the hold. The names of the intermediate decks vary in accordance with their number, which in turn varies with the size of the ship. A five-decked ship will have forecastle, upper, main, lower and platform decks ; a four-decked ship (*e.g.* cruiser) will have forecastle, upper, lower and platform decks, and a destroyer will have only forecastle, upper and lower decks. The decks of an aircraft carrier are described in Chapter III, page 61.

Parts of Decks (Fig. 8). Certain parts of any of these decks may also have a special name, and when situated below such parts are called " flats " or " lobbies " ; strictly speaking, however, a flat is a platform which does not run the length and breadth of a ship, and a lobby is a space giving access to one or more compartments. The flats and lobbies are named individually according to the principal adjacent compartments, *e.g.* Captain's Lobby, Gunroom Flat.

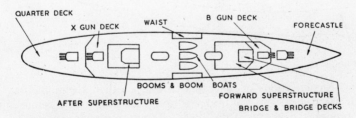

Fig. 8.—Arrangement of weather decks and superstructure of a cruiser

The arrangement of the weather decks and superstructure of a cruiser is shown in Fig. 8. The quarter-deck is the after part of the upper deck, the forecastle the foremost part of the forecastle deck, the waist the amidship portion on each side of the upper deck, and the booms the amidship portion of the forecastle or upper deck, where the boom boats are stowed underneath the crane.

The remainder of the weather decks are named after the type of armament situated in the vicinity, *e.g.* B Gun Deck.

Terms defining Position and Direction within a Ship

POSITION IN GENERAL

The landsman speaks of living IN a house, not ON a house, and naturally the seaman speaks of serving IN a ship—not ON a ship. When he joins her he goes " on board." He ascends the ship's side by a ladder which is rigged " outboard " (*i.e.* projecting beyond and outside the hull). When he steps " inboard " (*i.e.* within the guard rails round the ship's side) he finds himself " on deck." He is given a berth " between decks " (inside the hull) and to reach it he goes " below " (or as a landsman would say, " indoors " and " downstairs "). In a ship " ladders " give access to the decks below through " hatches," which are rectangular openings in the decks.

Positions in a ship are always reckoned in two directions :

(i) *fore-and aft*—*i.e.* relative to the ends of the ship ;

(ii) *athwartships*—*i.e.* across the ship, relative to the sides of the ship.

POSITION FORE AND AFT (Fig. 9)

In Fig. 9 the mast is " forward " (in the front part), and the bridge and funnel are " aft " (in the rear part). Right aft is an ensign staff, and right forward is a jackstaff. A man is standing amidships.

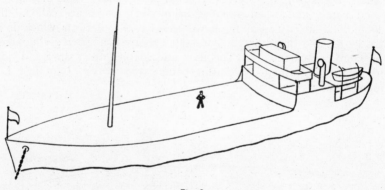

Fig. 9

Comparing positions of objects with one another, the funnel is " abaft " (behind) the bridge, and the bridge is abaft the mast but " before " (in front of) the funnel.

" Midships " describes the position of an object which is midway between the sides of the hull or midway between the stem and stern. The term " amidships " describes the position of an object which is in the amidship portion of the hull as distinct from the fore and after parts.

POSITION ATHWARTSHIPS (Figs. 10 and 11)

Position athwartships can be described relatively to either the fore-and-aft midship line or to the sides. Objects on either side of the fore-and-aft midship line are described as lying to port or starboard. The word " board " used to be the name for the side of a ship, and the terms " inboard " and " outboard " are used in the same way as the terms inside and outside to describe the position of objects relatively to the ship. In Fig. 10, for example, a ship is carrying three boats ; one is swung outboard to port, and the other two are stowed inboard to starboard.

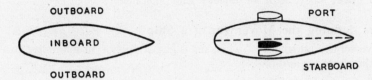

Fig. 10

When comparing the relative positions of the two boats stowed on the starboard side, the black boat can be described as lying inboard of the white boat, and the white boat can be described as lying outboard of the black boat. If, however, there is a risk of confusion between the positions of the boats relative to each other and relative to the ship it would be better to describe the white boat as lying nearer the ship's side.

When two boats' falls (i.e. ropes attached to the forward and after ends of a boat for hoisting her) are lying side by side on deck they are termed the " midship " and the " ship's side " fall respectively.

The position of an object can be clearly described by combining the two methods of reckoning, as shown in Fig. 11.

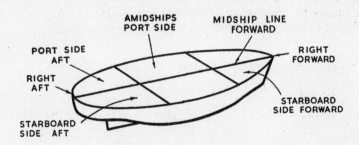

Fig. 11

MOVEMENTS OF OBJECTS ON BOARD

A seaman speaks of going forward, aft, below, on deck, and aloft (i.e. anywhere in the rigging of a mast). He uses the same expressions (always in relation to the ship) for shifting an object ; thus he may shift an object aft, or further forward, to port or starboard, or nearer the ship's side. (The terms inboard and outboard should not be used to describe the movement athwartships of objects within the ship.)

To " launch " is to drag or heave an object along.

To " lift and launch " is to lift the object and then heave it along.

To " ship " is to place an object in its position.

To " unship " is to remove an object from its position.

To " fend off " a boat is to prevent her from striking against anything that might damage her ; hence, " boat's fender."

To " fleet " is to shift an object a short distance.

Terms defining the Movement of a Ship

A vessel is " under way " when she is not at anchor, or made fast to a buoy or to the shore, or aground.

When actually moving through the water, a vessel has " way " on her ; if moving too fast she is said to have " too much way on." When she is moving ahead she is said to be making " headway " and when moving astern she is said to be making " sternway." She is said to " gather way " when she begins to move through the water, and she has " steerage way " when her speed is sufficient for her rudder to take effect.

A vessel moving sideways is said to be moving " broadside-on " (to port or starboard) ; if she is moving ahead and is also being blown sideways by the wind she is said to be making " leeway."

The question " How is the ship's head ? " means " in what direction is she pointing ? "

The " course " is the direction, by compass, in which the ship is being steered.

The " weather side " is the side of the ship facing the wind.

The " lee side " is the sheltered side of the ship.

A ship is described as " adrift " when broken away from her moorings and without means of propulsion. The term adrift also describes any floating object driven at random by wind and tide.

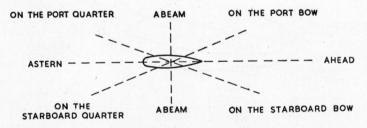

Fig. 12.—General relative bearings

Terms defining Direction and Position of Objects outside the Ship

RELATIVE BEARINGS (Figs. 12 and 13)

" Ahead," " astern " and " abeam " are relative bearings, in that they indicate directions as viewed from the ship and relative to her. In addition, when an object is midway between ahead and abeam it is said to bear " on the bow," and when midway between abeam and astern it is said to bear "on the quarter" (see Fig. 12). These terms are often used to indicate the approximate direction of an object.

A greater degree of accuracy in relative bearings is obtained by expressing them in terms of degrees from ahead to astern on each side of the ship. The horizon is divided in degrees, from zero right ahead to 180 right astern on each side of the ship, and everything to starboard is called green and everything to port is called red.

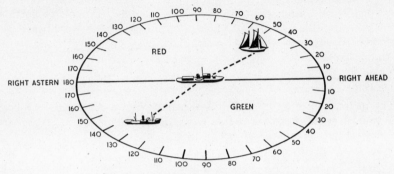

Fig. 13.—Red and green relative bearings

Thus, in Fig. 13, the sailing vessel would be said to bear "red 40" and the steamship "green 130" (the word "degrees" being always omitted).

When two ships are lying side by side they are said to be "alongside" one another. When two ships are on the same course and level with each other they are said to be "abreast" each other.

Fig. 14.—A compass card

COMPASS BEARINGS

These are directions relative to the direction of North, and they are expressed in degrees or by " points of the compass."

The Compass Card (Fig. 14) is divided into 360 degrees from North (zero), through East (090°), South (180°), West (270°), and so back to North. Bearings are always expressed in a group of three figures. The card may also be divided into 32 points each of $11\frac{1}{4}$ degrees. The principal points of the compass are North, East, South and West, which are called " cardinal points "; the " quadrantal points " are North-east, South-east, South-west and North-west; and the " intermediate points " are North-north-east, East-north-east, East-south-east, South-south-east, South-south-west, West-south-west, West-north-west, and North-north-west. The remaining 16 points are known as " by-points."

INCLINATION

The inclination of another ship is the angle between her line of bearing from your ship and her own course. It is measured in degrees from zero to 180, right or left, as illustrated in Fig. 15.

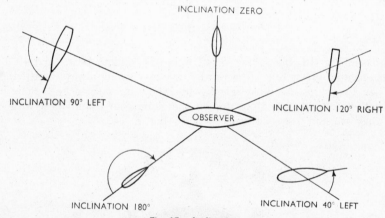

Fig. 15.—Inclination

TERMS RELATING TO SHIPPING, HARBOURS AND DOCKS
Draught and Loading Marks, Tonnage Measurements

DRAUGHT MARKS show the draught of a ship, and are usually painted at the bows and stern. They are cut in by chisel or centre punch and then painted, usually in roman numerals six inches high and six inches apart, or they may be metal figures of similar size welded to the hull. (See Fig. 16.)

23 FT. 6 INS.------ **XXIII**
23 FT.---------

22 FT. 6 INS.------ **XXII**
22 FT.---------

21 FT. 6 INS.------ **XXI**
21 FT.---------

Fig. 16.—Draught marks

When a ship is drawing, say, 22 feet forward and 22 feet 3 inches aft, the water-line at the bows will touch the lower edge of the numeral XXII and reach half way up the numeral XXII at the stern.

PLIMSOLL MARK AND LOAD LINES

These are marks on the sides of merchant ships to denote the greatest depth to which they may safely be loaded under various conditions, in accordance with the Ministry of Transport regulations. They are so named after Samuel Plimsoll, a Member of Parliament who rendered a great service to seamen by introducing these regulations to Parliament which were ratified under the Merchant Shipping Acts of 1876 and 1890. (See Fig. 17.)

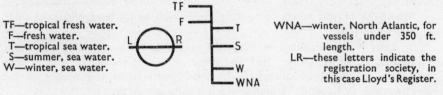

TF—tropical fresh water.
F—fresh water.
T—tropical sea water.
S—summer, sea water.
W—winter, sea water.

WNA—winter, North Atlantic, for vessels under 350 ft. length.
LR—these letters indicate the registration society, in this case Lloyd's Register.

Fig. 17.—Plimsoll mark and load lines

Load Water Line is a term chiefly used in H.M. ships to denote the position of the water-line when the ship is fully loaded with crew, stores, water, fuel, etc.

TONNAGE MEASUREMENTS

The tonnage of a ship can be expressed in terms of weight or of volume. When expressed by weight the unit of measurement in Great Britain is the " avoirdupois " ton of 2,240 pounds, and when expressed by volume the unit is a ton of 100 cubic feet. The tonnage of a vessel can be measured in a variety of ways, of which the following are the more usual :—

Displacement, which is the actual weight of the vessel represented by the number of tons weight of water she displaces when loaded with fuel, water, stores and crew on board. It is seldom used for merchant ships because of the great difference in their displacement when fully and lightly loaded. It is, however, the usual method of describing the tonnage of warships.

The following are various types of displacement in common use with the conditions they represent :—

DISPLACEMENT   CONDITIONS

SURFACE SHIPS

Deep or   Ship complete, fully equipped, and ready for sea as a fighting
Full Load.   unit.

Average   An assumed average battle condition in which part fuel and
Action   certain other items are considered consumed.

Standard   As Deep, but without fuel and reserve feed water.

Light   As Deep, with ammunition but without fuel, water, provisions
               and consumable stores.

SUBMARINES

Submerged   The weight of water displaced by the form of the ship totally
               immersed and which includes water in main ballast tanks
               but excludes water in free flooding spaces.

Surface   As Submerged, less main ballast tank water only.

Standard   As Submerged, less all fluids.

Gross Tonnage, which is the measure of the total internal volume of a ship reckoned in tons of cubic capacity. It is the usual method of expressing the tonnage of merchant ships.

Net Register Tonnage, which represents the earning capacity of a merchant ship and is a measure, in tons of cubic capacity, of that portion of her internal volume which can be used for carrying cargo or passengers. In other words it is her gross tonnage, less the spaces occupied by such items as the machinery, crew, bridge and cable lockers. This measurement is usually employed when computing costs such as harbour and port dues, and canal tolls.

Dead Weight Tonnage, which is the measurement in weight of the cargo, passengers, crew, stores, fuel and water which a vessel can carry when floating at her load draught. In other words it is the weight of the removable or expendable items which a ship can carry.

TONS PER INCH IMMERSION is the number of tons weight necessary to increase the overall draught of a ship by one inch. It will vary with the waterplane area of a ship at different draughts.

Docks, Basins, and Slips

A Dry Dock or Graving Dock (Fig. 18) is an excavation, faced with solid masonry, which is connected with a harbour, river or basin, and is of sufficient length, breadth and depth for ships of the size for which it is designed to be floated into it. Water is admitted through valves ("penstocks") to flood the dock, and after the ship is floated in and the entrance closed the water is pumped out, thus leaving the ship dry, resting on "keel blocks," and supported by "breast shores" and "bilge shores." Side keel blocks, and sometimes "cradles" in the wake of (below) concentrated weights, are also used for the heavier ships.

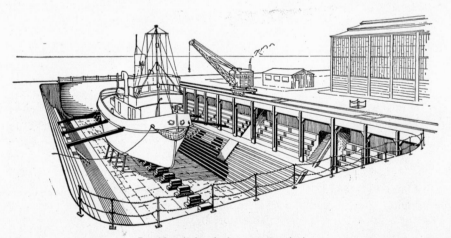

Fig. 18.—A dry dock or graving dock

The entrance is closed by a sliding "caisson" (pronounced *cassoon*), floating caisson, or "dock gates."

Some small dry docks are dependent on the rise and fall of tide to flood and drain them. The vessel to be docked is floated in at high water; the gates are then closed and, as the tide falls, the water is drained out through valves and the vessel settles on the blocks. When the dock is dry the drain valves are closed to prevent the water coming in as the tide again rises.

The processes of moving a ship into and out of a dry dock are called " docking " and " undocking," respectively.

A Floating Dock (Fig. 19) is a floating water-tight structure serving the same purpose as a dry dock, and it is capable of being submerged sufficiently to receive a floating ship by admitting water into the " pontoon tanks " which form the bottom of the dock.

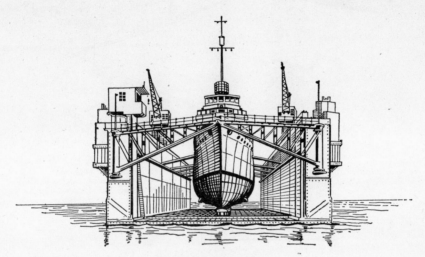

Fig. 19.—A floating dock

When the dock is sunk to a sufficient depth the ship is brought in and secured ; the pontoon tanks are then pumped out to the extent required to raise the dock until its " pontoon deck " and the ship are clear of the water. The ship rests on blocks on the pontoon deck and is supported by shores, as when in a dry dock.

A Basin or Wet Dock (Fig. 20) is an area of water which, except for its entrance is enclosed with walls of masonry and excavated to a sufficient depth to take floating ships. The water is shut in by caissons or gates, and is kept at a level sufficient to ensure that ships in it remain afloat irrespective of the level of the water outside. The entrance is usually through a " lock."

A Lock for a basin or wet dock is an excavated channel or approach, faced with masonry and fitted at each end with a caisson or gates through which ships can be floated to or from tidal waters without appreciably altering the level of the water in the dock or basin. Some locks are designed for use as dry docks.

In tidal waters a ship can, usually, only be locked in or out of a basin, or docked and undocked in a dry dock, at certain states of the tide.

A Camber is a made-up strip of foreshore which slopes into the water from above high water level to well below low water level. It is used for hauling up boats clear of the water for repair or refitting (see " patent slip "). The term is also applied to a small " dock " or " tidal basin " which has an open entrance and may dry out as the tide recedes.

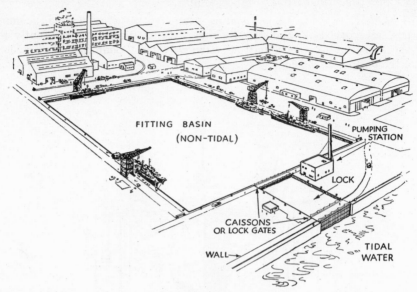

Fig. 20.—A basin or wet dock

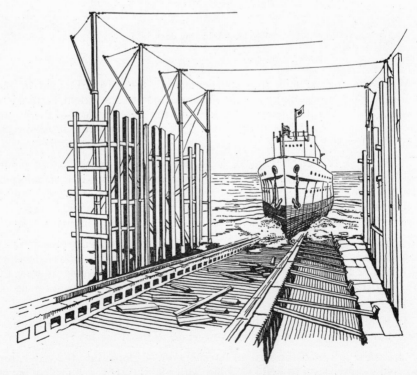

Fig. 21.—Launching a ship from a slipway

A Slipway (Fig. 21) is a sloping platform, erected on the foreshore of a deep river or estuary, on which ships are built and from which they are launched. It slopes down into the water, extends well beyond and below the water's edge, and is provided with " launching ways," " groundways " and " sliding ways " on which rests a " cradle " for supporting the hull of the ship while she is built. On launching, the cradle is released so that it slides down the slipway with the ship until she becomes waterborne.

A Patent Slip (Fig. 22) consists of a sloping runway, of masonry or concrete, which reaches well down into the water at high tide and has rails laid on it on which travels a cradle fitted with a wheeled carriage. The cradle is run out to receive the vessel and, when she is resting in it, the carriage is hauled up the runway by means of winches until she is clear of the water.

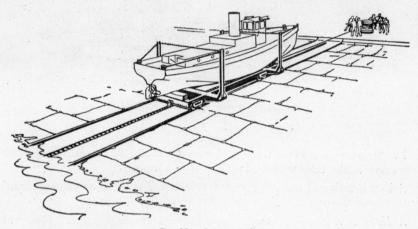

Fig. 22.—A patent slip

A Marine Railway is the term usually applied in Canada and the United States of America to a patent slip.

A Gridiron (or *Grid*) usually consists of baulks of timber which are laid parallel with one another and secured on the foreshore, below high water mark, in such a position that a vessel can be moved on to the grid at high water and left dry and resting on it at low water.

Jetties, Piers and Similar Structures

A Jetty is a platform built out from the shore, on piles, to reach water of sufficient depth for ships to berth alongside it.

A Pier is a narrow jetty which is built of masonry or on piles and usually extends seaward at right angles to the line of the shore. It may be used as a breakwater, or as berths for shipping.

Pens are bays, formed by a series of jetties or piers, for accommodating a large number of small ships in berths alongside.

A Mole or Breakwater is a long pier of heavy masonry built out on the seaward side of a harbour for protection ; it may be designed for berthing ships on its shoreward side.

Groins are of timber and board construction, and are built out on the foreshore between high and low water marks to prevent coast erosion by the scouring action of the sea.

Miscellaneous

Piles are baulks of timber with steel-pointed shoes which are driven into the harbour bottom. They are used for the foundations for the platforms of piers and jetties, or for facing the sides of concrete wharves. Some piles are made of steel sections which are embedded in rock and concrete.

Dolphins (Fig. 23) are mooring posts driven into the bottom of a harbour.

Fig. 23.—A cruiser moored to dolphins

The Stream is a general term used to describe the navigable channels and anchorages in the tidal waters of a river or an estuary.

A Trot is a line of moored buoys to which a number of small ships can be secured head and stern.

A Hard is a made-up strip of foreshore, sometimes built up over mud, which is used as a landing place for boats at low water.

A Creek is a narrow inlet or arm of the sea.

A Cove is a small bay, the greater part of which is land-locked.

A Floating Bridge is a form of ferry which is warped from shore to shore by hauling on wires or chains laid across the bed of the channel or river.

A Warp is a hawser, extending between ship and shore, by means of which a ship can be moved from one position to another without using her engines. The process of moving a ship in this manner is known as " warping."

Winding is a term used to describe turning a ship end for end when she is berthed alongside.

A Lighter is a vessel used for transporting cargo or stores to or from a ship.

A Dumb Lighter is a lighter without the means of self propulsion.

The Turn Around of a merchant ship is the period between her arrival and departure at her " terminal ports."

A Brow is a narrow platform forming a gangway between ship and shore ; it is called a " gang-plank " when laid between ship and ship.

A Pontoon can be any floating structure which may be used as a buoyant support. It may be used in salvage work to buoy up a damaged vessel, or it may be used to support a bridge across water. In tidal waters a flat-topped pontoon is used as a landing place for boats and ferries on a muddy foreshore, or alongside piers and jetties where the range of the tide is considerable ; such pontoons are connected with the shore or the jetty by a hinged bridge.

Between Wind and Water is a term used to describe that part of a ship's side near the water-line which is alternately submerged and exposed by the movement of the waves and the rolling of the ship. This term is also used to describe that part of sea walls, piles, etc., which is uncovered between high and low water.

Careening is a term used to describe the operation of exposing part of a ship's bottom for cleaning or repairs. This is done either by moving weights across the ship's deck so that she lists, or, if a small ship or boat, by allowing her to ground in shoal water on a falling tide. In tideless waters a small vessel can be careened by securing a heavy lighter alongside her, and then rigging tackles from her masthead to the lighter and heaving down on them so that they heel the vessel over.

SEA MEASURES

One *fathom* is equal to 6 feet. The fathom is the general unit of measurement for ropes, hawsers, depths of water and soundings.

One *cable* is equal to one-tenth of a nautical or sea mile and measures 608 feet, or roughly 200 yards. It is the unit of measurement for short distances. (The length of a ship's hempen anchor cable was formerly 101 fathoms, but nowadays the lengths of ships' anchor cables vary with the type and size of the ship and therefore have no relation to the cable measure.)

One *nautical mile* or *sea mile* is equal to 6,080 feet, or roughly 2,000 yards. It is the unit of measurement for long distances.

One *knot* is equal to a speed of one nautical mile per hour and is the unit of measurement of speed. A ship may be said, for example, to be " steaming at 15 knots." (The expression " knots per hour " is incorrect and should never be used to describe speed.)

CHAPTER II

Types of Ship

S HIPS, both warships and merchant ships, can be classified under "type" and "class." The term "type" is used to distinguish between ships built for different purposes, *e.g.* battleships, cruisers, liners, freighters, tankers, etc. The term "class" is used to distinguish between different ships of the same type, *e.g.* "Colony class cruisers," "Engine-aft freighters," etc.

Different types of ships can be recognised by certain distinctive features in their general appearance, because the general design of a ship depends mainly on the work she is required to perform. For example, the chief considerations in the design of a freighter are maximum carrying capacity, easy handling of cargo, and low running costs; but speed, manœuvrability and maximum hitting power govern the design of a cruiser, and so they differ widely in appearance.

In this chapter the distinctive features of the various types of warship, merchant ship, vessels and craft are described, and a glossary of the more common terms applied to the structure of a ship and her equipment is included to assist the novice in recognising the general features of any ship. *Many of these terms are applicable to several types of ships, and they should therefore not be read as referring only to the particular type of ship illustrated above them.*

WARSHIPS

The Battleship (Fig. 24)

Battleships carry the heaviest guns and combine great hitting power with fairly high speed and very heavy armour protection. They can be recognised by their great size; and by their upper works, which are concentrated amidships round the funnels so as to leave a clear field of fire for the turret guns. They displace from about 30,000 to 50,000 tons and are from about 600 to 900 feet long.

BRIDGE   A high superstructure from which the ship is navigated, and her armament largely controlled.

18

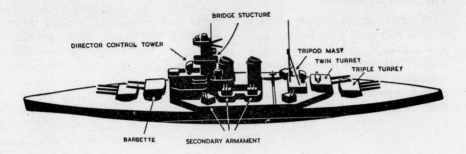

Fig. 24.—A battleship

TRIPOD MAST	A mast which is supported by two steel struts, instead of by rigging. This mast may carry control platforms, signal gear and other equipment.
DIRECTOR CONTROL TOWER	Protected revolving tower in which gunnery control instruments are situated.
ARMAMENT	Guns, torpedoes and other weapons carried by a warship. The main armament usually refers to the largest calibre guns, and the secondary armament to the next largest.
TURRET	Revolving box-like structure, housing one, two, three or four guns. A " twin turret " has two guns, a " triple turret " three, and a " quadruple turret " four guns.
BARBETTE	Circular armoured structure, surrounding gun machinery and surmounted by a turret.
ARMOUR	Hardened-steel plating, provided to withstand enemy shells, torpedoes, mines or bombs. It is fitted to the sides, decks, turrets, bridge, and other vital parts.
FLAG SHIP	Ship of a fleet or squadron which flies an admiral's flag, or the broad pennant of a Commodore.

The Aircraft Carrier

Aircraft carriers provide offensive power at very long ranges by using their aircraft to attack with bombs, rockets, torpedoes and mines. Their aircraft also intercept and destroy enemy air attack and air reconnaissance, and provide long-range reconnaissance for their own fleet. They carry defensive armament, but rely on the battle fleet for protection against enemy surface craft and submarines. Carriers may be recognised by the "flat-top" flight-deck. They displace from 20,000 to 50,000 tons and are from 700 to 1,000 feet long.

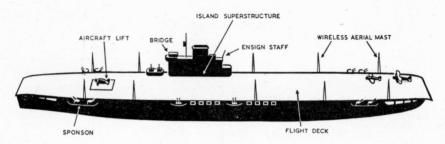

Fig. 25.—An aircraft carrier

FLIGHT DECK	Long flush uppermost deck of an aircraft carrier, used by aircraft for taking-off and landing.
ISLAND SUPERSTRUCTURE	Compact mass of superstructure (bridge, funnel, etc.) on the flight deck, usually on the starboard side.
SPONSON	Projection from the ship's side, usually for guns.
WIRELESS AERIAL MASTS	Light masts provided solely to support wireless aerials. Usually placed at the sides of the flight deck, and lowered outboard when flying is in progress.
WINDSCREENS	Collapsible or portable screens on the flight deck to shield aircraft from weather.
ENSIGN STAFF	Light pole from which the ensign is flown.
FLOATS AND RAFTS	Life-saving appliances carried in conspicuous and readily accessible positions.
AIRCRAFT LIFT	Power-operated platform for carrying aircraft up and down between the flight deck and the hangars below.
HANGAR	Accommodation for aircraft, below the flight deck.

The Cruiser

Cruisers are general purpose fighting ships and usually have great radius of action. They combine hitting power with speed and manœuvrability, and their turrets mount medium-sized guns which can be used effectively in all weathers. They can be recognised by their long and conspicuous upper works, and they displace from 4,000 to 16,000 tons and are from 450 to 700 feet in length.

Fig. 26.—A cruiser

POLE MAST	Vertical or raked tubular mast, in the form of a single pole.
FUNNEL	Tubular structure which carries smoke or engine exhaust clear of the ship. It may be raked or vertical, and of round, oval or pear-shaped cross-section. In a combined funnel, two or more funnels merge into one structure.
RAKED	Inclined from the vertical. The masts and funnels, and the stem and stern of a ship may be raked.
FUNNEL COWL	Cowl on the top of the funnel to deflect smoke and fumes away from the bridge and control positions.
BREAKWATER	Low barrier on the forecastle which prevents water sweeping aft along the deck in heavy weather or when steaming at high speed.
CATAPULT	Mechanical device for launching aircraft from a ship. It can be fixed or rotating.
CRANE	Lifting apparatus for handling aircraft, boats and other heavy weights.
BATTERY	A particular group of guns.
SUPERIMPOSED TURRET	A turret placed above another turret, so that its guns can fire over the top of the lower turret.
SQUADRON	A number of warships grouped into a unit under one command.

The Fleet Destroyer

Fleet destroyers, besides giving anti-submarine protection to the larger ships of the fleet, operate offensively in attacking the enemy with torpedoes. They are also the "messengers" of the fleet. In normal weather destroyers can achieve a high maximum speed, but their comparatively small size may necessitate a considerable reduction of speed in heavy weather. Recognised by their long, high forecastle, and lower upper deck, with long superstructures forward and aft. They displace from 2,500 to over 3,000 tons, and are about 360 feet in length.

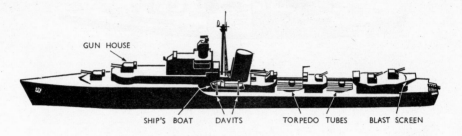

Fig. 27.—A fleet destroyer

TORPEDO TUBES	Tubes for firing torpedoes. They are fixed or rotating, and are mounted singly or in sets up to five, usually on the centre line in destroyers.
GUN HOUSE	Steel house enclosing the mounting and mechanisms of a gun, and accommodating the gun's crew.
BLAST SCREEN	Lip-shaped projection of a superstructure, mounting guns, which protects the deck or other guns below it from the blast of the guns on the superstructure.
SHIP'S BOATS	Boats carried by a ship, either at davits or in crutches on the booms; they include power-driven as well as pulling and sailing boats.
DAVITS	Curved steel supports, fitted in pairs at the ship's side, for carrying, launching and hoisting boats.
FLOTILLA	Two or more squadrons of destroyers, or smaller vessels, under one command.

The Submarine

Submarines attack the enemy's warships, fleet auxiliaries, troopships and merchantmen, but do not usually operate in company with the fleet. They also reconnoitre far in advance of the battle fleet, or off the enemy's coasts, and report his movements. They may displace from 250 to as much as 4,000 tons, and they vary in length from about 140 to over 300 feet.

Fig. 28.—A submarine

CONNING TOWER	A prominent superstructure projecting above the main hull of a submarine from which she is directed when on the surface.
PERISCOPE	Long vertical tube which can be raised or lowered at will and encloses a system of lenses and mirrors which gives an observer in a submerged submarine a view over the surface of the sea. Usually two periscopes are fitted, both projecting from the conning tower.
PERISCOPE STANDARDS	Fixed guides for the periscopes.
PRESSURE HULL	The inner hull of a submarine, which is constructed to withstand the pressure of water at the greatest depth for which the submarine is designed.
NET CUTTER	Hard-steel structure, fitted on the bow of a submarine, to enable her to cut through underwater nets and similar defences.
JUMPING WIRES	Wire ropes, leading from periscope brackets to bow and stern, to prevent the submarine from fouling nets, hawsers, mines and other obstructions.

Frigates

The term " frigate " is used nowadays to describe the three types of vessels known in the Second World War (1939–45) as sloops, frigates and corvettes. The vessels are smaller than destroyers and less heavily armed, and they do not carry torpedoes. They are classed as first, second and third rates according to their size, which ranges from about 1,000 to over 2,000 tons.

Their chief duties are to provide squadrons or convoys with protection against submarine and aircraft attack, and they differ in type according to the duties for which they were designed, e.g. anti-submarine or anti-aircraft. They may also be used, singly or in groups, to detect and hunt down enemy submarines in the open sea.

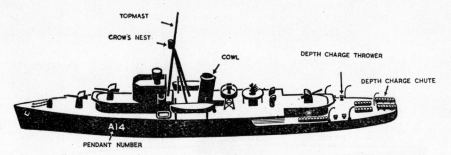

Fig. 29.—An anti-submarine frigate

TOPMAST	Lightly constructed, wooden upper mast.
CROW'S NEST	Barrel-shaped fitting on the foremast to protect the seaman look-out from the weather.
YARD	Spar rigged athwart a mast, nowadays used solely for signalling.
HALYARD	Light line, rove through a small block at the yard-arm or mast-head, for hoisting signal flags.
HOIST	Any group of signal flags or pennants which are " hoisted " at one time.
CALL SIGN	A letter and number from the signal code which are allotted to each unit of the fleet, and by which each unit is identified in naval signalling. In flag signalling, a ship identifies herself by hoisting the flags and pennants which represent her call sign.
GUN SHIELD	Steel plate structure fixed to the front of a gun to protect the working parts and gun's crew from shell splinters and the weather.
SILHOUETTE	Broadside outline of a ship. A " low silhouette " describes a ship of low free-board with low superstructures.
DEPTH CHARGE THROWER	Mortar-like mounting on the quarter deck, which fires depth charges well clear of the ship. Other depth charges are carried on rails and released from " chutes " over the stern.
DEPTH CHARGE RACKS	Racks near the stern to carry depth charges.
SWEEP	Wire rope device towed astern for cutting the mooring ropes of buoyant mines. Other forms of sweep deal with magnetic and acoustic mines.

DAN BUOY

Small buoy with a long thin spar to which is attached a large flag. It is generally used temporarily to mark swept channels and other areas.

Landing Ships and Craft

Special ships and craft of many types designed for landing assault forces and their guns, tanks, equipment and stores. These ships and craft vary widely in displacement and length, the largest of each type displacing about 4,000 and 600 tons respectively.

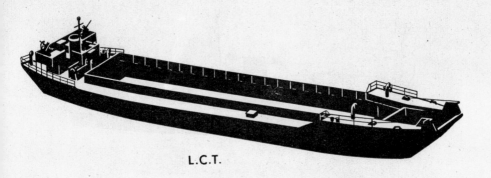

L.C.T.

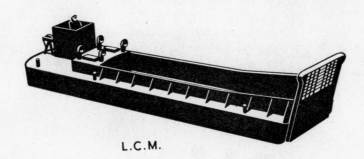

L.C.M.

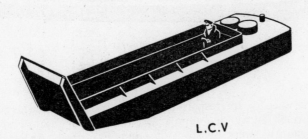

L.C.V

Fig. 30.—Landing craft (T—tanks, M—mechanised vehicles, V—vehicles)

Coastal Forces

These consist of motor torpedo boats, motor gunboats, motor launches, and other small vessels specially designed to operate in coastal waters off our own or the enemy's coast. They are built in large numbers to harass his coastal trade, or raid his coastal defences and harbours, and are also used to protect our own coastal shipping and harbours. They are very fast and highly manœuvrable.

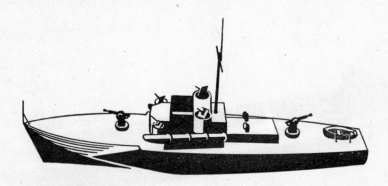

Fig. 31.—A motor torpedo boat

Minelayers

Some ships are specially constructed for laying mines. Mines can also be laid by aircraft, or by specially equipped submarines, destroyers and coastal craft.

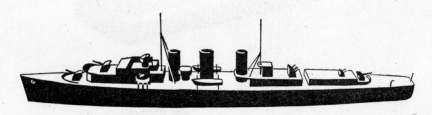

Fig. 32.—A minelayer

Minesweepers

Fleet minesweepers are responsible for sweeping mines wherever a fleet may be operating. In war the approaches to our commercial ports and naval bases are constantly swept by specially equipped armed trawlers and motor minesweepers working from coastal bases. They vary in size from the 1,200 tons displacement and 225 feet length of the fleet sweeper, to the 750 tons displacement and 150 feet length of the trawler.

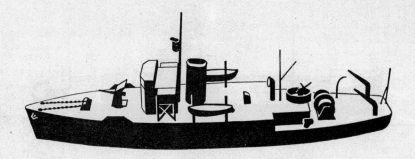

(i) A fleet minesweeper

(ii) A trawler minesweeper

Fig. 33.—Minesweepers

Harbour Craft

As their name implies, these are small craft designed to operate only in sheltered waters. They include a great variety of craft such as tugs, barges, launches, lighters, mooring lighters and tenders.

Fleet Auxiliaries

In ocean warfare the battle fleet may remain at sea for long periods, working many thousands of miles from its main bases. Fleet auxiliaries include depot and repair ships, tankers, store ships, hospital and other ships, which are equipped to supply the needs of the fleet at advanced anchorages and bases, and to replenish it at sea when necessary. They may range up to about 15,000 tons displacement, and most can only be distinguished from merchantmen by the colour of their paint work, and by their ensigns, minor details of their equipment and fittings. When a number of auxiliaries are concentrated for the purpose of supplying the needs of a fleet they are known collectively as the " Fleet Train."

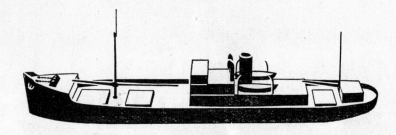

(i) A storeship

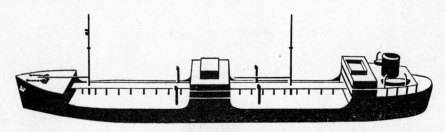

(ii) A fleet tanker

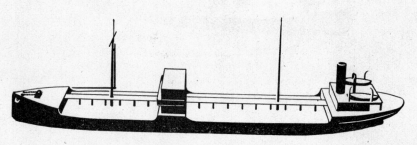

(iii) A harbour tanker (water or fuel)

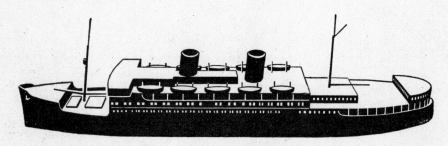

(iv) A transport

Fig. 34.—Fleet auxiliaries

MERCHANT SHIPS

Merchant vessels are more difficult to classify by type than warships because their duties are more numerous and varied, and one type of ship may often be used for many different purposes. Generally speaking, however, they belong to one or other of the following main types.

A Typical Merchant Ship

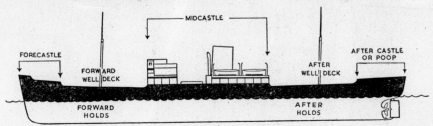

Fig. 35.—A typical merchant ship

HULL FORM	The type and shape of the hull.
AFTERCASTLE OR POOP	A raised portion of the hull at the after end of a merchant ship.
MIDCASTLE	A raised portion at the centre of the hull of a merchant ship.
WELL DECK	That portion of a merchant ship's upper deck between the forecastle and the midcastle, or the poop and midcastle.
HATCHES	Openings in the decks above the holds through which cargo is lowered and hoisted. When at sea they are covered with hatchboards supported on steel beams and covered with "tarpaulins" (sheets of tarred canvas).
CARGO	Any goods a ship carries in her holds. Cargoes of loose grain, coal, coke and mineral ores are termed "bulk cargo." When miscellaneous goods are carried they are termed "general cargo." Cargo may occasionally be carried on deck, when it is known as "deck cargo."
BALLAST	Water, sand, etc., carried in the bottom of a ship to make her seaworthy when carrying little or no cargo. The majority of vessels carry water ballast in tanks constructed under the flooring of the holds. Fuel-oil is also carried in similar tanks.
IN BALLAST	Term applied to a ship which has little or no cargo in her holds.

The Passenger Liner

Passenger liners are designed for the passenger carrying trade between the principal ports of the world. They vary in size from about 10,000 tons gross to the 84,000 tons gross of the *Queen Elizabeth*, and carry comparatively little cargo because most of their capacity is devoted to accommodation for passengers and their baggage, food and stores. Their speed varies from about 14 to 30 knots or more, and for this reason they usually carry mails as well. They can be distinguished by their size and long, high upper works, and, at night in peace-time, by the blaze of lights shining from their hulls and superstructures.

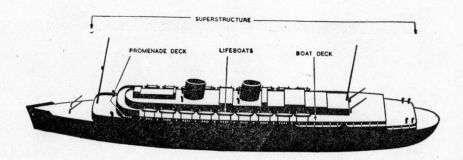

Fig. 36.—A passenger liner

SUPERSTRUCTURE OR UPPERWORKS	Structures or deck houses built upon the upper decks and the hull of a vessel.
PROMENADE DECK	An upper deck, used mainly by passengers, in the larger passenger carrying vessels.
BOAT DECK	The deck on which the life-boats of a merchant ship are stowed, and usually the highest deck.
LIFE-BOATS	Boats for saving life, carried by all merchant ships. They are usually slung from davits for lowering into the water.
OIL-BURNING	Descriptive of vessels in which fuel-oil is used for the boiler furnaces.

The Cargo-Liner

Cargo liners are vessels designed chiefly for carrying cargo but they usually have accommodation for a small number of passengers. The ocean-going cargo liners vary in size from about 5,000 to 15,000 tons gross with speeds of from 12 to as much as 18 knots. They can be distinguished from passenger liners by their numerous derricks for working the cargo and their smaller superstructures; and they can be distinguished from purely cargo-carrying vessels by their larger superstructures and the greater number of life-boats they carry.

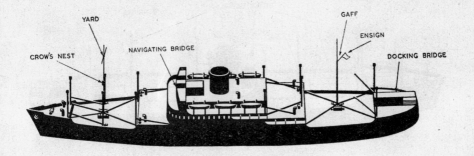

Fig. 37.—A cargo liner

LINER   Any ship which sails on a regular route with fixed ports of call.

NAVIGATING BRIDGE   The raised structure from which a vessel is steered and navigated. All navigating instruments, controls, signal flags and signal lamps are situated here.

DOCKING BRIDGE   A raised platform erected across the after part of the vessel; for use when manœuvring the ship into or out of her berth in a port.

ENSIGN   The national flag displayed by all vessels, usually on a flagstaff placed well aft or on a gaff fitted to the mainmast.

The Cargo Ship

These vessels are of many classes and varieties, and their gross tonnage varies from about 2,000 to 10,000 and their speed from about 10 to 15 knots. They are designed to carry all types of general cargo. They ply between all the ports of the world, and as they do not follow a regular route are often known by the term " tramps." They can usually be distinguished by the small extent of their upperworks and by their numerous masts and derricks.

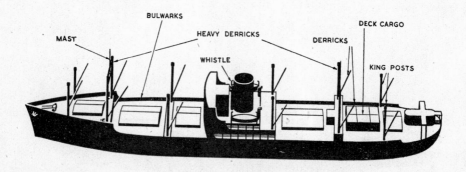

Fig. 38.—A cargo ship

DERRICK	A long spar (often of tubular steel), attached to the foot of a mast or kingpost, used for loading or discharging cargo.
HEAVY DERRICK AND JUMBO DERRICK	Larger and heavier types of derrick, which are usually clamped against the mast when at sea.
GOAL-POST MAST	A mast with its lower portion consisting of two tubular structures between which a platform is placed athwartships (so that they resemble goal-posts). The topmast is stepped into this platform.
KINGPOST	A vertical tubular structure resembling a lower mast and placed in the vicinity of any hatchway. Such posts erected in pairs athwartships are described as " twin king-posts," and should not be confused with goal-post masts.
STEAM WHISTLE OR SIREN	This is always fitted on the fore side of the funnel, usually near its top, and is operated by a lanyard from the bridge.

The Tanker

Tankers, as their name implies, are built to carry liquids of all kinds, from petrol or oil fuel to molasses. Their gross tonnage varies from 2,000 to as much as 50,000 tons, and their speed from 10 to 20 knots. Owing to the nature of their trade they are a very specialised type and normally ply only on certain ocean routes between a limited number of ports. Their propelling machinery is usually right aft because their cargoes are highly inflammable. They can be recognised by their small island superstructure and funnel aft, and by the absence of cargo derricks.

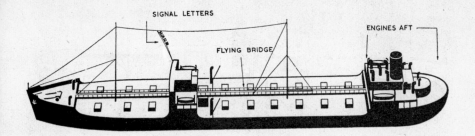

Fig. 39.—A tanker

MOTOR VESSEL	A vessel driven by internal combustion engines.
FLYING BRIDGE OR CATWALK	A raised gangway running the length of the ship and giving safe passage forward and aft when her upper deck is being swept by seas. Oil tankers always have a flying bridge.
SIGNAL LETTERS	A group of four letters allocated to a merchant ship for identification, and corresponding to the warship's " call sign."
BOW WAVE	The wave formed by the vessel's bows when under way.
WAKE	The disturbed water astern of a vessel which is caused by the turning of the propeller and the movement of the hull through the water.

2*

The Bulk Freighter

These freighters are designed to carry cargoes such as coal, ore and grain in bulk. Like the tankers, which sometimes they closely resemble, they are a specialised type of ship usually trading only between certain ports. Their speed varies from 10 to about 15 knots.

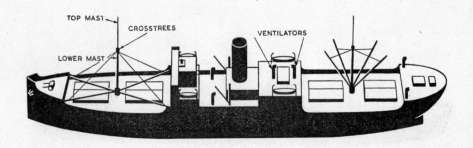

Fig. 40.—A collier (bulk freighter

VENTILATOR	Funnel-like fitting with a cowl-shaped top, projecting from the deck or from super-structure.
STEAMSHIP	A vessel in which the propelling machinery is driven by steam.
COAL-BURNING	Descriptive of vessels in which the fuel for the boiler furnaces is coal.
LADEN	Descriptive of a vessel which has a cargo on board.

The Coaster

Coasters are small cargo vessels, usually of under 2,000 tons gross and of slow speed, employed on coastal trade. They are not built for ocean trade and have a limited radius of action. They bear a close resemblance to their larger sisters, and often can only be distinguished from them by their smaller size.

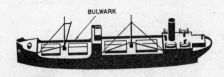

Fig. 41.—Coasters

RUBBING STRAKE	A heavy wooden guard, fitted permanently along the hull close above the water-line to protect the ship's plating when going alongside a wharf. Fitted only in coasters, small passenger vessels, and similar craft.
AUXILIARY SAILING VESSEL	A sailing vessel fitted with steam or motor propelling machinery.
BULWARK	Vertical plating or woodwork erected on deck at the ship's side to protect deck fittings and crew from the sea.

Steam or Motor Fishing Vessels

These vessels may be encountered in large numbers in northern waters, on the fishing grounds, around the coasts and in the open sea. They are small vessels of from about 70 to 500 tons gross, and can be recognised by their tall narrow funnel and sometimes by a small sail set abaft the mizzen mast. Their speed rarely exceeds 10 knots, and when engaged in fishing they are either stopped or proceeding at very low speed. The nets of trawlers and drifters may extend, astern and ahead respectively, for considerable distances under water.

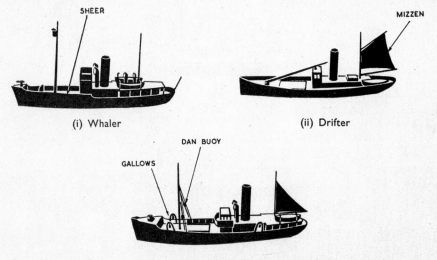

(i) Whaler   (ii) Drifter

(iii) Trawler

Fig. 42.—Fishing vessels

WHALER	A vessel similar to, but larger than, the trawler, and fitted with a harpoon gun well forward. (Not to be confused with the Service pulling and sailing boat illustrated in Fig. 206, page 194.)
TRAWLER	A small, ocean going fishing vessel, which tows a trawl astern and usually has her engines and boilers placed aft.
DRIFTER	A small steam or motor-driven vessel which drifts with a line of float-supported nets ahead of her when fishing.
PAREJA	Small coastal vessel resembling a trawler, seen in the Atlantic off the coasts of Spain and Portugal.
MIZZEN	Small sail carried aft by fishing vessels to assist their steering.
GALLOWS	A steel framework fitting, shaped like an inverted U, erected at the sides and near the bows of a trawler, and used for " shooting " and hauling in her trawl.
CRAFT	A term used to describe small vessels.

SAILING VESSELS

Until recently the prime test of a good seaman was his ability to handle a vessel under sail—because he had to pit his skill and wits against every vagary of weather, wind and sea, entirely unaided by mechanical propulsive power.

Sailing vessels no longer provide a commercially profitable means of transporting passengers or cargoes across the oceans, but many types of small sailing vessel are still to be found in coastal trade throughout the world, and in sufficient numbers to warrant a professional interest being taken in them by the modern seaman. Sailing, however, still provides the best medium for training a seaman to be alert, handy and observant, and has few equals as a sport.

Square Rig, and Fore-and-aft Rig

Sailing vessels are classified by their " rig," which is a term covering masts, yards, booms, gaffs, standing and running rigging, and sails. There are two main types of rig, viz. : " square rig " in which sails are bent to yards carried athwart the mast, and " fore-and-aft rig " in which the sails are bent to masts, booms and gaffs in the fore-and-aft line of the ship. Fore-and-aft rig has superseded square rig, which is seldom seen nowadays.

Masts and Sails

To thoroughly understand the different rigs of the present day sailing vessels and craft a knowledge of the rig of the older vessels is useful because it is from them that the principles and nomenclature of modern rigs derive.

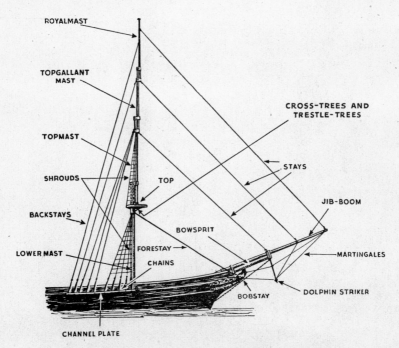

Fig. 43.—Foremast rigging of a square-rigged sailing vessel

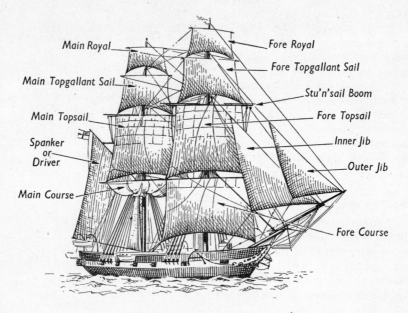

Main Royal

Main Topgallant Sail

Main Topsail

Spanker
or
Driver

Main Course

Fore Royal

Fore Topgallant Sail

Stu'n'sail Boom

Fore Topsail

Inner Jib

Outer Jib

Fore Course

H.M. TRAINING BRIG "MARTIN"

Fig. 44.—Masts and sails of a square-rigged sailing vessel

A mast (see Fig. 43) is stayed athwartships by " shrouds," and forward and aft by " forestays " and " backstays." When masts are stepped one above the other they are called successively the lower mast, topmast, topgallant mast and royal mast. On the top of each mast is a mast cap, and the platform at the foot of the lower mast is called a " top." " Tressel-trees " are the heavy fore-and-aft timbers which support the tops, and " crosstrees " are the athwartship timbers to which are secured the shrouds of the uppermasts.

In ships with more than two masts they are called successively, from forward aft : foremast, mainmast, mizzenmast and jiggermast. In vessels with only one mast it is named the mainmast. In vessels with two masts their

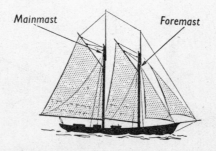

Mainmast   Foremast

Fig. 45.—A schooner

names are determined by their size and position :—if the foremost mast is the larger it is called the mainmast, and the other is called the mizzenmast ; but if the after mast is the larger it becomes the mainmast, and the foremost mast becomes the foremast (see Figs. 45 and 46). The first part of the name of each sail and item of rigging is taken from the mast which supports it, or to which it is attached, *e.g.* " fore topgallant stay," " main topsail," " mizzen topsail yard," " jigger gaff," etc.

The naming of the sails is shown in Fig. 44 which illustrates the 41-gun training brig H.M.S. *Martin* under " plain sail " in 1905, the year when training in sail ended for officers and men of the Royal Navy. It should be noted that she is carrying single topsails and topgallant sails which was common practice in warships, but in merchant ships which carried much smaller crews the topsails and in some cases the topgallant sails were divided into two sails and named upper and lower topsails and topgallant sails respectively. The studding-sail (stun'sail) booms shown were spars which could be run out as extensions of the yards to carry small rectangular studding-sails which in favourable circumstances were set to increase the " press of sail " and the speed of the vessel. To further increase the press of sail some " taunt," *i.e.* tall-masted, vessels were able to set additional sails above the royals, and these were called, in ascending order, " skysails," " moonrakers," and " stargazers." The sails before the foremast were called " headsails," and in vessels with a long bowsprit and jib-boom a full set would comprise a " fore staysail," a " fore-topmast staysail," an " inner " and an " outer jib," and a " flying jib."

In the simplest form of fore-and-aft rig the two chief sails are the foresail and the mainsail, and in Fig. 47 and shown the names for parts of these sails.

Classification (Figs. 48 and 49)

In the heyday of the sailing era nearly all the large vessels, both men-of-war and merchantmen, were " ship-rigged," *i.e.* they were three-masted vessels, square-rigged on each mast, and they were termed " ships." Smaller vessels were usually fitted with only two masts, square-rigged on each, and these were called " brigs." The fore-and-aft rig was in those days usually limited to

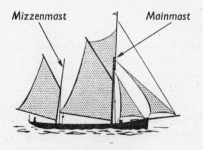

Fig. 46.—A ketch

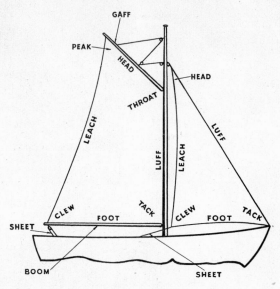

Fig. 47.—Parts of a foresail and a mainsail

small vessels and craft, those with two or more masts being called " schooners." Square rig, however, entailed having a large crew to work the ship efficiently, and as the wages and status of seamen in general rose in the merchant service, so, for the sake of economy, fore-and-aft rig gradually replaced square rig, because it was easier to handle and therefore required fewer men to work the ship. Before and during this transition period many vessels carried a combination of the two rigs in one form or another, and each form was given a specific name ; thus a three-masted vessel, square-rigged on the foremast and mainmast and with fore-and-aft rig on her mizzen, was called a " bark " or " barque," but if only her foremast were square-rigged and the other two masts were rigged fore-and-aft she was called a " barquentine," while a two-masted vessel, square-rigged on her foremast and with fore-and-aft rig on the other mast, was called a " brigantine," and a schooner carrying one or two square-rigged topsails on her foremast was called a " topsail schooner." Of these types the only true survivors nowadays are schooners, topsail schooners and a few brigantines and barquentines. The sailing craft of today are classified by a variety of names which denote the manner in which their masts are stepped or rigged, the cut of their sails, their port of origin, or a general term denoting their country of origin.

Thus a two-masted vessel with masts of nearly equal height and disposed as in Fig. 45 would be called a schooner, but if the after mast were the smaller and stepped further aft the vessel would be called a " ketch " if her mizzen-mast were stepped before the tiller, and a " yawl " if it were stepped over or abaft the tiller head. The mizzen of a ketch is usually much larger than that of a yawl, the former being designed primarily to help in driving the boat along, whereas the purpose of the latter is chiefly to aid the steering of the vessel.

Single-masted vessels are sometimes classified as sloops and cutters, and the difference between these two very similar rigs has constituted a controversial subject among seamen over a very long time, because these rigs have undergone many changes in the last 200 years or so. In modern parlance it is generally accepted among yachtsmen that a cutter has two working headsails, *i.e.* a fore staysail and a jib, whereas a sloop has only one working headsail, the fore staysail. The term cutter may, however, be used in a general sense to describe a fast or handy craft of any description, such as the 12-oared, general-purpose, pulling and sailing cutter of the Royal Navy.

These various rigs may be qualified by a term describing the cut of the main sails of the vessel, the six main types being the lugsail, the lateen sail, the gaff rig, the gunter rig, the Bermudian rig, and the spritsail rig.

A lugsail is a rectangular sail, taller than it is broad, with its head supported by a yard ; if the yard can be dipped from one side to the other of the mast as the vessel goes from one tack to the other the sail is called a " dipping lug," but if it cannot so be dipped the sail is called a " standing lug." A two-masted lug-rigged vessel is called a " lugger," and it was a favourite rig for fishing and small trading craft around our coasts. There are, however, few, if any, of these craft afloat nowadays, but the lugsail can be distinguished in many other types of vessel still in use.

The lateen sail also has its head supported by a yard, but the yard is much longer than that of the lugsail and the sail is either triangular, or nearly triangular with a very short luff, a long head, and a long leach. The lateen rig is found largely in the Mediterranean, and in near and middle-eastern waters.

Gaff rig describes a four-sided sail with its head supported by a spar, called a " gaff," the lower end of which abuts on the mast as in Fig. 46. The foot may or may not be bent to a boom, and as the gaff is usually set at a wide angle to the mast a triangular sail, called a " gaff topsail," can be set between the gaff and the upper part of the mast. This rig is common among small sailing craft.

The gunter rig is similar to the gaff rig but here the mainsail is almost triangular and its gaff is hoisted close against the mast, which latter is much shorter than that of the gaff rig for the same sail area. There is no gaff topsail with this rig, but the foot of the sail is usually bent to a boom.

The Bermudian rig consists of a tall triangular mainsail with the full length of its luff bent to the mast and its foot bent to a boom. The gunter and Bermudian rigs are the most common nowadays for racing and pleasure craft.

The spritsail rig consists of a four-sided sail supported diagonally from tack to peak by a spar or " sprit." This rig can be seen in the sprit-sail barges of the Thames Estuary, and is common in small craft in the Eastern Mediterranean.

BARQUENTINE
(Mediterranean)

TOPSAIL SCHOONER
(British Isles)

TWO-MASTED SCHOONER
(Baltic)

THAMES SAILING BARGE
(Spritsail rig)

PILOT CUTTER
(Cutter rig)

Fig. 48.—Types of sailing vessels

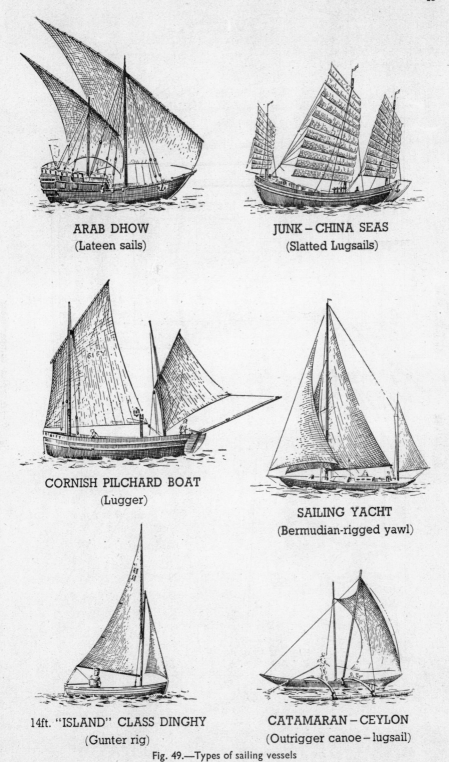

ARAB DHOW
(Lateen sails)

JUNK – CHINA SEAS
(Slatted Lugsails)

CORNISH PILCHARD BOAT
(Lugger)

SAILING YACHT
(Bermudian-rigged yawl)

14ft. "ISLAND" CLASS DINGHY
(Gunter rig)

CATAMARAN – CEYLON
(Outrigger canoe – lugsail)

Fig. 49.—Types of sailing vessels

44

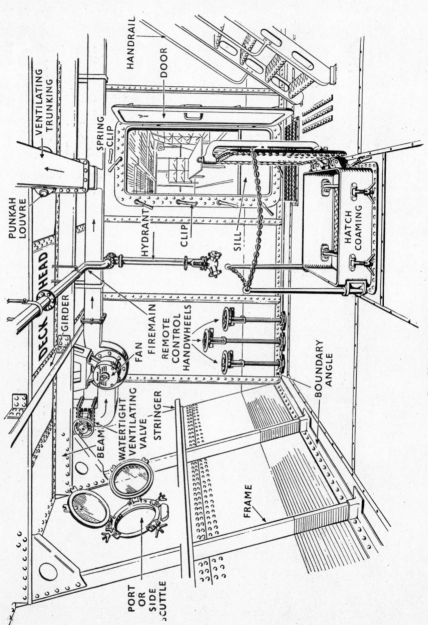

VENTILATING TRUNKING

HANDRAIL

DOOR

PUNKAH LOUVRE

SPRING CLIP

DECK HEAD

HYDRANT

CLIP

SILL

HATCH COAMING

GIRDER

FAN

FIREMAIN

REMOTE CONTROL HANDWHEELS

BEAM

WATERTIGHT VENTILATING VALVE

STRINGER

BOUNDARY ANGLE

FRAME

PORT OR SIDE SCUTTLE

Fig. 50.—A typical compartment

CHAPTER III

Design and Construction of Warships

INTERNAL FITTINGS

ALL the fittings in the hull of a warship are not described in this chapter, but descriptions of the more common fittings are given here to enable the seaman to maintain them in an efficient condition.

Constructional Components and Fittings of a Compartment

The structural components and fittings found in a typical " living space " of a warship are illustrated in Fig. 50.

Underfoot is the " deck " and overhead is the " deck-head " ; the lands-man's terms of floor and ceiling are not used because in a ship each describes something quite different, as is explained in the section of this chapter headed " Elementary Ship Construction." A wall of a compartment is called a " bulk-head," except where it is formed by the side of the hull when it is known as " the ship's side." Bulkheads can be water-tight or non-water-tight, and strict rules govern the opening and closing of the doors in a water-tight bulkhead. Decks within the hull are always water-tight, and strict rules govern the opening and closing of their hatches. " Frames " and " stringers " form parts of the hull structure (see pages 67 and 68), and they support and strengthen the ship's side plating.

Forced ventilation of compartments is provided by electric fans and trunking, and is assisted by natural ventilation through hatches and through scuttles cut in the ship's side.

The fire-main runs throughout the length of the ship, and connections for hoses, called " hydrants," are fitted in most of the main compartments.

Other fittings illustrated are described below.

WATER-TIGHT HATCHES (Fig. 51)

Decks are pierced by rectangular or circular openings, called " hatches," to allow access to the compartments below. A hatch is fitted with a " coaming " to prevent shallow flood water from flowing below, and a lid called a " hatch cover " is hinged to it. The hatch cover has a rubber sealing strip let into its inner side where it bears on the edge of the coaming, so that, when clamped down by means of wing nuts working on threaded bolts hinged to the coaming, the hatch cover makes a water-tight joint with the coaming.

Special attention should be paid to the maintenance of a good bearing surface between hatch cover and coaming ; neither the edge of the coaming nor the rubber should ever be painted, and the latter should be kept in good condition by cleaning it with a damp cloth and dusting it with French chalk.

The hatch cover should always be lowered in position, never let fall, and the wing nuts should be screwed home hand taut, not hammered home. The threads of the wing nuts should be kept lightly greased and never be painted.

Some hatch covers are fitted with water-tight escape manholes, fitted with double clips to enable them to be opened from either side. Ladders with hand chains or hand rails are provided and these should always be correctly secured in position before the hatchway is used. Guard chains and stanchions, or handrails, are provided round the tops of hatchways, and these should always be set-up correctly ; for obvious reasons it is dangerous to sit upon or lean against the guard chains or handrails. Before descending a hatchway always make sure that the hatch cover is securely clipped back in the open position. In war, each hatchway should be provided with a Jacob's ladder for use if the main ladder is displaced by the shock of an explosion.

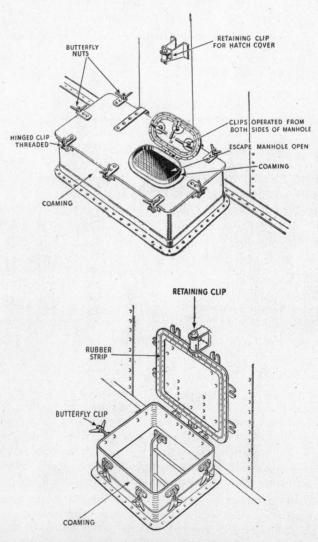

Fig. 51.—Hatches

Hatch covers are fitted with an air plug, the purpose of which is to ascertain before opening the hatch whether the compartment below is flooded ; it is also used for testing the water-tightness of the compartment below by pumping air into it and seeing whether the air pressure is maintained.

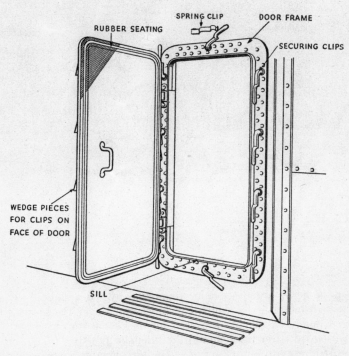

Fig. 52.—A water-tight door

Doors (Fig. 52)

The openings in bulkheads are called " doorways," and they are closed by hinged water-tight doors. These doorways are made water-tight by means of a rubber strip in the door, similar to that in a hatch cover, but the door is clamped shut by double clips and wedges, operable from either side, instead of by winged nuts and bolts. The same care should be taken of doors as of hatches to maintain them in a water-tight condition. The clips and wedges should be kept clean and dry, but the clips should not be removed for cleaning as their reassembly is a skilled job. It is most important that the clips should always be brought *down* (not up) on to the wedges, so that their own weight will tend to clamp the door shut ; they should be clamped hand-tight, not hammered home.

Scuttles

Above the waterline, light and air are admitted through " scuttles " or " portholes " cut in the ship's side. They are closed by hinged " sidelights " of thick glass, which are made water-tight by a rubber strip when secured by

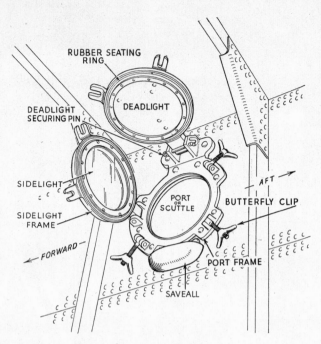

Fig. 53.—A scuttle

winged nuts, and the scuttles can be reinforced by " deadlights," which are circular, hinged, metal plates which can be clamped over the scuttles by the same winged nuts. Deadlights are used for darkening ship at night and for keeping the scuttle water-tight should the sidelight glass be broken ; they are always secured in position in action. In hot climates " windscoops " are provided which fit the scuttles and assist in circulating air from outside around living spaces. In war, light-tight windscoops are issued for use when the ship is darkened.

The same care should be given to the maintenance of scuttles in a water-tight condition as is given to doors and hatches.

Remotely Controlled Valves

There are many valves which, because of their importance to the safety of the ship, can be operated from one or more places in addition to the compartment in which they are situated ; those of the magazine flooding arrangements are examples. This remote control is usually transmitted by rod gearing, which may pass through several compartments and decks and is operated by a hand wheel at each position.

It should be remembered that this remote control system is designed for use in emergency, and that it must therefore be ready to function at a moment's notice. No gear should ever be hung on the hand wheels or rod gearing ; and the joints, crown wheels and deck glands should be kept lightly greased and never be painted over ; the tallies on the hand wheels should be kept clean so that they are easily legible.

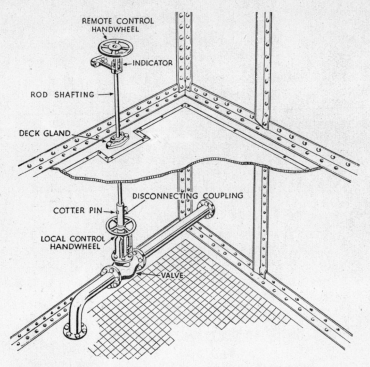

REMOTE CONTROL HANDWHEEL

INDICATOR

ROD SHAFTING

DECK GLAND

DISCONNECTING COUPLING

COTTER PIN

LOCAL CONTROL HANDWHEEL

VALVE

Fig. 54.—Remote and local control of a valve by handwheel and rod gear

Electrical Equipment

A warship's electrical equipment is as important to her fighting and navigational efficiency as are her main engines, and the ship's safety and the comfort of her crew are largely dependent upon its correct functioning.

The care and maintenance of the electrical equipment is the responsibility of the Electrical Branch, and in no circumstances should others interfere with it. Any defects should be reported at once to the Electrical Office, where the necessary steps will be taken for their repair. Notes on certain electrical equipment are given below.

Emergency Lanterns

These are small battery-operated handlamps, kept in special stowages between decks for use in emergency. Their purpose is to illuminate important spaces or gangways if the main lighting system fails. Men's lives, or even the safety of the ship, may depend upon their accessibility and correct functioning, and therefore on no account should they be moved from their stowages or switched on by unauthorised persons.

Telephones

A description of the various telephone systems is given in Volume II of this manual. Telephones and broadcast transmitters, including handsets, headphones, transmitters and microphones, are delicate instruments and must therefore be handled with care. Flexible leads of such instruments should be kept free of turns and not be pulled forcibly ; this applies particularly to the long leads fitted to telephone headsets. When a flexible lead has to be plugged into a socket, care must be taken to ensure that the plug is properly engaged and held firmly in it. Water or liquid of any description must be kept away from all telephone and broadcasting apparatus.

Radio

A warship carries numerous radio installations, including wireless telegraphy, radio telephony and radar. They are placed as far as possible in offices to protect them from the weather, dirt and shock, but certain parts of them may be in exposed positions about the ship. Parts usually exposed and very easily damaged with serious results unless treated with care, are :—

   (i) aerials and their " feeders " (or " leads ") ;

   (ii) radar indicator units (on the bridge, in gun directors, target indicating rooms, gunnery calculating positions, action information spaces, etc.) ;

   (iii) radio telephone microphones and small transmitters (in spaces such as the Air Direction Room).

The three greatest enemies of radio equipment are water (especially salt water), dirt and ill-usage ; remarks on these are given below.

Water.—Most of these radio installations use high voltages (from about 400 to 20,000 volts). Protection against these high voltages by adequate insulation is a great difficulty. Water, especially salt water, conducts electricity, and if it reaches radio equipment the insulators will be rendered useless and the high voltages will " flash over," causing burning and serious damage throughout the equipment. Even when salt water is dried out the difficulties are not overcome, because the grains of salt remain, absorb moisture from the air, and start the trouble all over again. The following precautions should therefore be taken :—

   (i) hoses should not be used near radio equipment, or near the ventilation to radio rooms ;

   (ii) as little water as possible should be used when scrubbing decks near radio equipment ; it should not be splashed about, and the deck should be wiped dry with a cloth ;

   (iii) ventilation to radio rooms should be kept running, and radiators be switched on when necessary to keep the air warm and dry.

Dirt.—Dust and dirt, like water, will conduct electricity. Dust in a ship usually consists of tiny particles of metal, carbon and other conductors of electricity, and a film of such dust over insulators will allow the high voltage to discharge through them. In the vicinity of radio equipment, tobacco ash, cigarette ends, pipe dottle, and other refuse should therefore always be placed in a closed tin, and a moist cloth should be used for dusting because a dry duster merely scatters or disturbs the dust instead of removing it.

Ill-usage.—Radio equipment is extremely delicate and may easily be seriously damaged ; no unauthorised person is therefore allowed to interfere with or alter the setting of any radio equipment.

Care should be taken not to break, crush, dent, bend or chafe the leads to and from the aerials.

Ordinary paint being a conductor of electricity, no leads or aerials should be painted except with the special paint provided, and then only if a definite order is given to do so.

Electrical Dangers

The operation of all electrical devices depends on electrical power, which is transmitted through the conducting wires and cables which run through most compartments.

To prevent leakage of the power all conductors have to be insulated from the metal parts of the ship, and this insulation is provided by layers of non-conductive material between the current-carrying conductor and the protective water-tight cover of the cable.

If this insulating material is damaged in any way, or rendered ineffective by water or damp, the resultant leakage of electric power may be dangerous. For this reason the cap of any plug socket which is no longer in use should always be replaced ; rubber-covered cable must not be painted because the oil in the paint will rot the rubber ; cables must never be chipped or scraped, and nothing must be hung from them or the cable plating overhead.

Just as hoses are more likely to leak than the ship's fire-mains, so flexible electric cables on portable apparatus are more likely to leak than the ship's permanent wiring, and a leak of electricity at 220 volts can easily cause death.

No attempt should be made to repair electric irons, portable drills, electric chipping hammers wandering leads, or any other portable electric apparatus, because such repairs of equipment by inexpert persons may lead to serious injury or loss of life.

INTERNAL ARRANGEMENTS

The internal arrangements of a warship vary according to the type and size of the vessel and the constantly changing requirements of sea warfare, but there is a certain similarity in the general lay-out of most warships.

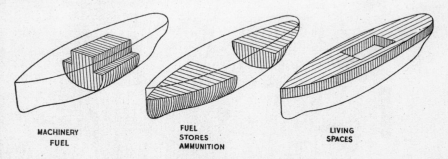

MACHINERY
FUEL

FUEL
STORES
AMMUNITION

LIVING
SPACES

Fig. 55.—General allocation of space in the hull of a warship

In Fig. 55 is shown a typical allocation of space in the interior of a warship' hull for machinery, stores and ammunition, and living quarters ; this allocation, together with that for the armament, is one of the basic factors of warship design.

52

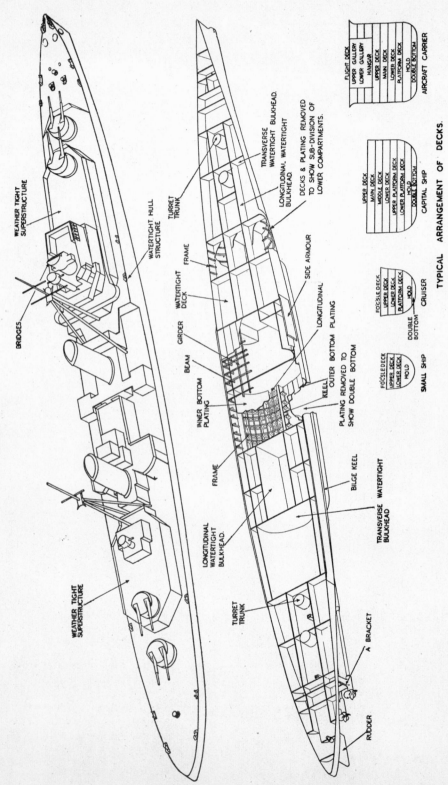

WEATHER TIGHT
SUPERSTRUCTURE

WEATHER TIGHT
SUPERSTRUCTURE

BRIDGES

WATERTIGHT HULL
STRUCTURE

TURRET
TRUNK

WATERTIGHT
DECK

GIRDER

BEAM

INNER BOTTOM
PLATING

FRAME

LONGITUDINAL
WATERTIGHT BULKHEAD.

TURRET
TRUNK

TRANSVERSE WATERTIGHT

BILGE KEEL

A BRACKET

RUDDER

TRANSVERSE
WATERTIGHT BULKHEAD.

LONGITUDINAL WATERTIGHT
BULKHEAD

DECKS & PLATING REMOVED
TO SHOW SUB-DIVISION OF
LOWER COMPARTMENTS.

FRAME

SIDE ARMOUR

LONGITUDINAL

KEEL

OUTER BOTTOM
PLATING

PLATING REMOVED TO
SHOW DOUBLE BOTTOM

FLIGHT DECK		
UPPER GALLERY		
LOWER GALLERY		
HANGAR		
UPPER DECK		
MAIN DECK		
LOWER DECK		
PLATFORM DECK		
HOLD		
DOUBLE BOTTOM		

AIRCRAFT CARRIER

UPPER DECK		
MAIN DECK		
MIDDLE DECK		
LOWER DECK		
UPPER PLATFORM DECK		
LOWER PLATFORM DECK		
HOLD		
DOUBLE BOTTOM		

CAPITAL SHIP

FO'C'SLE DECK		
UPPER DECK		
LOWER DECK		
PLATFORM DECK		
HOLD		
DOUBLE BOTTOM		

CRUISER

FO'C'SLE DECK		
UPPER DECK		
LOWER DECK		
HOLD		

SMALL SHIP

TYPICAL ARRANGEMENT OF DECKS.

Fig. 56.—Water-tight sub-division of a cruiser

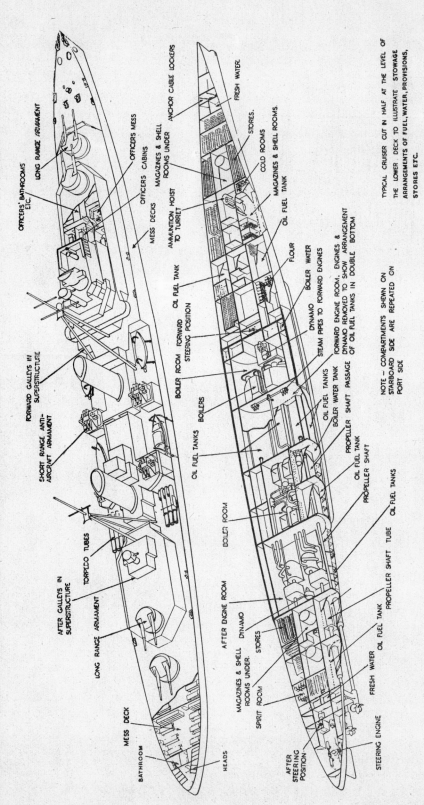

OFFICERS' BATHROOMS ETC.

LONG RANGE ARMAMENT

OFFICER'S MESS

OFFICER'S CABINS

MESS DECKS

AMMUNITION HOIST TO TURRET

MAGAZINES & SHELL ROOMS UNDER

ANCHOR CABLE LOCKERS

FRESH WATER.

STORES.

COLD ROOMS

MAGAZINES & SHELL ROOMS.

OIL FUEL TANK

FORWARD GALLEYS IN SUPERSTRUCTURE

SHORT RANGE ANTI-AIRCRAFT ARMAMENT

OIL FUEL TANK

BOILER ROOM FORWARD STEERING POSITION

FLOUR

DYNAMO BOILER WATER

STEAM PIPES TO FORWARD ENGINES

FORWARD ENGINE ROOM. ENGINES & DYNAMO REMOVED TO SHOW ARRANGEMENT OF OIL FUEL TANKS IN DOUBLE BOTTOM

AFTER GALLEYS IN SUPERSTRUCTURE

TORPEDO TUBES

OIL FUEL TANKS

BOILERS

OIL FUEL TANKS

BOILER WATER TANK

PROPELLER SHAFT PASSAGE

OIL FUEL TANK

PROPELLER SHAFT

LONG RANGE ARMAMENT

BOILER ROOM

AFTER ENGINE ROOM

DYNAMO

STORES

MAGAZINES & SHELL ROOMS UNDER.

SPIRIT ROOM

OIL FUEL TANKS

PROPELLER SHAFT TUBE

MESS DECK

BATHROOM

HEADS

AFTER STEERING POSITION

FRESH WATER

OIL FUEL TANK

PROPELLER SHAFT TUBE

STEERING ENGINE

NOTE — COMPARTMENTS SHEWN ON STARBOARD SIDE ARE REPEATED ON PORT SIDE

TYPICAL CRUISER CUT IN HALF AT THE LEVEL OF THE LOWER DECK TO ILLUSTRATE STOWAGE ARRANGEMENTS OF FUEL, WATER, PROVISIONS, STORES ETC.

Fig. 57.—Internal arrangements of a cruiser

The main and auxiliary machinery is usually situated midway between bow and stern, and, together with its fuel, is kept for protection as far as possible below the waterline. Stores and ammunition are situated before and abaft the machinery space, and as far as possible below the waterline. Living spaces are usually arranged above the waterline and near the ship's side, so that side scuttles can be provided for light and ventilation.

More detailed descriptions of the interior arrangements of a warship are given on the following pages, and illustrated by the sectional drawings of a small cruiser (Figs. 56 and 57). These illustrations should be taken only as a general guide to the text.

In aircraft carriers the internal arrangements below the level of the upper deck are very similar to those of other warships of the same size, but above this deck they are very different ; a short description of the lay-out of an aircraft carrier is therefore given at the end of this section and illustrated in Fig. 60.

Water-tight Subdivision (Figs. 56 and 57)

The decks and main bulkheads divide the hull into a number of main water-tight spaces, and these are sub-divided into smaller water-tight compartments which house the various items of the ship's equipment. This water-tight sub-division is of vital importance to the safety of the ship if her hull is damaged below the waterline, because it confines any ingress of water to the immediate vicinity of the damage instead of allowing it to flow unchecked throughout the ship.

Water-tight decks and bulkheads have, however, to be pierced by hatches and doorways to allow access to the various compartments, and they have also to be pierced for electric leads, piping, ventilating trunking, shafting, etc., led into or through the compartments. Wherever this occurs, however, each opening is made water-tight by special fittings, and it is essential to the safety of the ship that the water-tightness of each such fitting be maintained in an efficient condition, and that such fittings as doors. valves and hatches are opened only when necessary. Special rules are therefore laid down for the opening and closing of all doors, hatches, valves and other water-tight openings situated near or below the waterline.

Ventilation (Fig. 58)

Most compartments in the ship must be supplied, either continuously or intermittently, with fresh air to enable the crew to live and work in them ; ventilation is also necessary for the preservation of stores and provisions. This air is provided in one of two ways, known as " natural " or " forced " ventilation, each of which introduces fresh air into the compartment through an " inlet " and allows the foul air to escape through an " exhaust."

Natural ventilation is provided through scuttles in the ship's sides, through sky lights, ventilators and cowls in the weather decks, and through doorways and hatches. This natural ventilation is only provided to compartments which have direct access to the air, i.e. to those adjacent to the ship's sides or immediately below the weather decks, and then only when considerations of water-tight integrity permit.

Most compartments, however, have no direct access to the air, so they have to be supplied by a system of forced ventilation in which fresh air is drawn by electric fans from various positions above the weather decks and forced through trunking to the various compartments. The foul air is exhausted back to the weather decks through trunking, either naturally or by exhaust fans.

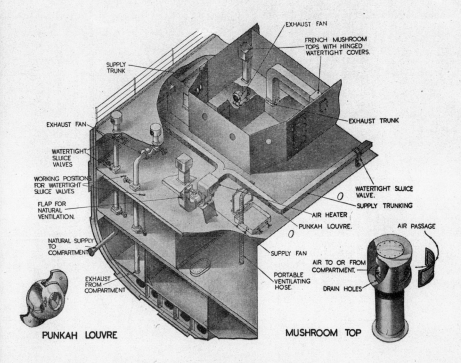

Fig. 58.—Typical ventilation system of a warship

One fan can supply several compartments, and the system is designed to change the air in each compartment every few minutes. To do this the air must circulate freely inside each compartment and along the whole length of the supply system ; consequently, stopping or slowing down a fan which is apparently supplying too much air to one compartment may have the effect of entirely depriving other compartments of their fresh air. The same effect may result if valves or louvres are interfered with to give a compartment more than its fair share of air.

The trunking of the ventilation system provides a means whereby flood water may flow from a flooded compartment to another compartment. To guard against this, all trunking is provided with a valve which can be closed to make it water-tight wherever it passes through a water-tight deck or bulkhead.

" Air Conditioning " is a form of forced ventilation in which the air is kept dry and at a constant temperature by special machinery. The doors and hatches of all compartments thus ventilated must always be closed immediately after use.

56

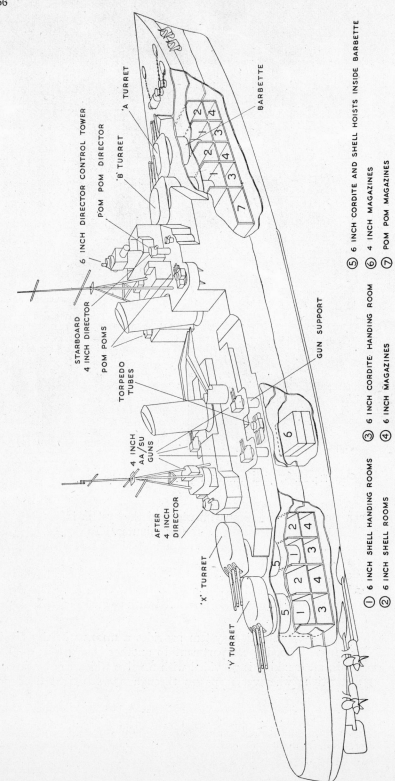

6 INCH DIRECTOR CONTROL TOWER

POM POM DIRECTOR

'A TURRET

'B' TURRET

BARBETTE

STARBOARD
4 INCH DIRECTOR

POM POMS

TORPEDO
TUBES

GUN SUPPORT

4 INCH
AA/SU
GUNS

AFTER
4 INCH
DIRECTOR

'X' TURRET

'Y TURRET

① 6 INCH SHELL HANDING ROOMS   ③ 6 INCH CORDITE HANDING ROOMS   ⑤ 6 INCH CORDITE AND SHELL HOISTS INSIDE BARBETTE

② 6 INCH SHELL ROOMS   ④ 6 INCH MAGAZINES   ⑥ 4 INCH MAGAZINES

⑦ POM POM MAGAZINES

Fig. 59.—Typical armament lay-out of a cruiser

Armament (Fig. 59)

This term includes all offensive weapons such as guns, torpedo tubes and depth-charge throwers. There are many different types of armament, and the following descriptions are only intended to be read in a very general sense.

Guns.—Battleships and cruisers carry their heavy guns in armoured revolving turrets, mounting two, three, and sometimes four guns each. The turrets are usually mounted on the middle-line of the ship, before and abaft the amidships superstructure, to allow as clear a field of fire as possible. The main armament of smaller ships is similarly placed, but the guns are mounted, singly or in pairs, in lightly armoured turrets or behind gun shields. Although turret guns can be laid and fired independently, they are trained on the target by the movement of the turret itself, which revolves on the top of a ring bulkhead outside which is an armoured tube called a " barbette." The armoured barbette extends from the deck on which the turret is situated to below the armoured deck, and below the armoured deck are the magazines and shell rooms in which the ammunition is stowed. The ammunition is conveyed to the guns by mechanical hoists through trunks in the barbette.

The medium guns revolve on " roller paths " and " gunrings " fixed to the deck, which in turn are supported by tubes bolted to the next deck below and known as " gun supports." The magazines for these guns are situated in the bottom of the hull as nearly under the guns as possible, and their ammunition is fed to them, by mechanical hoists, through small trunks which lead from the magazines through the various decks to a position in the vicinity of the guns.

Close-range weapons are mounted where their arcs of fire are least interrupted by superstructures, funnels and masts. Their supply of ammunition is stowed ready to hand in the vicinity of the weapons, and is replenished by hand from their magazines as required.

Torpedoes, tubes and depth charge throwers.—Torpedoes are carried in torpedo tubes fixed to a turn-table called a " mounting," which may carry three, four or five tubes. The mounting can be trained abeam, and the torpedoes are fired into the water by compressed air or an explosive charge. The torpedo is a heavy and cumbersome weapon to handle and stow, and re-loading is a comparatively lengthy operation ; for this reason a ship's outfit of torpedoes is usually limited to one full broadside from each mounting with which she is equipped.

A depth-charge is a projectile used against submarines, and is carried in appreciable numbers by destroyers and other craft. They can be launched over the stern by means of " chutes," or projected a short distance on either side of the ship from " throwers " situated on the after part of the upper deck, the throwers being operated by an explosive charge.

Armour

In the larger ships, the propelling machinery, magazines and certain other vital equipment are usually protected by armoured plating secured to the adjacent part of the hull. On account of its weight the amount of armour must be kept to a minimum ; all vital equipment is therefore grouped in as short a length of the ship as possible, and then protected by a box-like citadel of armour plating which extends from below the waterline on each side, across the decks, and over the bulkheads at each end. Some protection is also afforded to vital equipment by placing it below the waterline.

3

Propelling Machinery

A warship is usually propelled by steam-driven turbines, the steam being supplied from oil-fired boilers. These turbines are commonly known as " the main engines," and their number and position depend upon the number of propellers with which the ship is equipped ; usually one set of turbines drives each propeller shaft. The main engines, and the boilers which feed them, are situated in water-tight compartments known as " engine-rooms " and " boiler-rooms." In the larger ships there may be two or more engine-rooms, and two or more boiler-rooms, to guard against the complete immobilisation of the main propelling machinery by one hit from a torpedo or mine. In Fig. 57, for example, it will be seen that the cruiser has four propellers, two engine-rooms, and two boiler-rooms ; each boiler-room is situated next to the engine-room which it supplies, and the two groups are separated by a water-tight section. The two outer propeller shafts are driven by the forward group, and the two inner propeller shafts by the after group. Should the forward group be put out of action by a lucky torpedo hit abreast its dividing bulkhead the after group will still be able to provide the ship with a fair turn of speed.

The supplies of fuel and water for the boilers are stored in tanks built into the bottom of the hull.

The ship may be driven by one or more propellers, which are keyed to shafts driven by the main engines. The shafts lead through water-tight shaft tunnels, and are supported at intervals by bearings known as " plummer blocks " ; they emerge at the after end of the hull through a shaft tube fitted with a water-tight gland. Where shafts are not on the centre line of the ship a supporting bearing is fitted close to the propeller, which is secured to the hull by a bracket known as the " 'A' bracket " or " shaft bracket."

Auxiliary Machinery

In addition to supplying steam for the main engines the boilers must supply steam for numerous machines ; some of these, such as lubricating and feed pumps, are auxiliaries for the main engines and boilers, and others, such as the dynamos for generating electricity, are necessary for the general work and life of the ship. Most of this machinery is situated in or near the engine and boiler-rooms and is known as the " auxiliary machinery."

Steering Gear

The direction in which a ship moves is controlled by her rudder, which is situated abaft the propellers and operated by machinery known as the " steering gear." The steering gear is driven by hydraulic and electric power, and is connected by a system of pipes to the steering wheel in the forward steering position ; being a vital installation it is, in larger ships, protected by armour.

Living Spaces

These comprise messes, mess decks, cabins, and their associated bathrooms, galleys, canteens and recreation spaces, also the ship's administrative and technical offices. They are usually situated immediately below the upper and forecastle decks, provided with lighting and heating, and furnished for the needs of the officers and men.

Store and Provision Rooms

Sufficient stores are normally carried by a warship to enable her to maintain all her equipment in running order for periods varying between three and six months without recourse to supply bases or dockyards, and their number and type is therefore very considerable. For the most part they are stowed in store-rooms situated low down in the hull, before and abaft the machinery spaces.

A sufficient quantity of provisions is normally carried by a ship to feed her crew for a period of three months and these are augmented as opportunity occurs by fresh provisions, such as meat, fruit and vegetables. The " dry " provisions are stowed in well ventilated " provision rooms " in the vicinity of the living spaces. Fresh meat is stowed in " cold rooms " which are maintained at the required temperature by refrigerating machinery. Fresh vegetables may be stowed in cold rooms, or in well ventilated stowages on or near the upper deck.

Fresh Water Tanks and Supply System

Water for drinking, cooking and washing is carried in tanks situated forward and aft in the hull. From these tanks it is pumped up to gravity tanks in the superstructure, whence it is fed by gravity through pipes to the various drinking-water tanks, pantries, galleys, washplaces and bathrooms throughout the ship. Storage of sufficient fresh water to provide for the domestic purposes of a warship's crew throughout any but a very short voyage would constitute an uneconomical use of weight and space ; fresh water is therefore distilled on board from the surrounding sea water by means of " evaporators," in which the sea water is boiled by steam from the boilers, and the resulting steam condensed into fresh water which is pumped into the storage tanks. The evaporators have also to provide a sufficient supply of fresh water for the boilers and, because their output is limited, strict economy in the use of fresh water must be observed on board a ship.

Distribution of Steam and Electric Power

The chief forms of power in a warship are steam and electricity. Steam pipes are more vulnerable than electric cables and more difficult to repair or replace, and for this reason the use of steam to drive machinery is usually confined to the main machinery spaces and to other parts of the ship behind armour. Electricity is generated by dynamos, situated either in the engine and boiler rooms, where they are driven by steam engines, or in " dynamo rooms " situated outside the main machinery spaces, where they are driven by internal combustion engines called " diesels." This differentiation guards against complete failure of electric power should the boilers be put out of action.

Distribution of Electric Power.—In most ships electricity is produced at 220 volts D.C. ; it is conducted by main electric cables led round the ship, as far as possible below the waterline or behind armour, from which it is tapped by leads to feed the various electric appliances and machines. In small ships the supply of power is distributed from one or more centralised switchboards, but in larger ships it is distributed from a " ring-main " system. This system consists of heavy armoured cables which are led round inside the armoured part of the ship in the form of a ring, and fed through special switch-gear by all the dynamos. By means of various types of switches, electrically, mechanically or hand-operated, electric power can be distributed to, or cut off from, any part of the ship. The ring-main system of distribution ensures that if one section of the ring-main, or one of the dynamos, is put out of action, current can still be supplied by the undamaged dynamos through the undamaged part of the ring-main ; by breaking the necessary switches, any damaged part of the system can be isolated and repaired in safety from electric shock.

Electric power at a lower voltage than 220 is supplied to numerous instruments, including radio equipment, from conversion sets called " transformers," which are fitted in small compartments such as the " low-power rooms " and " radar-power rooms."

Fire-main System

This consists of a system of pipes running throughout the ship and fed with salt water under pressure by steam and electrically driven pumps. It can be distinguished from other pipe systems because it is painted a bright red colour. Hydrants with hose connections are fitted in the fire-main at intervals, so that all parts of the ship can be reached by hoses. The fire-main also provides water for the spraying systems fitted in magazines for drenching the ammunition when endangered by fire.

In addition to providing water for fire fighting, this system provides water for the ships sanitary services, and also for scrubbing decks and cleaning the anchors and cables when weighing anchor.

Pumping and Flooding

In most ships a system of pipes called the " main suction " runs throughout the greater part of the ship, usually below the lower deck, and is led to the various compartments and spaces situated low down in the hull. The system can be connected with any or all of the electrical hull and fire pumps, and the fire-and-bilge pumps and pumps in the machinery spaces, so that any flood water in any of the compartments served can be pumped out. Flood water in compartments not connected with the system can be pumped out by portable electric pumps.

Some compartments, such as the magazines and spirit room, can be flooded direct from the sea by opening the " sea cocks " fitted in the bottom of the hull. Other compartments can be flooded if necessary by means of the fire-main.

Aircraft Carriers

Types of Carriers

There are at present (1953) two main classes of aircraft carriers, Fleet Carriers and Light Fleet Carriers.

Fleet Carriers are usually armoured and have a maximum speed of over 25 knots. They carry the maximum anti-aircraft armament that is possible without obstructing the flight deck and other flying arrangements. Their hangar capacity is at least 30 aircraft.

Light Fleet Carriers are somewhat smaller than Fleet Carriers, usually unarmoured, and have a speed of from 21 to 28 knots. Their anti-aircraft armament is lighter than that of Fleet Carriers and they have a hangar capacity of from 20 to 30 aircraft.

In the Second World War (1939–1945) a class known as Escort Carriers was largely used. They were converted merchant ships and their use was generally confined to trade protection or assault in combined operations landings. Most of these have now (1953) been re-converted to merchantmen.

LAY-OUT AND GENERAL ARRANGEMENTS (Fig. 60)

The uppermost deck is called the " flight deck " and is flush from bows to stern, without a break except for the lifts. At each end the flight deck curves downwards to form what is known as the " round-downs."

On the starboard side of the flight deck are the funnel, mast, bridge, and various flying and armament control positions, grouped together in a super-structure known as the " island."

On each side of the flight deck are sponsons which carry the armament and the various flight deck control positions. At the forward and after ends of the flight deck, on each side, are the " safety nets " where the members of the deck handling party are stationed when aircraft are taking-off or landing.

The equipment of a carrier includes a mobile crane, tractors for towing aircraft, portable wind barriers called " palisades," and fork trucks for lifting and transporting light stores or equipment.

Across the after part of the flight deck run a number of " arrester wires," which are raised a few inches off the deck when aircraft are landing-on, but otherwise lie flat on the deck. These wires render when caught by the arrester hook with which deck landing aircraft are fitted, but are hydraulically braked and controlled so as to bring the aircraft to a standstill within a short distance of its touch down.

Led across the flight deck amidships are two or three " safety barriers " of wire rope. These are raised when aircraft are landing-on, but otherwise lie flat on the deck. Their purpose is to stop any aircraft which miss the arrester wires when attempting to land, thus allowing the forward part of the flight deck to be used as an aircraft park while aircraft are landing-on.

A " catapult and track " are fitted at the forward end of the flight deck to enable aircraft to take-off from the carrier when she is at anchor, or when the remainder of the flight deck is obstructed.

Below the greater part of the flight deck are situated the hangars, which are divided by fire curtains into sections. On each side of the hangars and before and abaft them are the workshops, offices, and stowages for stores and equipment. Living spaces are usually before and abaft the hangars and on the decks below. Below the " hangar deck," which corresponds to the upper deck of other vessels, the internal arrangements are very similar to those of battleships or cruisers.

OPERATION OF AIRCRAFT

When aircraft are landing-on or taking-off, the carrier steams into the wind at a speed which gives an airflow over the deck of about 30 knots.

To take-off, aircraft are parked on the after part of the flight deck and

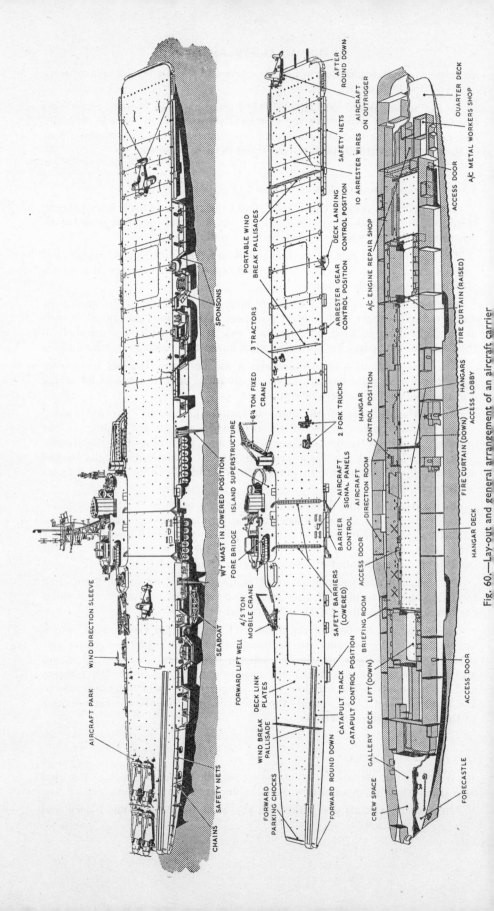

Fig. 60.—Lay-out and general arrangement of an aircraft carrier

stowed close to one another with their wings folded ; their positions before take-off are arranged so that they will be airborne before they reach the forward round down. The aircraft take-off singly, and when each one's turn comes it taxies to the fore-and-aft midship line, spreads its wings, and takes off when flagged by the Deck Control Officer.

Aircraft land on the flight deck singly. After each has landed, the arrester wire is disengaged from the aircraft's arrester hook and hove taut ready for the next one. The safety barriers are then lowered and the aircraft is taxied to the forward lift and struck below on it ; the safety barriers are then raised again ready for the next aircraft.

While the carrier is steaming head to wind at a constant speed for landing on or flying off her aircraft she presents a very vulnerable target, especially for submarine attacks ; these operations therefore require a special organisation and method of control so that they can be carried out as quickly as possible. The flying organisation, internal administration and routine of an aircraft carrier are not, however, within the scope of this book, and are dealt with in other books of reference and regulations.

ELEMENTARY SHIP CONSTRUCTION

Hull Stresses

The hull of a ship must be strong enough to withstand all the stresses imposed upon it by encountering heavy seas, or by resting on the blocks of a dry dock ; it must also be sufficiently strong to withstand vital damage in the event of collision or grounding. The most important requirement of a warship's hull is that it should withstand damage in action.

The stresses to which a ship may be subjected are illustrated in Fig. 61. The most important are the " hogging " and " sagging " stresses, caused by pitching head-on into heavy seas, which tend to break her back. When a ship rolls heavily in a sea-way she is subjected to " racking " stresses which tend to distort her sides and upper deck, and a combination of both pitching and rolling subjects her to " torsional " stresses which tend to twist her hull about its fore-and-aft axis. In addition, the pressure of the water against the underwater surface of the hull tends to bend the hull plating inwards. A concentration of weight " between decks " along the middle line of a ship tends to draw the top sides of her hull inwards ; the opposite effect is produced when the ship rests on her keel in a dry dock, also her sides then tend to sag outwards and have to be supported by bilge and breast shores.

Hull Form

The hull of a ship can be compared with a box, the ends of which are " faired off " to form the bows and stern, and the underwater portion of which is shaped to reduce its resistance to the water when moved through it. The bottom is rounded to meet the sides, this rounding being called the " bilge " and its degree varying with the type and size of the vessel. Most merchant ships and battleships have a nearly rectangular cross section for the greater part of their length, the bottom being flat, the sides vertical, and the bilges sharply rounded, but high-speed vessels such as cruisers and destroyers have rising bottoms and less sharply rounded bilges.

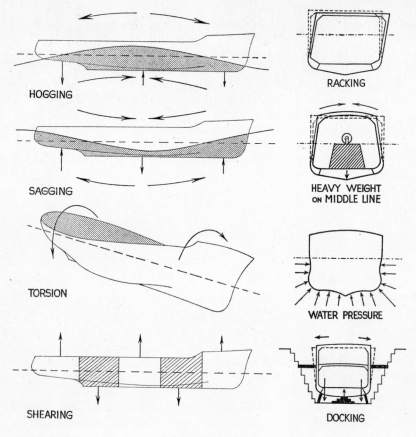

Fig. 61.—Hull stresses

The gradual broadening of the underwater part of the hull under the bows from the stem to the main body of the hull is called the " entry," and the corresponding narrowing under the quarters towards the stern is called the " run." Cruisers, destroyers and other high-speed vessels have a " fine entry " and a " fine run," while ships designed essentially for large carrying capacity, such as freighters, have a comparatively " bluff entry " and " bluff run."

Hull Plating (Figs. 62 and 63)

The outer surface of the hull is built of steel plates, which are welded or riveted to each other and to the main internal structural members of the hull. The plating covering the bottom is known as the " outer bottom plating," and that covering the sides is generally known as the " side plating." The thickness of the plates varies with their position in the hull, the thickest or heaviest being usually found over the bottom and at the deck edges amidships. In the larger warships, armour plating made of

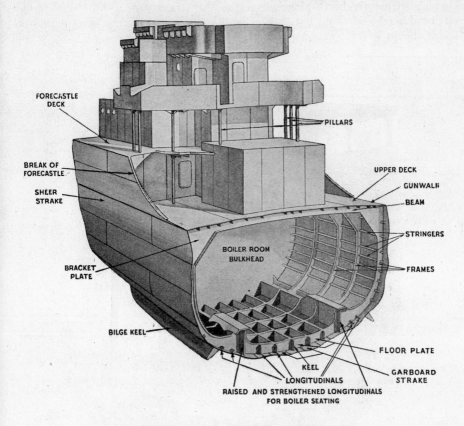

FORECASTLE DECK

PILLARS

BREAK OF FORECASTLE

UPPER DECK

GUNWALH

SHEER STRAKE

BEAM

STRINGERS

BOILER ROOM BULKHEAD

FRAMES

BRACKET PLATE

BILGE KEEL

FLOOR PLATE

KEEL

GARBOARD STRAKE

LONGITUDINALS

RAISED AND STRENGTHENED LONGITUDINALS FOR BOILER SEATING

Fig. 62.—Cross section of a destroyer through " A " boiler-room

thick slabs of specially toughened and hardened steel is secured to the side plating of those parts of the hull within which are situated the more vital items of her equipment, such as the magazines, shell rooms, and propelling machinery ; this armour plating usually runs from a few feet below the waterline to upper-deck level and across the decks.

The short sides of each plate are called the " ends," and the long sides the " edges." Plates are joined end to end to form a panel of plating which runs forward and aft and is known as a " strake." The joint between the ends of any two plates in a strake is known as a " butt," and that between two strakes is known as a " seam." Some strakes run continuously throughout the length of the hull, but others, particularly those around the turn of the bilge, may run only for a short distance amidships. The heaviest and most important strakes are the " garboard strakes " which run each side of the keel, and the " sheer strakes " which are the topmost strakes next below the upper deck ; the sheer strakes run continuously throughout the length of the hull and give considerable longitudinal support to its structure. The strakes each side are usually lettered alphabetically from the keel outward and upward, the garboard strake being known as the "A" strake and the next strake as the " B " strake, and so on up to the sheer strake. In cross channel steamers and other vessels

3*

which frequently berth alongside jetties the strake just above the waterline is reinforced and protected with a baulk of timber, which is faced with steel and known as the " rubbing strake."

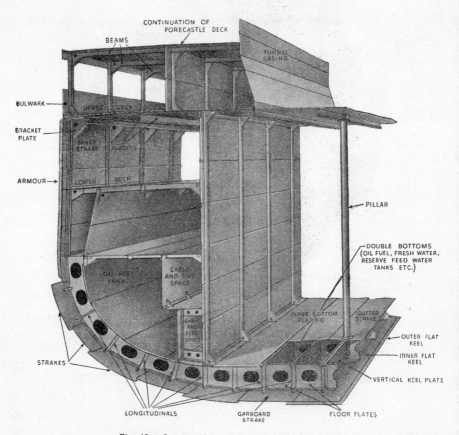

Fig. 63.—Section through a cruiser (amidships)

Main Members of the Hull Structure (Figs. 62 and 63)

The main members of the internal structure of the hull are the " keel," the " stem," the " stern post," the " frames," the " longitudinals," the " beams " and " girders," the " decks " and the " bulkheads." These all combine to support and strengthen the shell of the hull and enable it to withstand the various stresses to which it may be subjected.

THE KEEL, STEM AND STERN POST (Fig. 64)

The most important structural member of the hull is the keel, which forms the backbone of the ship. It is constructed of horizontal and vertical keel plates and runs throughout the length of the hull, to the stem at its fore end and to the stern-post at its after end. In small vessels the vertical keel may project a few inches from the bottom to form a bar keel, which helps to counteract the tendency of the vessel to roll.

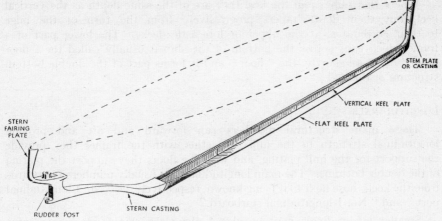

Fig. 64.—Keel, stem and stern post

The lower plate of the keel, called the " flat keel plate," forms the centre strake of the outer bottom plating and is frequently fitted in two thicknesses. On this is built the " centre vertical keel," which is constructed of plates and angles to form a continuous girder of " I " cross-section and the height of which usually determines the depth of the " double bottoms." On the top of the vertical keel is built the " gutter strake," which forms the centre strake of the inner bottom plating. At either end of the midships section the cross section of the lower keel plate begins to take the shape of a " V," which becomes progressively sharper to conform to the finer lines of the hull at its entry and run.

The stem can be a single casting or forging, or, like the keel, can be built up of shaped plating and angles. The stern post is more complex, and in most ships has to take the weight of the rudder. It may consist of a single casting or forging, continued with shaped plating and angles. The stem and the stern post provide the anchorages for the extremities of the strakes of the outer plating.

FRAMES (Fig. 65)

The frames of a ship can be likened to the ribs of a skeleton. Their lower ends are secured to the keel, whence they extend outwards and upwards to the upper deck, and, with the longitudinals, form the main support of the shell plating. The frames conform to the shape of the hull and are closely spaced at intervals throughout its length. The spacing between the frames varies with the method of construction of the ship and with the position of the frames in the ship ; generally speaking, they are spaced closer together at the bows and quarters, and in the wake of heavy side armour. In large ships the intervals may be as much as from 4 to 6 ft. amid-

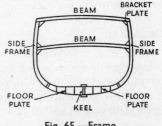

Fig. 65.—Frame

ships, and from 2 ft. 6 in. to 3 ft. at the bows and stern, while in small ships the intervals may be as small as from 1 ft. 9 in. to 2 ft. 6 in.

Where the frames join the keel they are of the same depth as the vertical keel, but their depth tapers progressively from the turn of the bilge to their extremities at the upper or forecastle decks. The lower part of a frame which runs across the bottom of the ship is usually called the "floor plate" or, more shortly, the "floor," and it forms part of the double bottom structure of the hull.

LONGITUDINALS

These main structural members run forward and aft and provide longitudinal strength to the hull. Together with the frames they provide the support for the hull plating, and with the floors they support the plating of the double bottoms. The main longitudinals are usually numbered outwards from the keel, those next to it being known, respectively, as "No. 1 longitudinal port" and "No. 1 longitudinal starboard."

Smaller longitudinals may be placed along the ship's side where extra strength above the double bottoms is required, particularly at the bows and stern, and these are usually known as "stringers."

DOUBLE BOTTOMS

The keel, with the floors of the frames and the bottom longitudinals, form the cellular structure extending about two-thirds the length of the hull known as the double bottoms. They are covered by a layer of water-tight plating called the "inner bottom" or "tank top," and thus prevent the ship becoming flooded should the outer bottom plating be holed. The double bottoms, in addition to contributing greatly to the strength of the hull, provide storage space for oil fuel and fresh water. In some merchant ships they enclose the ballast tanks, which can be filled with seawater to give additional stability to the ship when she is lightly loaded ; when in this condition the ship is said to be "in ballast."

The double bottoms of most merchant ships and some warships extend across the bilges to their turns, and the inner bottom or tank top is flat and forms the deck of the engine-rooms, boiler-rooms, cargo-holds and store-rooms. In cruisers and some larger warships the double bottoms may extend up to the waterline and thus form part of the underwater protection of the ship against mine or torpedo.

The bottom and sides of the holds of merchant ships are usually sheathed with a layer of wooden planks as a protection for the cargo, this sheathing being known as the "ceiling."

BULKHEADS

The term "bulkhead" is used by the seaman to describe any wall of a compartment which is not formed by the ship's side. Bulkheads can therefore be water-tight or non-water-tight, and transverse or longitudinal, and they may either serve as partitions between compartments or form part of the main structure of the ship.

The hull is divided vertically and athwartships, by "main structural bulkheads," into a number of water-tight sections. These bulkheads usually extend between the frames from the bottom of the hull to the main deck above the waterline, but in places they may be continued up to the upper and forecastle decks. In addition to dividing the ship into water-tight sections these bulkheads appreciably contribute to the transverse and longitudinal strength of the hull.

The interval between transverse bulkheads is determined by the type of ship and her manner of construction ; generally speaking they are spaced closer together at the forward and after ends of the hull than amidships. The forward bulkheads help the bows to withstand the impact of the waves and form a barrier against the ingress of water in the event of collision ; the after bulkheads help to strengthen the hull against the thrust of the propellers and the stresses of pitching and rolling. The positions of the bulkheads in the main body of the hull are largely determined by the spaces required for boiler and engine-rooms, cargo holds, magazines, shell-rooms, and other main features of the ship's design. In a freighter the main structural bulkheads may provide the only water-tight division of the hull, but in warships and passenger liners, where a tier of decks runs almost continuously forward and aft, the hull is sub-divided by water-tight decks and longitudinal and transverse water-tight bulkheads into what is virtually a honeycomb of water-tight compartments. This water-tight compartmentation provides a great measure of safety to the ship should her hull be holed below the waterline, as it enables the resultant flooding to be confined to a small portion of the hull.

DECKS, BEAMS AND PILLARS

The hull is divided horizontally by decks which, in a warship, run continuously from stem to stern except where they are broken by the main machinery spaces ; in a freighter their continuity is further broken by the holds. Non-continuous decks may be found in many ships, and these are usually called " flats " or " platforms." The number and names of the decks vary with the type and size of the ship. In warships, decks up to and including the upper deck are made water-tight wherever possible, and with the bulkheads they thus complete the water-tight compartmentation of the ship ; in addition, they lend considerable transverse and longitudinal strength to the hull.

A deck is formed of strakes of steel plates which extend forward and aft and are joined together in the same way as the hull plating. The plates forming the outer strakes are heavier than the remainder and are known as the " stringer plates," and the edges where they join the side plating are known as the " boundary angles." Decks above the waterline are usually " cambered " (*i.e.* arched) to aid the drainage of any surface water to the gutters, called " waterways," which extend fore and aft at the sides of the decks. From these waterways the water is drained over the ship's side by pipes called " scuppers " which usually run to just above the waterline. Weather decks are usually covered with a layer of wooden planking which, in addition to affording a safe foothold for the crew in wet weather, helps to insulate the spaces below them against heat and cold. The edge where the upper deck meets the ship's side is known as the " gunwale " ; this term survives from the early days of wooden ships when the hull was strengthened longitudinally by one or more heavy strakes called " wales," the one supporting the main gun-deck being then known as the " gun-wale." In many ships, particularly merchant ships, the ship's side abreast the waist and well-decks is built up several feet above the upper deck by a strake of plating joined to the gunwale and known as the " bulwarks " ; these form a protecting breakwater against heavy seas, and prevent the crew from being washed overboard or falling overboard, and they are pierced at intervals with openings, fitted with hinged flaps, called " washports," to allow the escape of any water shipped in a seaway.

Decks are supported by beams which extend athwartships between the frames, and by girders which extend forward and aft between the beams. The beams are usually joined to the frames by " brackets " or " knee plates," which thus unite the beams, frames and decks in contributing to the transverse strength of the hull. " Pillars " assist the beams and girders in supporting the decks over large compartments, around large hatchways, and below heavy equipment.

BILGE KEELS

These take the form of two, long, narrow, fore-and-aft girders, which are built out from the hull at the turn of the bilge on each side of the ship to check her rolling in a seaway.

Stations

To enable any position in the hull to be described with accuracy the frames are numbered consecutively from forward to aft and known as " stations," and the main transverse bulkheads are numbered in accordance with the stations of the frames between which they run ; in addition, the decks are numbered consecutively from top to bottom, the uppermost deck being called No. 1 deck. Thus for example, the position of a fitting can be described as lying on the middle line, on No. 3 deck, between numbers 73 and 74 stations.

CHAPTER IV

Routine, Passing Orders, and Organisation

ROUTINE

Time and Watches

THE seaman uses the 24 hour clock and his day is divided into seven periods called watches. The day starts at midnight and the time is recorded in four figures, of which the first two denote the hour and the last two the minute. The following table shows the difference in the recording of time by civil and naval methods.

Name of Watch	Duration in Naval time	Duration in Civil time
Middle	0000 to 0400	midnight to 4 a.m.
Morning	0400 to 0800	4 a.m. to 8 a.m.
Forenoon	0800 to 1200	8 a.m. to noon.
Afternoon	1200 to 1600	noon to 4 p.m.
First Dog	1600 to 1800	4 p.m. to 6 p.m.
Last Dog	1800 to 2000	6 p.m. to 8 p.m.
First	2000 to 2400	8 p.m. to midnight

The purpose of dividing the period between 1600 and 2000 into the two " dog watches " is to provide an odd number of watches in the 24 hour day so that the port and starboard watches will keep a different watch each day.

The seaman, unlike the civilian, does not speak of the morning, afternoon, and evening, but of the morning, forenoon, afternoon and dog watches.

Striking the Ship's Bell

The time is indicated by striking the hours and half-hours on the ship's bell throughout each watch, in accordance with the table below ; the time thus indicated is called " one bell," " two bells," etc., according to the number of times the bell has been struck.

First half-hour	one bell,
first hour	two bells,
first hour and a half	three bells,
second hour	four bells,
second hour and a half	five bells,
third hour	six bells,
third hour and a half	seven bells,
fourth hour	eight bells.

This sequence is repeated in each watch, with the exception of the last dog watch ; seven bells, for example, can therefore indicate 0330, 0730, 1130, 1530, or 2330, and so when quoting the time by this method the name of the watch is added ; 1030, for example, is described as "five bells in the forenoon." Time in the last dog-watch is marked as follows :—1830 by one bell, 1900 by two bells, 1930 by three bells and 2000 by eight bells.

Except for marking the time the ship's bell is only struck to indicate the position of the ship when at anchor in a fog or bad visibility, or to sound the general alarm in the event of fire or other emergency. The fog signal is the rapid ringing of the bell for about five seconds every minute. For a general alarm the bell is rung rapidly for considerably longer than five seconds, and this is usually followed by a bugle call or a " pipe " indicating the nature of the emergency and giving orders for dealing with it. The general alarm is only sounded by order of the Commanding Officer.

SILENT HOURS

The term " silent hours " denotes the period of the night watches, between the times of " pipe down " and calling the hands, when it is customary not to mark the time by the ship's bell in order to avoid unnecessarily disturbing the watch below and the day-men. During the silent hours the watch next on deck is called by the pipe " all the (named) watch," the call being made much less loudly than in daytime. At five or ten minutes to the hour for relieving the watches the bell may be struck once, softly, as a signal for the relieving watch to muster, this strike being called " little-one-bell."

Daily Harbour and Sea Routines

Normal every-day life in a ship is regulated in accordance with a time-table known as the " routine." This routine must cover the general activities of the ship and her crew wherever she may be, and so there will be a " harbour routine " and a " sea routine " for both weekdays and Sundays, and these will differ for home and foreign stations, and for winter and summer. Although these routines must vary considerably with the type of ship and the station on which she is serving the principles on which all routines are based are governed by the *Queen's Regulations and Admiralty Instructions*, and there are therefore certain main features which are common to all.

Examples of typical daily harbour and sea routines are shown on pages 73 and 74. From these it will be seen that the day is divided into three main periods ; the first from 0535 to 0900, the second from 0900 to 1600, and the third from 1600 to 2200. In the first period the hands are called, and the ship is cleaned inside and out and made generally shipshape for her day's work. The second period, which covers the forenoon and afternoon watches, is devoted to the maintenance and repair of the ship and her armament and equipment, and to the training and instruction of her crew. In the third period facilities are given to the crew for leisure, and for recreation and shore leave if in harbour, and the ship and her equipment are prepared for the night.

In the tropics it is usual to start the day's work earlier and " pipe down " when the hands go to dinner.

EXAMPLE OF
DAILY HARBOUR ROUTINE

(Times marked * are to be reported to the Commander.)

0505	Call men under punishment.
0515	Call duty R.P.O., disciplinary P.O., and bugler.
0530	Call the hands ; lash up and stow hammocks ; men under punishment to muster.
0535	Cooks to the galley for cocoa.
*0550	" G."
0555	Out pipes.
0600	Hands fall in ; clean ship and lower boats ; duty boats' crews scrub out and fuel boats ; off boat ropes.
0630	Up guard and steerage hammocks.
*0650	Cooks to the galley ; uncover guns ; respread awnings.
0700	Hands to breakfast and clean ; clean mess deck brightwork.
0745	Guard and band (Summer).
0750	Out pipes ; duty boys of forenoon watch to muster.
0800	Colours (Summer) ; both watches for exercise, stand fast cooks and sweepers ; hands to brightwork stations ; clean messdecks and flats.
0820	Commander's requestmen and defaulters.
0835	Quarters clean guns.
0845	Guard and band (Winter).
*0855	" G," return rags ; morning watchmen out pipes.
0900	Colours (Winter) ; both watches of the hands, or Divisions.
1030	Stand easy.
1040	Out pipes, hands carry on with work.
1115	Up spirits.
1130	Afternoon watchmen and relief boats' crews to dinner.
*1150	Cooks to the galley ; grog call.
1200	Hands to dinner ; pipe leave and any general orders.
1220	Duty boys of afternoon watch to muster.
1230	Men under punishment to muster (1315 on make-and-mend days).
1305	" G."
*1310	Out pipes.
1315	Both watches of the hands fall in.
1420	Stand easy.
1430	Out pipes, hands carry on with work.
1530	First dog-watchmen to tea (make-and-mend days, men under punishment secure).
1540	Clear up decks (make-and-mend days, both watches fall in).
*1550	Cooks to the galley ; emergency party to muster.
1600	Hands to tea, or evening quarters ; clean into night clothing ; libertymen to clean (liberty men " fall in " in accordance with boat routines).
1630	Men under punishment to muster.
1700	Engine-room department to evening quarters ; duty hands fall in—up fresh provisions (in dockyard—emergency party to muster ; exercise Fire Stations).
1800	Duty part of the watch fall in ; hoist boats ; rig boat ropes and stern fasts ; rig cinema ; cover guns (at Sunset if earlier).
1830	Hands to supper ; men under punishment secure ; duty boats' crews clean into night clothing.
2015	Cooks and sweepers clear up mess decks and flats ; duty part of the watch of the hands fall in, clear up decks, slope awnings, close water-tight openings.
*2040	First post ; duty hands, night boat's crew, and men under punishment and stoppage of leave to muster.
2045	Rounds ; boys turn in.
2100	Last post.
2145	Duty hands fall in, unrig cinema.
2200	Pipe down.
2230.	Chief and petty officers pipe down.

EXAMPLE OF
DAILY SEA ROUTINE

(Times marked * are to be reported to the Commander.)

0340	Call morning watchmen.
0350	Morning watchmen to muster.
0505	Call men under punishment.
0515	Call duty R.P.O., disciplinary petty officer and bugler.
0530	Call the hands (stand fast middle watchmen) ; lash up and stow hammocks ; men under punishment to muster.
0535	Cooks to the galley for cocoa.
0545	Morning watchmen to muster ; sweep down decks, place washdeck gear.
*0550	" G."
0555	Out pipes.
0600	Hands fall in ; clean ship.
0630	Up guard and steerage hammocks ; open water-tight openings (as ordered by O.O.W.).
*0650	Cooks to the galley ; watchkeepers of forenoon watch to breakfast and clean.
0700	Hands to breakfast and clean ; clean messdeck brightwork.
0735	Out pipes ; seaboat's crew and lowerers of forenoon watch to muster.
0800	Both watches for exercise, stand fast cooks and sweepers ; hands to brightwork stations ; clean messdecks and flats.
0820	Commander's requestmen and defaulters.
0835	Quarters clean guns.
*0855	" G " ; return rags ; morning watchmen out pipes.
0900	Both watches of the hands, or Divisions.
1030	Stand easy.
1040	Out pipes, hands carry on with work.
1100	Up spirits.
1130	Watchkeepers of the afternoon watch to dinner.
*1150	Cooks to the galley ; grog call.
1200	Hands to dinner.
1225	Seaboat's crew and lowerers of afternoon watch to muster.
1230	Men under punishment to muster (1315 on make-and-mend days).
1305	" G."
1310	Out pipes.
1315	Both watches of the hands fall in ; stand fast watchkeepers of the forenoon watch.
1345	Watchkeepers of the forenoon watch to muster.
1430	Stand easy.
1440	Out pipes, hands carry on with work.
1530	First dog-watchmen to tea (make-and-mend days, men under punishment secure).
*1540	Clear up decks (make-and-mend days, both watches fall in).
1600	Hands to tea or evening quarters ; clean into night clothing.
1630	Men under punishment to muster.
1820	Cooks to the galley.
1830	Hands to supper ; men under punishment secure.
1950	First watchmen to muster.
2015	Watch fall in ; duty part clear up decks, non-duty part close water-tight openings ; cooks and sweepers clear up mess decks and flats for rounds.
*2040	Men under punishment to muster.
2045	Rounds ; boys turn in.
2130	Pipe down ; seaboat's crew and lowerers unrig cinema.
2200	Chief and petty officers pipe down.
2340	Call middle watchmen.
2350	Middle watchmen to muster.

Make-and-Mend

Originally known as "make and mend clothes," this was a half-holiday set aside weekly (usually on Thursdays) for the ship's company in which to repair and replace their kit. In those days few articles of clothing were supplied from store and most were usually made by the men themselves.

Nowadays, make-and-mends are usually granted on every Saturday when circumstances permit, and in addition, when the ship is in harbour, an extra make-and-mend may occasionally be granted for organised recreation and sports.

Guard and Steerage

The steerage used to be right aft by the rudder head, and near or around this flat were berthed the officers, who, together with the guard and any passengers, were allowed to lie in later than the remainder of the hands and were roused by the call " Guard and steerage."

Nowadays, " Guard and steerage " may apply to Gunroom and Branch Officers who sling their hammocks, Chief Petty Officers, watch-keepers, excused day-men, bandsmen, and officers' servants and boats' crews on duty after 2200 on the previous evening.

PASSING ORDERS

Piping and the Boatswain's Call

Piping is a naval method of passing orders, especially routine orders, and every seaman should know how to use a " boatswain's call " and how to pipe an order. Orders thus passed are known as " pipes."

The use of the boatswain's call in English ships can be traced back with certainty to the days of the Crusades, A.D.1248. In former days it was worn in English ships and fleets as an honoured badge of rank, probably because it had always been used for passing orders. As long ago as 1485 it was worn as the badge of office of the Lord High Admiral of England, and by his successors in office up to 1562. Thereafter it was used throughout the English fleets for passing all orders, and since about 1671 it has always been known as the boatswain's call. Nowadays, the boatswain's call and chain are the badge of office of the Chief Boatswain's Mate, quarter-masters and boatswain's mates.

The expression " to pipe " means, generally, to make the sound of the boatswain's call and to give the spoken order which may qualify it. Many pipes, however, are orders in themselves and do not require any verbal addition afterwards.

A boatswain's call (Fig. 66 (i)), can be tuned by scraping away and enlarging the wind edge of the hole in the " buoy," until it will sound if the mouth of the " gun " is held directly into a moderate wind.

The boatswain's call is held between the index finger and thumb, the latter being on or near the " shackle " (Fig. 66 (ii)). The side of the buoy rests against the palm of the hand, and the fingers close over the gun and buoy hole in such a position as to be able to throttle the exit of air from the buoy to the desired amount. Care must be taken that the fingers do not touch the edge of the hole in the buoy, or of the hole in the end of the gun, otherwise all sound will be completely choked.

A great variety of notes and tones may be obtained with the boatswain's call by manipulating the fingers and varying the breath blown into the mouth of the gun, but certain notes and tones are only used in piping in the Royal Navy and these, together with the method of producing them, are described below.

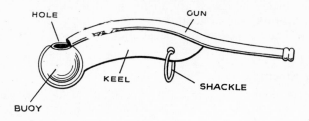

(i) The boatswain's call

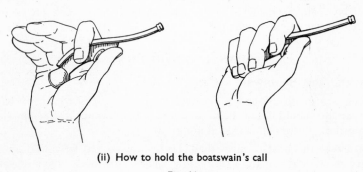

(ii) How to hold the boatswain's call

Fig. 66

There are two main notes, the " low " and the " high," and there are three tones ; these tones are the " plain," marked on the chart (Fig. 67) with a steady line, the " warble," marked with a wavy line, and the " trill," marked with a cross-hatched line.

The plain low note is produced by blowing steadily into the mouth of the gun with the hole of the buoy unobstructed by the fingers. The plain high note is produced by throttling the exit of air from the hole of the buoy ; this is done by closing the fingers around the buoy, taking care not to touch the edges of the hole or the end of the gun. Intermediate notes can be obtained by throttling to a greater or lesser degree.

The warble is produced by blowing in a series of jerks, which results in a warble similar to that of a canary.

The trill is produced by vibrating the tongue while blowing, as in rolling the letter " R."

The chart shows the various " pipes " used in the Royal Navy today. The figures at the top of each diagram represent seconds of time. The nature, continuity and tone of the notes are indicated by the various lines, and the degree of their slope indicates the speed of ascent or descent of the notes.

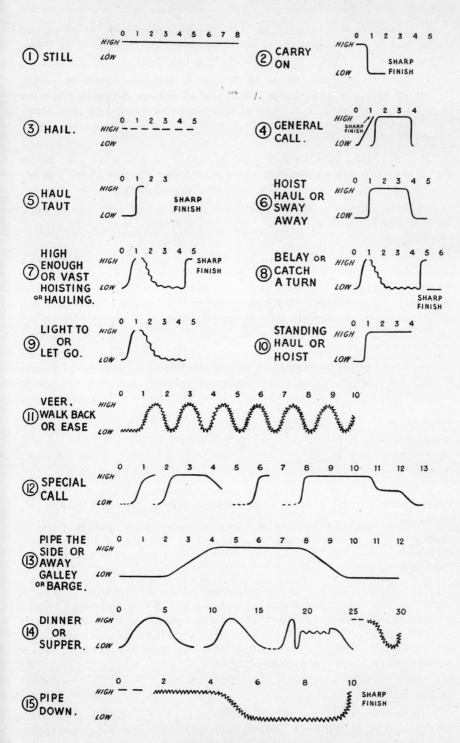

Fig. 67.—Piping chart

Pipes

(1) Except for Nos. 3, 4, 12 and 13, the pipes are an order in themselves and require no verbal addition ; *e.g.*, it is incorrect and superfluous to follow the pipe for dinner by the words " Hands to dinner."

(2) The " Still " is used to call all hands to attention as a mark of respect, or to order silence on any occasion, or to stop all work in the vicinity in order to prevent an accident. It is followed at the required interval by the " Carry on," and, in the last example, usually not until verbal orders have been given to remedy what was wrong.

(3) The " Hail " was formerly used to call all boatswain's mates, but is used nowadays to attract the attention of a particular person in an unobtrusive manner, the coxswain of a boat or a member of the gangway staff, for example.

(4) Particular attention must be paid to the hoisting and hauling pipes. These can be used when manning purchases or falls, or working the capstan by hand.

(5) No. 4 pipe precedes any routine order such as " Up spirits " or " Out pipes," or any short order such as " Able Seaman Smith lay aft " ; it draws attention to the order. No. 4 pipe also precedes the calling away of any boat's crew, except that of the barge for which No. 13 pipe is used. With the exception of the barge the crew and not the boat is referred to when piping, examples of the relevant pipes being " Awa-a-a-y first motor boat's crew," and " Awa-a-a-y barge."

(6) No. 12 pipe precedes the calling of the hands and is followed by the order " Lash up and stow," In practice it is customary considerably to amplify this pipe, a typical example being : " Heave out ! Heave out ! Heave out ! Show a leg ! Show a leg ! Lash and carry ! Lash and carry ! Rise and shine ! Rise and shine ! Heave out, lash up and stow ! Heave out, lash up and stow ! Heave out, lash up and stow !," and this may be followed by a short description of any adverse weather such as : " Gale and rain," or " Ice and snow," to warn those below to put on suitable clothing.

When calling the watch at night the pipe is followed by the words " A-a-a-ll the (requisite) watch," given in a low but clear voice and repeated once.

This pipe also precedes some out-of-routine order or information of general interest to the ship's company, which in turn is preceded by the words " D'ye hear there ! " ; for example, " D'ye hear there ! The last mail will close at noon today."

(7) A routine pipe and its accompanying order is not repeated ; the words " at once " or " at the double " are superfluous and should not be used because all seamen are expected to obey an order as quickly as they are able. In general, piping is reserved for passing orders and information of importance ; it should not be used for trivial matters, or for purposes which could be served equally well by using a messenger.

Bugle Calls

The more important routine orders are passed by the bugle in ships which carry a bugler. Most of these bugle calls are an order in themselves and require no qualification by pipe, so that if, for example, " Both watches for exercise " are required to muster in the usual place, on the forecastle, the bugle call "Both watches for exercise" should not be followed by some such order as "Both watches for exercise fall in on the forecastle." If, however, the watches were required to muster in an unaccustomed place, *e.g.* on the quarterdeck, the bugle call would be followed by the order "Muster on the quarterdeck." It is the duty of all hands to learn and recognise the standard bugle calls and pipes.

Verbal Orders

It is most important that all verbal orders should be brief and concise, and to avoid the possibility of any misunderstanding the method of giving verbal orders has been standardised throughout the Service.

This standardization includes a special phonetic alphabet which is given below and which must be mastered.

THE PHONETIC ALPHABET

Letters

A	ALFA	J	JULIET	S	SIERRA
B	BRAVO	K	KILO	T	TANGO
C	CHARLIE	L	LIMA	U	UNIFORM
D	DELTA	M	MIKE	V	VICTOR
E	ECHO	N	NOVEMBER	W	WHISKEY
F	FOXTROT	O	OSCAR	X	X-RAY
G	GOLF	P	PAPA	Y	YANKEE
H	HOTEL	Q	QUEBEC	Z	ZULU
I	INDIA	R	ROMEO		

Numbers

0	ZERO	5	FI-YIV
1	WUN	6	SIX
2	TOO	7	SE-VEN
3	THUH-REE	8	ATE
4	FO-WER	9	NI-NER

ORGANISATION

Command

A warship is commanded by an officer of the Executive Branch who is known as the Commanding Officer or the Captain. He may be of any rank from Captain to Lieutenant, depending upon the size and type of the ship he commands.

Next in importance to the Captain is the Executive Officer, who may be of any rank from Commander to Sub-lieutenant. He is specially appointed to carry out executive duties in the ship, and he is responsible to the Captain for the fighting efficiency of the ship, the general organisation and routine of the ship's company, and the discipline, morale and welfare of everyone on board her. In ships where the Executive Officer is of Commander's rank he is known as the Commander, otherwise he is known as the First Lieutenant ;

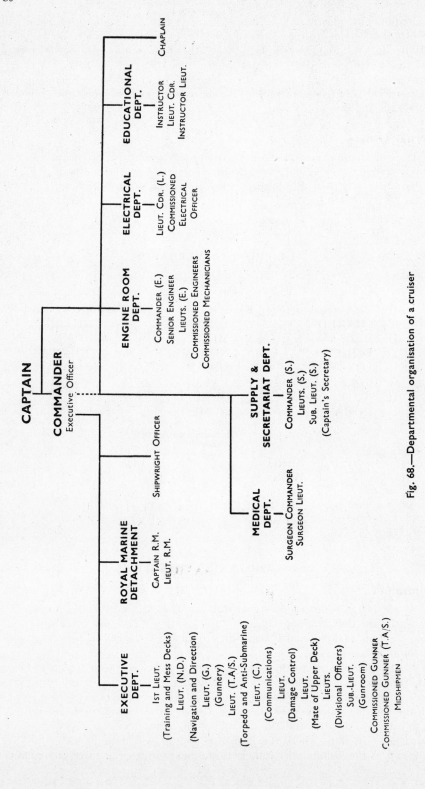

CAPTAIN

COMMANDER
Executive Officer

EXECUTIVE DEPT.

1st Lieut.
(Training and Mess Decks)
Lieut. (N.D.)
(Navigation and Direction)
Lieut. (G.)
(Gunnery)
Lieut. (T.A/S.)
(Torpedo and Anti-Submarine)
Lieut. (C.)
(Communications)
Lieut.
(Damage Control)
Lieut.
(Mate of Upper Deck)
Lieuts.
(Divisional Officers)
Sub.-Lieut.
(Gunroom)
Commissioned Gunner
Commissioned Gunner (T.A/S.)
Midshipmen

ROYAL MARINE DETACHMENT

Captain R.M.
Lieut. R.M.

Shipwright Officer

MEDICAL DEPT.

Surgeon Commander
Surgeon Lieut.

SUPPLY & SECRETARIAT DEPT.

Commander (S.)
Lieuts. (S.)
Sub. Lieut. (S.)
(Captain's Secretary)

ENGINE ROOM DEPT.

Commander (E.)
Senior Engineer
Lieuts. (E.)
Commissioned Engineers
Commissioned Mechanicians

ELECTRICAL DEPT.

Lieut. Cdr. (L.)
Commissioned Electrical Officer

EDUCATIONAL DEPT.

Instructor Lieut. Cdr.
Instructor Lieut.

Chaplain

Fig. 68.—Departmental organisation of a cruiser

in ships where the Executive Officer is a Commander the officer of the Executive Branch next in seniority to him is known as the First Lieutenant.

In the event of the death or incapacity of the Captain the command of the ship devolves upon the senior surviving officer of the Executive Branch ; if no officer of the Executive Branch survives it devolves upon the senior surviving rating of the Seaman Branch.

In the temporary absence on leave or duty of the Captain the command of the ship for the time being is vested in the senior officer of the Executive Branch on board.

Departments

The men who man a warship are known collectively as her " ship's company," and for administrative purposes the ship's company is divided into " departments " which correspond with the various branches of the Service. Fig. 68 shows the departmental organisation of a cruiser.

The senior officer of each department is known as the " Head " of his department, and he is responsible to the Captain for the efficiency of his department and the work it carries out.

Watches

A continuous watch must be kept in a ship, both day and night and at sea or in harbour, to ensure her safety and to ensure her readiness for any duty she may be called upon to perform. A proportion of her complement of officers and men must therefore always be on watch, either actively engaged or standing-by at immediate notice. The number of officers and men on watch depends upon the type of ship, whether she is at sea or in harbour, and the duties on which she is engaged. In order to provide a continuous watch to suit every occasion, and to allow adequate periods for the rest and recreation of the men, a ship's company is divided into watches and parts of watches, in each of which there are sufficient men of the various branches, and with the necessary technical qualifications, to carry out any duty which the watch, or part of a watch may be called upon to perform.

Watch Systems

In the Royal Navy there are two types of watch organisation, known respectively as the " Two-watch " and the " Three-watch " systems.

In either system each watch is divided into two parts, and in large ships each part may be divided into two " sub-divisions." A part of a watch, or a sub-division, is the smallest body of men that is used to work or fight the ship.

The men off watch carry out their general ship's duties during working hours in accordance with the routine in force at the time. Whether the seamen work in two or three watches depends upon the type of ship and the arrangement of her armament, and they may be changed from the one to the other according to the duties she has to carry out. The Engine-room Department usually work in three watches except when steaming at full power for prolonged periods ; other departments usually conform to the system adopted for the seamen.

Two-watch system.—In the Two-watch system the men are equally divided into the " Starboard watch " and the " Port watch," and each watch is equally

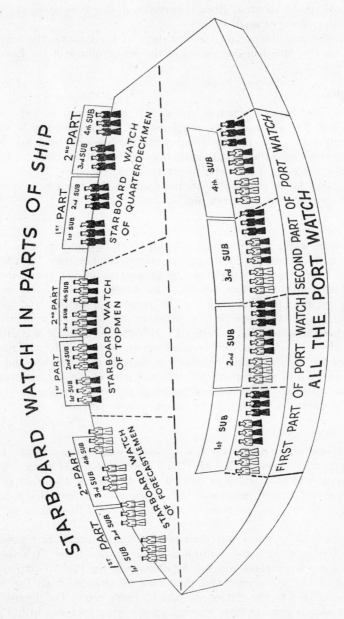

STARBOARD WATCH IN PARTS OF SHIP

2ND PART · 1ST PART

4th SUB · 3rd SUB · 2nd SUB · 1st SUB

STARBOARD WATCH OF QUARTERDECKMEN

2ND PART · 1ST PART

4th SUB · 3rd SUB · 2nd SUB · 1st SUB

STARBOARD WATCH OF TOPMEN

2ND PART · 1ST PART

4th SUB · 3rd SUB · 2nd SUB · 1st SUB

STARBOARD WATCH OF FORECASTLEMEN

4th SUB · 3rd SUB · 2nd SUB · 1st SUB

FIRST PART OF PORT WATCH | SECOND PART OF PORT WATCH

ALL THE PORT WATCH

Fig. 69

divided into the " First part " and the " Second part." With this system the men can be worked " watch-and-watch," *i.e.* four hours on and four hours off at sea, or one day on and the next day off in harbour, or in four watches, that is four hours on and twelve hours off at sea, or one day on and three days off in harbour. In general ship work, and for manning the armament in wartime, this system provides for three-quarters, a half, or a quarter of the ship's company to be used at any time ; see Fig. 69.

Three-watch system.—In the Three-watch system, the men are divided into " Red," " White " and " Blue " watches, and each watch may be divided into its first and second parts. With this system the men can be worked in " three watches," *i.e.* four hours on and eight hours off at sea, or one day on and two days off in harbour. The system provides for two-thirds, one-third, or one-sixth of the ship's company to be used for any work or duty required.

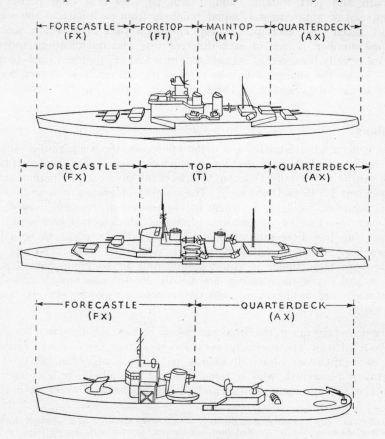

Fig. 70.—Parts-of-ship

Parts-of-Ship

For purposes of cleaning, maintenance and general shipwork a warship is divided into what are known as " parts-of-ship." The number and names of these parts depend upon the type and size of the ship ; in a battleship there will usually be four, *i.e.* " Forecastle (F.X.)," " Foretop (F.T.),"

" Maintop (M.T.)," and " Quarterdeck (A.X.) " ; a smaller ship may be divided into three parts, *i.e.* " Forecastle (F.X.)," " Top (T.) " and " Quarterdeck (A.X.)," or into only two parts, *i.e.* " Forecastle (F.X.) " and " Quarterdeck (A.X.)." (The abbreviations shown in brackets are those used when marking the gear belonging to the respective parts of ship ; A.X. (for " after-castle ") is used instead of Q.D. as it is easier to mark, and the quarterdeck now replaces the after-castle of former days.)

Seamen petty officers and men are detailed for each part-of-ship in approximately equal numbers from each part of the watch, and they are then known as Forecastlemen, Foretopmen, Maintopmen, Topmen, Quarterdeckmen, etc., according to the part to which they are allocated.

Fig. 69 shows the division of a ship's company into parts-of-ship and starboard and port watches, and it will be seen that each part-of-ship is composed of approximately equal numbers from each part of the watch. Care is taken that each part-of-ship and each part of a watch contains an equal number of men of each different rate and qualification, and that they are equally balanced as regards seniority and experience. Each part-of-ship is under the charge of two or three petty officers (one to each watch) known as the First, Second, or Third " Captain of the Top."*

Divisions

For general administrative and welfare purposes, the whole ship's company is divided into a number of " divisions," which correspond with the departments of the ship (*e.g.* " Supply Division," " Electrical Division," " Communication Division " and " Boys Division "). The number of seamen in a ship of any size is, however, too large for them to be grouped in a single division, and they may therefore be divided into divisions which correspond with their parts of ship (*e.g.* Forecastle, Top and Quarterdeck divisions), or with their watches (*e.g.* Starboard and Port, or Red, White and Blue divisions). The Engine-room Department is also too numerous to be grouped in a single division, and engine-room ratings are usually divided into four divisions, one for artificers and mechanicians, and the remaining three for stokers, one for each watch.

The main principle of the divisional system is that each division is composed of a body of men who normally work and mess together and who therefore know each other well. Each division is under the charge of an officer of the department concerned, who is responsible for the administration, training, instruction, advancement, welfare and general efficiency of everyone in it.

---

* The term " top " originated in the days of sail, when the crew of a " ship of the line " with three masts would be divided into fo'c'slemen, foretopmen, maintopmen, mizzen-topmen, quarterdeckmen, waisters, and idlers or daymen. The topmen were able-bodied and ordinary seamen who, with a small number of boys, worked aloft on the masts and yards and were regarded as being the cream of the seaman complement. The older and less active able seamen and ordinary seamen, supplemented by boys, were allocated to the forecastle and quarterdeck. The waisters were made up of old or infirm seamen, and landsmen or " greenhorns " ; they worked in the waist of the ship, " had little else of duty than hauling, swabbing decks, picking oakum and other menial tasks ", and were looked down upon by all on board. The daymen or idlers comprised the artisans, such as the carpenter and sailmakers, and others such as the cooks ; they were not allocated to watches or parts-of-ship, worked regular hours during the day, and had " every night in ", but they had to turn to at the order " All hands ".

CHAPTER V

Rope and its Usage

IN this chapter are described the various types of rope with which a seaman works, and the manner in which he uses them. Rope of any kind can be described as belonging to one of two main types, *i.e.* :—

cordage (which is rope made of vegetable fibres), and
steel wire rope.

The chapter has been divided into four main sections, headed as follows :—

(i) Construction and Characteristics of Cordage and Wire Rope ;

(ii) Handling of Cordage, Wire Rope and Hawsers ;

(iii) Bends and Hitches ;

(iv) General Rope Work.

In Volume II of this manual a chapter is included which describes more advanced work in rope. It is divided into four sections headed :—

(i) Knots and General Advanced Work in Cordage ;

(ii) Hawsers, and their Handling, Care and Maintenance ;

(iii) Splicing of Wire Rope ;

(iv) Types, Supply, Strengths and General Notes on Cordage and Wire Rope.

CONSTRUCTION AND CHARACTERISTICS OF CORDAGE

Construction and Types

Though it is not necessary to go deeply into the process of ropemaking, an elementary knowledge of its principles is desirable.

Ropes are made from vegetable fibres each of which is only about five feet long, and the first process is to comb these fibres out in a long even ribbon, as shown in an exaggerated form in Fig. 71.

Fig. 71.—Fibres of a rope

The ribbons are then twisted up into yarns, and the twist thus given binds the fibres firmly together so that they hold by friction when the yarn is subjected to strain. The shorter the length of the fibres used the harder this twist must be to give the necessary strength to the yarn. This process is known as spinning, and yarns are said to be spun left or right-handed, according to the direction of twist.

Next, a certain number of yarns are twisted together to form strands which, at the Admiralty Ropery, are each 150 fathoms in length when completed.

The number and size of the yarns required to make each strand depends on the size of the rope it is intended to make. This stage is known as twisting the strands, and again, the twist can be left or right-handed.

Three or four strands are now made up into a left or right-handed rope. This process is called "laying" and is always carried out in the opposite direction to that used in the previous stage of twisting the strands; it is, moreover, distinct from the simple spin or twist, and is twofold, in that :—

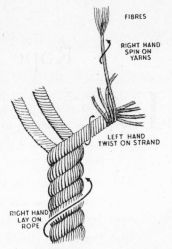

Fig. 72.—Component parts of a right-handed hawser-laid rope

    (i) the strands are twisted up together to form the rope, and

    (ii) at the same time the strands are rotated individually in the direction of their original twist.

Were this not done, laying the strands together would tend to untwist the yarns in each strand.

As the rope is thus laid up its length contracts like a coiled spring, thus giving it a certain amount of elasticity. The harder the twist given in laying, the shorter will be the resultant rope, and, in practice, three strands of 150 fathoms lay up into a rope about 120 fathoms in length.

Three strands so laid up constitute a "hawser-laid rope" (Fig. 72), which is the type of cordage most commonly used.

Fig. 73.—Shroud-laid rope

Fig. 74.—Cable-laid or water-laid rope

Four-stranded rope laid up round a heart or centre is known as "shroud-laid rope" (Fig. 73). It is somewhat weaker than three-stranded rope of a similar size, but is less liable to stretch.

Three hawser-laid ropes, each of 120 fathoms, laid up together in the opposite direction to that of their own lay will form a "cable-laid," or "water-laid rope," 100 fathoms in length. (Fig. 74.) Such a rope is weaker than a hawser-laid rope of equal size, but by reason of its construction it is more elastic and is therefore used where elasticity is the chief requirement, as in towing. Furthermore, cable-laid rope, being more solid in construction, is more resistant to chafe and does not absorb water so readily as hawser-laid rope.

Direction of the Lay

In the Royal Navy hawser-laid rope is normally laid up right-handed ; that is, the strands twist away from the eye in a right-handed spiral, as in Fig. 72.

The direction of the lay can also be seen at a glance when the rope is viewed from the side, as illustrated in Fig. 75 (i).

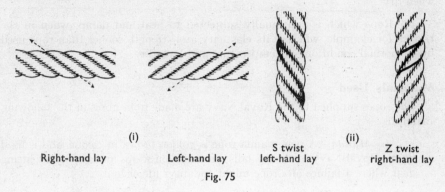

(i)

Right-hand lay   Left-hand lay

S twist
left-hand lay

(ii)

Z twist
right-hand lay

Fig. 75

In the rope trade, right-hand lay is described as " Z twist " and left-hand lay as " S twist," the letters indicating the direction of the lay when the rope is viewed from above (Fig. 75 (ii)).

In a normal right-handed rope :—

fibres are spun right-handed to form yarns ;
yarns are twisted left-handed into strands ; and
strands are laid up right-handed into rope.

Left-handed ropes, in which each component is made in exactly the opposite direction, are found in commercial practice, but the only such cordage supplied to the Royal Navy is hammock lashing and marline.

Description

In the Royal Navy cordage is described by reference to the circumference of the rope measured in inches, and to the material from which it is made ; $4\frac{1}{2}$-inch manila for example. In the United States and other countries rope is measured by its diameter and this practice is gaining ground in Great Britain. The size of a strand is that of the rope from which it was taken ; thus a 2-inch strand is one taken from a 2-inch rope. The length of a rope is measured in fathoms.

General Characteristics

(i) The strands tend to fly apart unless the end of the rope is whipped (*i.e.* firmly bound) with twine.

(ii) The rope will stretch under load but may be expected to regain its normal length when slack, provided that the load applied is well within the breaking stress of the rope ; a greater load, however, even if it does not part the rope, will cause a permanent extension in its length and thereby render it unfit for service. The older and more worn the rope, the less elasticity it will possess and the weaker it will become.

(iii) Rope under load will tend to twist in the opposite direction to that of its lay and thereby tend to unlay itself, but it should regain its normal form when slack.

(iv) Rope when wet will shrink in length in proportion to the amount by which it swells in diameter, but it will recover a proportion of its original length when dry.

(v) Rope which is continually subjected to heat and damp, when in the tropics for example, will lose its elasticity and strength sooner than rope used under normal conditions of temperature and humidity.

Materials Used

The ropes supplied to the Royal Navy are made from fibres of the following materials :—

(i) *Manila*. A new manila rope is golden brown in colour, and is used in the Royal Navy for boats' falls, ammunition whips and important lifting gear where a failure of a rope might endanger life or limb.

(ii) *Sisal*. This is hairy, of a pale straw colour, and is used for general purposes other than those mentioned above. Sisal is sometimes treated with tar to protect it from the weather ; it is then dark brown in colour and is known as " tarred sisal."

(iii) *Hemp*. This also is of a pale straw colour, but is hard and smooth in texture. It is at present only used in the Royal Navy for small lines (*e.g.* codline).

(iv) *Coir, or Grass Line*. This is very rough and of a coconut brown colour. It is much lighter and weaker than the others, but is more resilient and is useful because it will float on water.

The properties, strength, and other particulars of these different ropes, also details of " small stuff," are given in the chapter on rope in Volume II of this manual.

Care and Maintenance

Apart from necessary inspections, there is but one golden rule for the care and maintenance of cordage, that is—*not to stow it away when wet*. If this is unavoidable, however, the rope should be brought out and dried at the first opportunity.

Boats' falls, which are stowed on reels, have only too often to be reeled up wet and so are very liable to rot. Consequently, they should not be turned end-for-end without first being subjected to careful inspection throughout their whole length.

Strength

A rough method of finding the breaking load of manila, sisal, or hemp cordage is to square its circumference (in inches) and divide by 3, the answer being in tons. This allows for a good margin of safety for all types of cordage except coir.

The working load is found by dividing the breaking load by 6.

Example for 3-inch cordage :—

Breaking Load	*Working Load*
$\dfrac{(3)^2}{3} = 3$ tons.	$\dfrac{3}{6} =$ half a ton.

A nearer approximation to the specific breaking loads of new cordage is found by dividing the square of its circumference by 2·5 for ropes of size up to 6 inches, and by 2·6 for ropes of size above 6 inches.

To estimate the strength of rope which is well worn but in good condition, apply the formula as for new rope but use the actual and not the nominal circumference.

CONSTRUCTION AND CHARACTERISTICS OF WIRE ROPE

Construction

A wire rope is constructed of a number of small wires which extend continuously throughout its entire length ; these wires are twisted into strands, and the strands themselves are laid up to form the rope. With the exception of certain special types (*e.g.* minesweeping ropes, paravane ropes and ropes of purchases), all wire ropes used at sea consist of six strands ; the wires forming a strand are twisted left-handed around a jute or wire *core*, and the strands forming the rope are laid up right-handed around a hemp or jute *heart*.

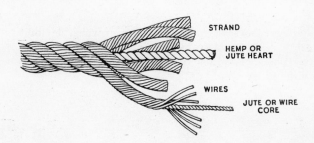

Fig. 76.—Construction of a steel wire rope

The hemp or jute heart has two functions :—

(i) it acts as a cushion into which the strands bed, allowing them to take up their natural position as the rope is bent or subjected to strain ;

(ii) it absorbs the linseed oil or other lubricant with which the rope should periodically be dressed, so that as the rope is stretched or flexed the oil is squeezed between the wires, thus lubricating them and minimising any friction between them.

A wire rope can be made flexible in one of two ways :—

    (i) by replacing the centre wires of each strand with a large core of jute or hemp, in which case strength is sacrificed to flexibility ; or

    (ii) by making up each strand with a large number of small-gauge wires round a wire core, in which case the full strength is retained.

Types

    Ropes used at sea are manufactured on the foregoing principles, and those supplied to the Royal Navy fall into the four following groups :—

    (1) *Steel Wire Rope* (S.W.R.) (Fig. 77).   This is used for standing rigging such as shrouds and funnel guys, and so is not required to be flexible. Its strands are therefore each made up of a small number of large-gauge wires, wound round a steel wire core.

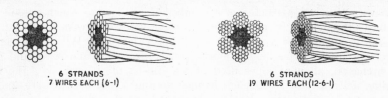

6 STRANDS
7 WIRES EACH (6-1)

6 STRANDS
19 WIRES EACH (12-6-1)

Fig. 77.—Steel wire rope for standing rigging

    (2) *Flexible Steel Wire Rope* (F.S.W.R.) (Fig. 78).   This is used for running rigging, hawsers, and other ropes in which flexibility is necessary. To make it flexible necessitates sacrificing a certain proportion of its strength, and its strands each consist of a number of medium gauge wires wound round a large jute core.

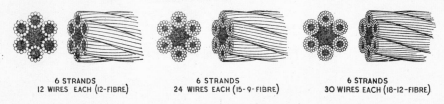

6 STRANDS
12 WIRES EACH (12-FIBRE)

6 STRANDS
24 WIRES EACH (15-9-FIBRE)

6 STRANDS
30 WIRES EACH (18-12-FIBRE)

Fig. 78.—Flexible steel wire rope for hawsers and running rigging

    (3) *Extra Special Flexible Steel Wire Rope* (E.S.F.S.W.R.) (Fig. 79). This is used where strength and flexibility are both essential.   The strands are constructed of large numbers of small gauge wires which are made of higher quality steel than are those used for the other two groups.   (The term " extra special " refers more to the quality of the steel than to the flexibility of the rope.)

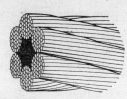 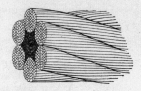

6 STRANDS
37 WIRES EACH (18-12-6-1)

6 STRANDS
61 WIRES EACH (24-18-12-6-1)

Fig. 79.—Extra special flexible steel wire rope for hoists and special purposes

(4) *Flexible Mild Steel Wire Rope* (F.M.S.W.R.). This is supplied in small sizes only ($\frac{11}{16}$-in. to $1\frac{1}{4}$-in.), and used for such purposes as seizing and serving. It differs from the foregoing groups in that it is made of pliable mild steel, is much weaker, and of different construction. The smaller sizes consist of a single strand only, and the larger ($\frac{1}{2}$-in. and above) are made up of four strands.

ⁿ addition to these main groups there are specially constructed wire ropes for equipment such as mine moorings and sweeps, paravane towing ropes, crane purchases, boats' falls, and sounding machines. Flexible copper wire rope is supplied in sizes from $\frac{3}{8}$ to $1\frac{1}{2}$-in. for use in the wake of magnetic compasses, *e.g.* for ridge ropes and jackstays of bridge awnings.

Description

In the Royal Navy wire rope is described by initials denoting the type of the rope (*e.g.* S.W.R., F.S.W.R. or E.S.F.S.W.R.), preceded by the circumference of the rope measured in inches, and followed by bracketed figures representing the number of strands in the rope and the number of wires in a strand, thus : 3-inch S.W.R. (6 × 7), or 3-inch F.S.W.R. (6 × 12), or 3-inch E.S.F.S.W.R. (6 × 37), for example.

Measurement

In the Merchant Navy and foreign navies, the size of wire rope may be measured by its diameter. When determining the size of a wire rope in this way it should be measured, at any point throughout its length, across its *largest diameter*. The following table shows a comparison between the circumference and diameter of different sizes of rope :—

CIRCUM-FERENCE in. m.m.	DIAMETER in. m.m.	CIRCUM-FERENCE in. m.m.	DIAMETER in. m.m.	CIRCUM-FERENCE in. m.m.	DIAMETER in. m.m.
1 25	$\frac{5}{16}$ 8	3 76	$\frac{15}{16}$ 24	5 127	$1\frac{15}{16}$ 40
$1\frac{1}{2}$ 38	$\frac{15}{32}$ 12	$3\frac{1}{2}$ 89	$1\frac{1}{8}$ 28	$5\frac{1}{2}$ 140	$1\frac{3}{4}$ 44
2 51	$\frac{5}{8}$ 16	4 102	$1\frac{5}{16}$ 32	6 152	$1\frac{7}{8}$ 48
$2\frac{1}{2}$ 63	$\frac{13}{16}$ 20	$4\frac{1}{2}$ 114	$1\frac{7}{16}$ 36	$6\frac{1}{2}$ 165	$2\frac{1}{16}$ 52

The length of wire ropes is measured in fathoms ; they are issued in coils whose lengths vary with the type and size of the rope ; usually the smaller the size of the rope the greater is the length of a coil.

The following list gives a general indication of the length of a coil of various types of wire ropes :—

> S.W.R. for standing rigging—150 and 200 fathoms.
> F.S.W.R. for hawsers and running rigging—150, 200, 240, 300 and 360 fathoms.
> E.S.F.S.W.R.—100, 150 and 300 fathoms.

Strength

The breaking load of wire rope differs in each type. It may be calculated approximately in tons by multiplying the square of the circumference by the figure indicated in the table below :—

F.S.W.R. up to 4½-inch	2
F.S.W.R. above 4½-inch	2½
S.W.R.	2¾
E.S.F.S.W.R.	3·6

The working load of wire rope is one-sixth of its breaking load for standing rigging and hawsers, and one-eighth for running rigging and slings.

Comparison with Cordage

Wire rope is from 5 to 9 times as strong as manila of equal size, and from 1½ to 2 times the strength of manila of equal weight. It is also much more durable than any fibre rope, and if treated correctly will give a long life of hard work.

Wire rope stretches only slightly under stress and for practical purposes it can be considered as non-elastic. Its lack of elasticity makes it very suitable for standing and running rigging, but is a disadvantage in operations such as towing where sudden heavy stresses are to be expected, because wire ropes will part if allowed to take the strain too quickly.

Like cordage, wire rope of normal lay will tend to twist in the opposite direction to that of its lay when under stress.

All wire ropes are much less flexible than fibre cordage, and great care must be taken with regard to the size and shape of sheaves, drums and bollards around which they have to pass.

The fundamental difference in the construction of wire rope and vegetable fibre cordage is that the former is built up of wires which are continuous throughout the length of the rope, whereas the latter is manufactured from fibres which are each only a few feet in length.

HANDLING OF CORDAGE

Elementary Rules

Four lessons which a seaman must learn before he handles a rope are explained below.

(i) *The Seaman's Knife.* The seaman should regard his knife as his best friend and should carry it with him wherever he goes ; without it he is like a joiner without his tools. The knife should be worn on a lanyard, either around the waist or the neck, and preferably stowed in a small, specially made pocket in the trousers or jumper. The lanyard should never be made as a running noose, otherwise it may strangle him.

The seaman's knife is a tool and not a weapon; the end of the blade should be rounded, not pointed, and the blade should be sufficiently deep and thick to cut without bending. The edge of the blade should be sharpened like a chisel to avoid wearing away the thickness and strength of the blade, and the hinge should be kept lightly oiled.

(ii) *Safety of Tools.* Whenever a seaman works aloft, or over the side, he must secure whatever tools he may be using with a lanyard secured to a part of the rigging or passed around his body. This is a commonsense precaution for avoiding possible injury to men working below him, or loss of the tools over the side.

(iii) *Rope Ends.* When a rope is cut its ends should at once be whipped to prevent it unlaying and thus rendering a fathom or more of the rope useless. An unwhipped rope's end is the trade mark of the land-lubber.

(iv) *Coiling down ropes.* A heaving line, or any line or rope which is being hauled in, should be coiled either in the hand or on the deck *as it is hauled aboard.* This is an elementary, seamanlike precaution to ensure that the line or rope is immediately ready for further use.

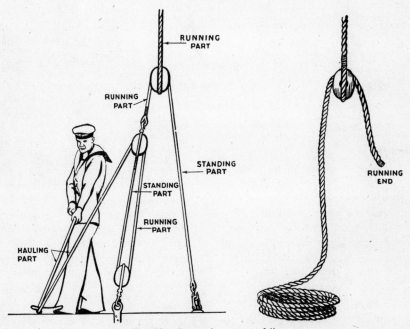

Fig. 80.—Parts of a rope or fall

Terms used when Handling Ropes (Fig. 80)

The following terms are used to define the different parts of ropes and tackles when in use :—

Bight.—The middle part of a rope between its two ends, or between two points of suspension. A rope is said to "hang in a bight" when hanging slackly between two points.

Standing Part.—That part of a rope which is made fast to a mast, deck, block of a tackle, or other fitting, in contrast to the hauling or running parts.

Hauling Part.—That part of a rope or a tackle which is hauled upon.

Running Part.—That part of a rope or tackle which runs through the blocks.

Fall.—The rope of a tackle.

Running End.—That part of a length of rope which first runs out from a coil, flake, or reel, or through a block or fairlead.

The Common Whipping

Ordinary twine is used for whipping. There are several types of whippings, examples of which are shown later in this chapter, but to be able to make a " common whipping," as described below, should suffice for the beginner :—

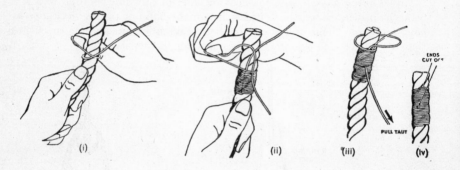

Fig. 81.—The common whipping

Place the end of the twine along the rope, as in Fig. 81 (i) ; pass turns of the twine over the rope against its lay, working towards the end of the rope, and haul each turn taut. Then lay the other end of the twine along the rope, as in Fig. 81 (ii), and pass the remaining turns over it, taking the bight of twine over the end of the rope with each turn. When the bight becomes too small to pass over the end of the rope, haul this second end of the twine through the turns which you have passed over it until taut, thus completing the last turn round the rope, and cut off the end. (Figs. 81 (iii) and 81 (iv)).

An alternative finish, which can be used when the whipping is on the bight of the rope, is to take the last three or four turns loosely over one finger and pass the end back through them. The turns are worked taut, and the end hauled taut as above.

Permanent Finishes for Rope Ends (Fig. 82)

Permanently to prevent a rope's end from unlaying, it is finished with one of the following alternatives instead of with a whipping :—

(i) *A backsplice.* The backsplice has the disadvantage that it will not reeve through a block intended for the rope.

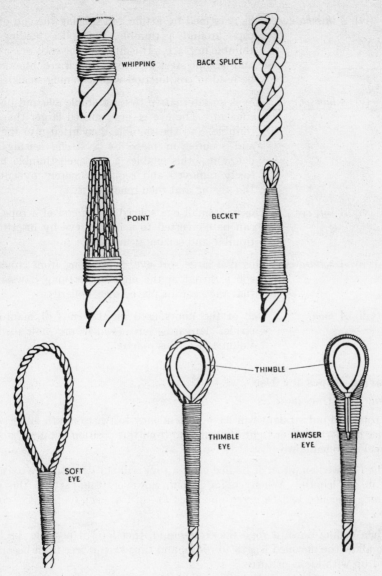

WHIPPING   BACK SPLICE

POINT   BECKET

THIMBLE

SOFT EYE   THIMBLE EYE   HAWSER EYE

Fig. 82.—Permanent finishes for rope ends

(ii) *A point.*   This is the most efficient and most ornamental method of ending a rope which is intended to pass easily through a block or eye (*e.g.* a boat's painter).

(iii) *A becket.*   A becket is a small loop fitted to the pointed end of a large fibre hawser, and is made from rope of about one-quarter the size of its hawser. It enables the hawser to be " tailed " with a line to facilitate handling it or reeving it through an overhead block.

(iv) *A thimble eye.* This is formed by fitting and splicing the end of the rope around a thimble, the splice holding the thimble in place. It is fitted in the ends of cordage and flexible steel wire ropes which are intended to be used in conjunction with a joining shackle.

(v) *A hawser eye.* This is an alternative to the thimble eye and just as efficient. The eye is first spliced larger than the thimble, and the thimble then fitted into the eye and secured in place by a strong seizing just below it ; this enables a damaged thimble to be easily removed and replaced, merely by cutting the seizing and then renewing it.

(vi) *A soft eye.* This is a small eye spliced in the end of a rope. It can be converted to a hawser eye by inserting a thimble and seizing it into place.

(vii) *A bollard eye.* This is a large soft eye, 5 feet long from crown to splice, fitted in the ends of berthing hawsers so that they can be placed over bollards.

(viii) *A knot.* One of the knots used on the ends of manropes, rudder lanyards, etc., which are described in Volume II of this manual.

Preparing Ropes for Use

COILING AND UNCOILING

A rope laid out straight will have no tendency to twist or turn either way, whether its lay be left or right-handed, and from this position it can be stowed on a reel or coiled down.

When stowed on a reel or hauled off it a rope will not develop any twists or turns in its length. When coiling down, however, the part of the rope remaining uncoiled will be given one twist or turn as each loop in the coil is formed.

When coiling down a rope the end should, therefore, if possible, be kept free to allow the uncoiled length to rotate and thus keep it free from becoming snarled up with kinks or turns.

Similarly, a rope which is run off a coil will acquire a twist or turn for every loop in the coil, but if the end is kept free the rope will usually free itself of these turns when hauled out straight.

One method of avoiding these turns, should the end of the rope not be free, is to turn the coil round while coiling down the rope, thus turning the coil into a reel. Another method, as when coiling direct from a reel, is to allow as long a length as possible between reel and coil ; this length will absorb the turns until the end of the rope is free from the reel, and so can be freed of its turns. Similarly, when coiling down a rope which is led through a block, as in a boat's fall for example, the coil should not be made too near the block, otherwise a slight check may cause a kink to develop in the rope as it is running through and thus choke the luff of the block.

(i) Coiling down with the end made fast—kinks developing

(ii) Result of coiling down left-handed

Fig. 83

COILING DOWN (Fig. 83)

Cordage is very resilient and will absorb a number of turns in its length without becoming snarled if the length is sufficient and the turns correspond with the lay of the rope ; if the turns are against the lay, however, it will quickly become snarled. For this reason rope of right-hand lay is always coiled down right-handed, and rope of left-hand lay is always coiled down left-handed.

TO COIL A ROPE FOR RUNNING (Fig. 84)

Lay the rope as straight as possible along the deck ; begin coiling it down close to where the standing part is made fast, and lay each loop flat upon the one below it until the bare end is reached. The size of the loops should be as large as stowage space permits.

The running part is now underneath the coil, so turn the coil over and the rope should then run out freely when required. Remember that the running part or end should always be on the top of any coil.

4*

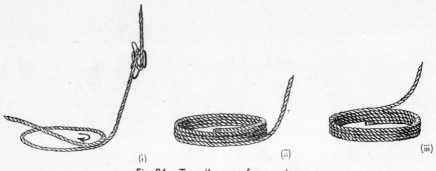

(i)   (ii)   (iii)

Fig. 84.—To coil a rope for running

To Thoroughfoot a Rope

This is the most effective way of taking a large number of turns out of a rope. First determine whether the turns it is required to remove are left or right-handed. Then, to remove left-hand turns, coil down left-handed, dip the end through the coil and haul the coil out straight. To remove right-hand turns, coil right-handed and proceed as before.

If the bight of the rope is badly snarled, thoroughfoot the end for only a few fathoms at a time, repeating this operation as often as necessary.

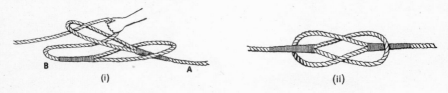

B   A
(i)   (ii)

Fig. 85.—(i) Thoroughfooting. (ii) Cow hitch

Thoroughfooting also describes the method of joining two ropes by their soft eyes (see Fig. 85). The eye of rope A is passed through the eye of rope B, and the bight of B is then hauled through the eye of A, thus joining the ropes by their eyes. The result is known as a " cow hitch." This method is not used for joining two ropes temporarily, because it may take some time to unhitch them.

To Under-run

The bight of a rope, hawser, or cable secured between two points is under-run to ensure that it is not foul of any object and is free to run if required. For example, a mooring rope is under-run for examination by hauling up its bight from the sea bed over the bows and stern of a boat (see Fig. 86).

A tackle is under-run by separating its running parts to ensure that the fall is correctly rove and has no turn or kinks in it.

To Coil a Small Line in the Hand (right-hand lay) (Fig. 87)

When coiling in the right hand hold the rope with the right thumb pointing towards the end, and when coiling in the left hand the left thumb should point towards the bight. The coil will then form correctly.

Fig. 86.—Under-running a mooring rope

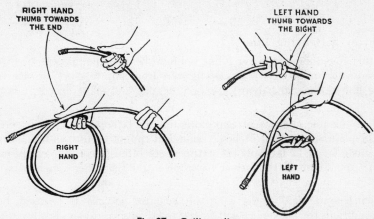

Fig. 87.—Coiling a line

To Flake Down a Rope

A rope which may have to be paid out quickly should be flaked down in as long flakes as stowage space allows. When flaked a rope does not acquire as many turns as when coiled, and it will therefore run out with less chance of becoming snarled. Care should be taken that each turn at the end of a flake is laid over that immediately preceding it to ensure that the upper turns are given no opportunity to catch in the lower turns as the rope runs out.

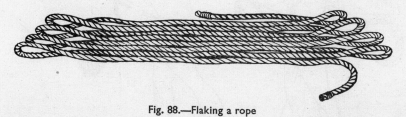

Fig. 88.—Flaking a rope

To Cheese Down (Fig. 89)

When a neat stow is required for a short end of rope, such as a ladder check line or the tail of an awning earring, it may be " cheesed down " as shown below. This method should never be used when the rope will be required to render quickly through a block.

Fig. 89.—Cheesing down a rope

To Throw a Heaving Line

As its name implies, a heaving line is a light flexible line that can be thrown. It is used as a " messenger " to pass hawsers from ship to shore, or vice versa. Old log line and signal halyard are very flexible and make excellent heaving lines.

A heaving line consists of approximately 17 fathoms of $1\frac{1}{4}$-inch cordage, tarred or plain, and well stretched ; though it cannot be thrown much further than a distance of 12 fathoms the extra length often proves extremely useful. One end should be fitted with a backsplice and the other weighted with a " monkey's fist," a small sand bag, or a heaving line knot.

When heaving against the wind the weighted end has to be used, but in other conditions the backsplice will go just as far, and, as it looks less formidable, it is more likely to be caught by the man to whom it is thrown. To weight the monkey's fist with a heavy nut, as is sometimes done, is dangerous and inexcusable.

Fig. 90.—Throwing a heaving line

To prepare a line for throwing it should be wetted, and from 12 to 13 fathoms should be coiled carefully in the left hand, using rather small coils. One-third of the line is taken in the right or throwing hand ; the line is then thrown with the right arm straight, and it must be allowed to run out freely from the coil in the left hand. The most frequent cause of bad casts is failure to have this coil properly clear for running.

There is more than one method of heaving a line and most good throwers have their own variations. Some men take rather less than half the coil in the right hand and throw both halves together, letting go with the right hand before the left. This method is very effective but harder to learn, and to achieve a good throw by the first method is generally sufficient. Many seamen think they can heave a line further than they can ; 70 feet is a good cast.

Before heaving a line the standing end must be made fast, to the top guard rail for example, with a clove hitch. Many a good throw has been rendered abortive and valuable time wasted through omitting to secure the standing end first. As soon as the heaving line has been caught the standing end should be léd in through the required fairlead and bent to the hawser. Remember that a heaving line is only meant to take the strain of the weight of the hawser while it is being passed ashore or into the ship.

Belaying

When a rope will have to be cast off while still under strain it cannot be secured with a bend or a hitch, except perhaps a slipping one. It is therefore belayed to a fitting made for the purpose, such as a cleat, staghorn, or bollard.

The action of belaying consists of taking sufficient turns round the fitting concerned to hold the rope by friction when it takes the strain to which it is subjected. Generally speaking four complete turns should be sufficient, but the number of turns may have to be increased according to the degree of friction existing between rope and fitting. A wet and slippery rope or bollard, or a smooth cleat or staghorn and a well worn rope, may require extra turns.

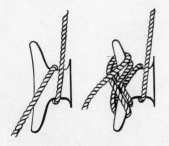

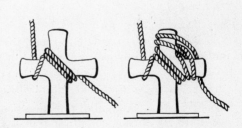

Fig. 91.—Belaying a rope to a cleat   Belaying a boat's fall to a staghorn

To Belay a Rope to a Cleat or Staghorn. Take initial turns as shown in Fig. 91, then continue with figure-of-eight turns round the horns of the cleat or staghorn as many times as are required. It will be seen that when the figure-of-eight turns are removed the rope is ready to be checked under control. A rope belayed to a cleat or a staghorn must be ready for casting off at a moment's notice, therefore the turns should not be completed with a half hitch because this may jam them.

Cleats are not suitable for belaying wire rope.

To Hang a Coil on a Belaying Pin or a Cleat (Figs. 92 and 93).

Whenever possible a coil of rope should be hung up clear of the deck so as to keep the deck clear and the rope dry.

To hang a small coil, proceed as shown in Fig. 92.

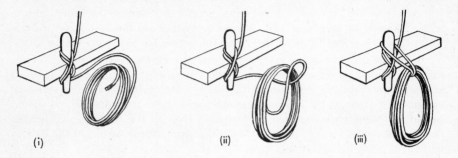

Fig. 92.—Hanging a small coil on a belaying pin

To hang a large coil, proceed as shown in Fig. 93.

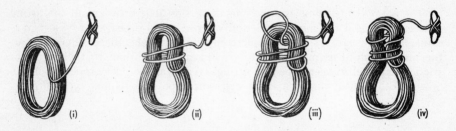

Fig. 93.—Hanging a large coil on a cleat

Handling New Rope

Opening a New Coil (Fig. 94). A length of rope is supplied to a ship in a compact, machine-wound coil, stopped with yarns or strands.

To open up a new coil of rope below 6 inches in size a seaman should roll it over until the outside end of the rope is at the top and pointing directly at him. If the rope is of right-hand lay, he will then turn the coil over towards his left and lay it flat on its side ; conversely, a coil of left-handed rope must be turned over to the right. The stops are now cut and the inner end of the rope pulled out from the centre (Fig. 94 (i)). The rope will then leave the coil correctly : counter-clockwise for a right-handed rope, and clockwise for a left-handed one. It can then be coiled down right or left-handed according to the lay of the rope.

With rope of 6-inch size or larger the twisting involved in the preceding

(i) Opening a new coil of small rope

(ii) Opening a new coil of large rope

Fig. 94

method is not acceptable and the coil must be unreeled in the opposite way to that in which it was made up. The coil should be placed on a turntable, or slung so that it can be revolved (Fig. 94 (ii)) ; then unstop the outside end and haul off.

To Cut off a length of Rope from a New Coil. Rope used for general purposes is hauled from the coil, as previously described, and cut to the length required, as follows :—

First, the rope is whipped at each side of the position at which it is to be cut, to prevent the strands from flying apart. If a small rope it is then cut with a knife, but if a large one it must be laid across the edge of an axe and cut by hitting it with a piece of wood. It should not be cut by striking it with an axe as it is very difficult to hit twice with the axe in exactly the same place.

Whenever a length of rope is cut off a coil, a label, on which should be clearly stated either the length cut off or the length remaining, should be attached to the coil.

A length of rope should never be cut unnecessarily. If too long for a temporary purpose it may be shortened by one of the methods described on pages 124 and 125 or it may be used on the bight, *i.e.* doubled.

Storage

Coils of new rope should be stowed clear of the deck, in a cool, well ventilated, dry place, to allow the air to circulate freely around them. Used rope should be hung in loose coils if this is practicable. No cordage should be stowed in contact with bare ironwork, and if practicable it should be stowed clear of bulkheads. If cordage has to be stored in the open it should be protected from sunlight to prevent it from deteriorating ; cordage made from vegetable fibres is very susceptible to deterioration caused by the sun's rays.

Examination

Cordage made from vegetable fibres is very susceptible to rot from the effects of damp and mildew, and it is a wise precaution, particularly in the tropics, carefully to examine new rope before it is put into service. To examine a rope for signs of deterioration, open out the strands anywhere along its bight and look closely at their inner surfaces ; if any dust or broken fibres fall out or can be rubbed off it is a sure sign of dry rot ; if their inner surfaces are much darker than their outer surfaces it is a sign of dampness ; and if there is a light grey film of dust on their inner surfaces it is a sign of mildew.

Rope which is suspect should never be tested by hanging a proof load on it, because, though it may pass the test without apparent failure, the load may be just sufficient to strain the fibres and disturb their grip on each other, and if this occurs the rope will probably part the next time it is used. It is more economical in the long run to discard rope which is suspect, particularly if it is intended to use it for hoisting.

HANDLING OF WIRE ROPE

Wire rope is much less resilient, and therefore much less tractable, than cordage. It resists being bent, does not absorb turns readily, and is therefore much more liable to kinking and snarling, and tends to spring out of a coil, or off a drum or bollard. If handled correctly, however, it can be used for most of the purposes to which cordage is put, but bends and hitches cannot be made in it.

Kinking and Crippling

Because of its construction and comparative lack of flexibility, wire rope requires more care in handling than cordage ; if carelessly handled it may suffer serious damage through kinking and crippling.

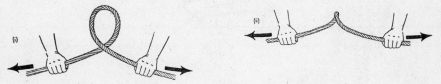

Fig. 95.—Incorrect way of removing a kink in wire rope

Kinking (Figs. 95 and 96). Any loop or turn in a wire rope can very easily be pulled into a kink, which permanently damages it. If a kink is seen to be about to develop it should be removed as indicated in Fig. 96, and no attempt should be made to pull it out in the manner shown in Fig. 95.

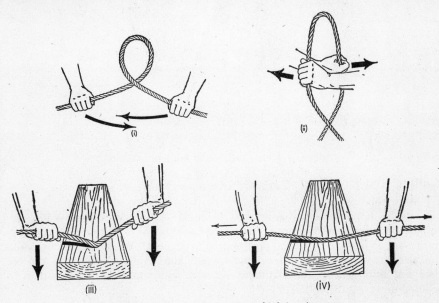

Fig. 96.—Correct way of removing a kink in wire rope

Crippling (Fig. 97). If a wire rope is bent at too acute an angle, or led over a sharp edge, it will be seriously damaged by distortion of its strands, which may result in a permanent kink or even in the rope parting. A rope so led is said to form a " bad nip," and this results in it being " crippled." (To " freshen the nip " is to veer or heave in a foot or two of a rope while it is under strain, a tow rope for example, so as to bring a fresh portion of the rope to take the chafe where it passes through fairleads or around bollards.)

To prevent crippling, a wire rope which will come under strain should never be led through a shackle or ring bolt to alter the direction of its lead. In addition, it should not be led around a bollard or drum of a diameter less than 4 times the circumference of the rope, and if it has to run through a block the diameter of the sheave should be at least 6 times the circumference of the rope.

(ii)

Fig. 97.—Examples of bad nips

Coiling and Uncoiling

Wire rope, especially long lengths of it, should be stowed on reels, but where this is not practicable it must be coiled down. Wire rope is less able to absorb turns than fibre rope ; when coiling down it is therefore all the more necessary to have the uncoiled portion free to revolve. Where this is impossible an alternative is to use left-handed loops, called " Frenchmen," in the coil (see Fig. 98). These " Frenchmen " serve to counteract the twists put in by coiling down right-handed.

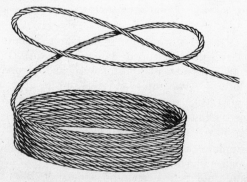

Fig. 98.—A " Frenchman "

"Frenchmen" are also necessary when coiling down a wire rope of which some portions have contracted a left-hand set (as will occur when a rope belayed left-handed round a bollard has been subjected to strain). Such portions will resist being coiled right-handed and each loop must be allowed to become a "Frenchman."

It is wise to stand clear when rope is being hauled off a coil containing "Frenchmen" as such turns are very liable to jump up.

A coil of wire rope should always be well stopped to prevent the coils from springing out of place.

Fig. 99.—Running a wire rope from a coil

The best way to run a wire rope out from a coil is to roll the coil along the deck, as shown in the left-hand sketch of Fig. 99. If the rope is hauled off the top of the coil, as shown in the right-hand sketch, it will soon become snarled unless the end is free to rotate and the turns in the rope are taken out as each loop comes off the coil.

Handling of New Rope

To Unreel a New Rope (Figs. 100, 101 and 102). New wire ropes are supplied either in machine wound coils or on cable drums. They must be taken off the coils or drums in the correct manner, or kinks will quickly develop.

Do not haul the end off the top of the coil or drum, but unreel the rope in one of the following ways :—

A small coil can be rolled along the deck, but if space does not permit, or the rope is heavy, place the coil on a turntable and lash down two strong battens crosswise on the top of the coil (Fig. 100). This will prevent any chance of the rope springing up over the top of the coil and kinking. Then cut the stops, and haul the rope off the coil as it rotates on the turntable.

To unreel the rope from a drum, pass a shaft through the drum and support the

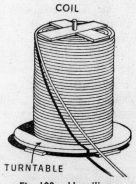

Fig. 100.—Uncoiling a new wire rope

shaft at either end, thus allowing the drum to revolve ; then cut the outer stops and unreel the rope off the drum (see Fig. 101 (i) and (ii)).

(i)   (ii)

Fig. 101.—Unreeling a new wire rope

To coil down a small rope from a drum, upend the drum as shown in Fig. 102, and lap the rope off the top of the drum, lapping off each turn anti-clockwise. The twist put in the rope as each turn is lapped off is cancelled out automatically by coiling the rope down clockwise.

Fig. 102.—Lapping-off and coiling down a small wire rope

To Cut off a Length of Wire Rope.—The rope should be very firmly whipped about one inch on each side of the position at which it is to be cut, then placed on the top of a bollard or similar hard surface, and the strands then cut with a hammer and cold chisel or with a wire cutter ; various types of wire cutters are now supplied and these should be used when available.

Whenever a length of rope is cut off a coil or a drum the coil or drum should be clearly labelled or marked, either with the length cut off or the length remaining.

Making a Temporary Eye with Bulldog Grips (Fig. 103)

A temporary eye, either soft or thimble, can be made in wire rope by using " bulldog grips," which are screwed clamps holding the two parts of the rope together.

It is most important that the grips should be fitted with the U-bolt over the tail end of the rope and the bridge on the standing part, as shown in Fig. 103.

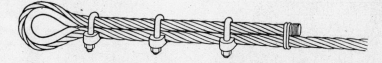

Fig. 103.—Making a temporary eye with bulldog grips

Bulldog grips are supplied in various sizes to fit each size of rope. Should the correct grip for a certain rope not be available the next largest size should be used.

Three grips should be used on all ropes up to three inches in circumference, four grips on ropes over three inches and up to four inches in circumference, and five grips or more on ropes of over four inches circumference. Their spacing should be about three times the circumference of the rope.

Grips are apt to mark or crush the rope, and both grips and rope should be frequently inspected for security and wear.

Grips should not be used to join two wire ropes together.

HANDLING HAWSERS

As the name implies, a hawser was originally a heavy, fibre, cable-laid rope which was led through the hawse-pipe for use in connection with the ship's anchors, or for towing. Nowadays the term is applied to any long length of heavy rope, made of fibre or wire, which is specially fitted and supplied to a ship as part of her outfit and used for heavy duties such as towing, berthing and working ship.

Safety Rules

Before working hawsers, the seaman should learn the simple rules for safety, which are illustrated in Fig. 104 and briefly described below :—

(i) Look at the lead of the rope or hawser and determine which is the running end, the standing part, the hauling part, and which part forms a bight or a coil.

(ii) Never stand within a bight or a coil ; the dangers of doing so are illustrated in Fig. 104 (i), (ii), (iii) and (iv).

(iii) A rope which is being surged from bollards through a fairlead is liable to part at the fairlead. If this happens the parts may spring back and anyone standing between the fairlead and the bollards may be hurt.

(iv) A seaman always keep a good lookout aloft and should seldom be caught unaware of what is happening above him. No seaman stands below an object which is being hoisted or lowered if he can avoid it. (See Fig. 104 (v).)

The warning cry to those below if something above them is about to be let fall, or may be accidentally falling, is " *Stand from under !* "

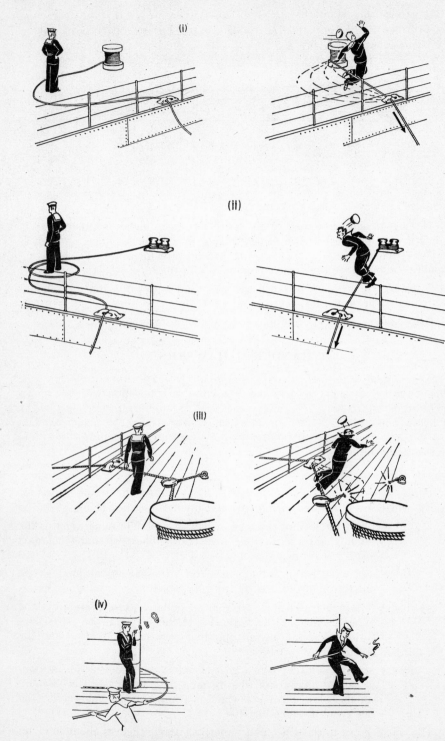

Fig. 104.—Never stand within a bight or coil

Fig. 104 (v).—Never stand underneath a hoist

Orders and Terms used in Handling Hawsers, Ropes and Cables

Note : In the course of his normal work the seaman uses the word " strain " as meaning the pull or tension on a rope (*e.g.* " take the strain " and " a rope under strain "), which is the sense given in the dictionary. In the mechanical sense, however, the term strain is applied to distortion of material resulting from force or stress applied to it, and this distinction must be remembered when dealing with mechanisms.

HEAVING :—

A heave :	A pull on a rope or cable, a throw or cast with a rope.
To heave :	To throw a rope, or to pull on a rope or cable either by hand or power.
Heave !	The order to give a strong pull together.
Heave in !	The order to heave in with the capstan.
Heave hearty !	An order for an extra strong pull by hand.
One, two, six, heave !	An order to men hauling on a rope to make them heave together, repeated as necessary.

HAULING :—

A haul :	A pull on a rope by hand.
To haul :	To pull by hand.
To haul hand over hand :	To haul a rope in quickly with alternate hands.
Haul taut !	An order to take down the slack and take the strain.
Haul away !	An order to haul in steadily.
Avast hauling ! and *Avast !*	Orders to stop hauling.
Hold fast !	To hold a rope under strain so as to keep it from moving.

HOISTING :—

A hoist !	A system designed for lifting, or the load which is lifted.
To hoist :	To lift.
Hoist away !	The order to haul away on a rope when hoisting something with it.
High enough !	The order to stop hoisting.
Marry !	The order to bring two ropes together side by side and handle them as one. Also a term used in splicing, meaning to butt two ropes' ends together with their respective strands interlocking.

LOWERING :—

Lower away !	The order to lower steadily.
Avast lowering !	An order to stop lowering.

GENERAL :—

Handsomely :	Slowly, with care (*e.g.* " lower handsomely ").
Roundly :	Smartly, rapidly.
Walk back !	An order to ease a rope back or out while keeping it in hand, or the order to pay back a rope or cable for a short distance when brought to the capstan.
Light to !	The order to fleet a rope back along the deck so as to provide enough slack for belaying it.
Veer !	The order to pay out rope or cable when brought to the capstan.
To check :	To ease out a rope steadily by hand while keeping a strain on it.
To snub :	Suddenly to restrain a rope or chain cable when it is running out.
To surge :	To check a rope under strain while rendering it round a bollard or capstan. Also to let chain cable run out freely by its own weight.
To render :	A rope is said to render when it surges under strain around a bollard, cleat, or staghorn.
Well, or Enough !	Orders to stop heaving, hoisting, hauling, lowering, checking, etc. " Enough " is usually applied only to hoisting and lowering, and is preceded by " High " or " Low," respectively.
To back up :	To haul on the hauling part of a rope when passed round a bollard or similar fitting so that you assist the bollard to hold it. Also to reinforce men already handling a rope.

Take a turn !	An order to pass a turn round some fixture so that it takes most of the strain if the end of the rope is held or backed up.
To belay :	To secure a rope, usually to a bollard, staghorn, or clear. (*Note :* The order " Belay " is also used to cancel a previous order.)
To make fast :	To secure a rope, usually to a ring, lizard, or fixtures other than those mentioned against " belay."
Cast off !	The order to free and let go a rope which has been belayed or made fast.
To fleet :	To move an object, or work a rope or tackle, in a series of stages or " fleets."

BENDS AND HITCHES

Our forefathers devised various bends, hitches and knots as a means of quickly making fast a rope so that it would hold under strain and yet could be cast off easily when required. These must be learnt by every seaman before he can be of use to his ship.

Strength of Knotted Ropes

All knots, bends, or hitches, reduce the strength of a rope in that portion of it where the knot, bend, or hitch is made. This reduction varies from 40 to 60 per cent., and it should be borne in mind when putting a load on a knotted rope. If, for example, two 3-inch manila ropes were joined by a reef knot, the working load of the knotted ropes should be reduced from 13 hundredweight to 6½ hundredweight.

Terms used

The following terms are used when describing the formation of the various bends and hitches :—

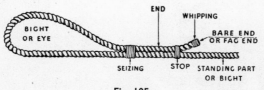

Fig. 105

Bight.—The middle part of a length of rope. This term also refers to a loop of rope, and " to make a bight " is to form a loop.

End.—The short length at either end of a rope, which may be formed into an eye, or used for making a bend or a hitch with which to secure it. The end of a rope is also that length of rope left over after making such an eye, bend, or hitch. The " bare end," or " fag end," is the extreme end of a length of rope.

Standing Part.—The part of the bight of a rope which is nearest the eye bend, or hitch, in contrast to the end.

Stopping.—A light fastening for temporarily holding in place a rope or any other object. It is not meant to bear any strain other than that required to keep the rope or other object in place.

Seizing.—A seizing is used to fasten two ropes, or two parts of the same rope, securely together, to prevent them moving in relation to each other.

Whipping.—The binding around the bare end of a rope for preventing the strands from unlaying.

Elements of Bends and Hitches

Most bends and hitches consist of a combination of two or more of the elements illustrated in Fig. 106.

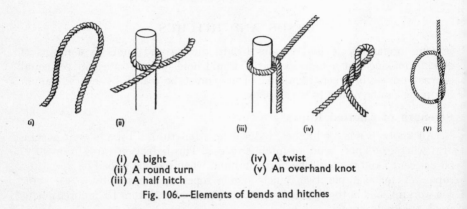

(i) A bight	(iv) A twist
(ii) A round turn	(v) An overhand knot
(iii) A half hitch	

Fig. 106.—Elements of bends and hitches

Bends, Hitches and Other Fastenings Used at Sea

Reef Knot (Fig. 107). The reef knot consists of two overhand knots made consecutively, and is used as a common tie for bending together two ropes of approximately equal size. It is not liable to come undone when there is no strain on the knot, but it is not reliable if the ropes are of unequal size or very slippery unless the ends are seized back to their standing parts.

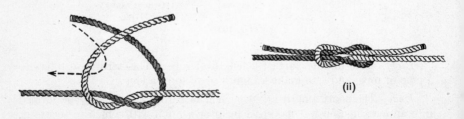

Fig. 107.—Reef knot

To form a reef knot care must be taken to cross the ends opposite ways each time they are knotted (*i.e.* right over left, then left over right, or vice versa), otherwise the result will be a "granny," which will either slip or jam, depending upon whether it is made with or against the lay of the rope; a granny is also very liable to come undone when there is no strain on the knot, and for these reasons it is never used by seamen.

Figure-of-eight Knot (Fig. 108).   This knot is used to prevent a rope unreeving through an eye or a block.

Fig. 108.—' Figure-of-eight ' knot

Marline Spike Hitch (Fig. 109).   This hitch is for securing a marline spike, or similar object, into the bight of a line.   Figure 109A indicates its employment when hauling taut a serving or lashing with a marline spike.

It can also be used to secure a sling or the bight of a rope to a hook when the strain on both parts of the bight is approximately equal (Fig. 109B).

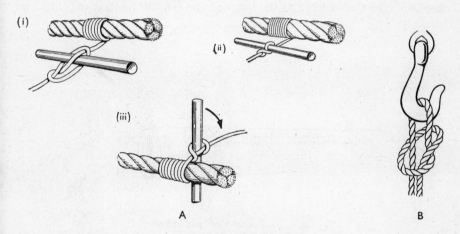

A

B

Fig. 109.—Marline spike hitch
A—On a marline spike
B—On a hook

Marling Hitch (Fig. 110).   This is used for lashing long bundles such as sails, hammocks, and awnings.   It will be seen from the illustration that in each hitch the end is passed down through the bight, thus jamming that part against the bundle and enabling the lashing to be hauled taut.

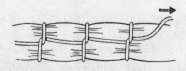

Fig. 110.—Marling hitch

The operation of binding together ropes or yarns by a succession of closely spaced marling hitches is known as "marling down." Marling is usually begun with a timber hitch if no eye is spliced into the end of the lashing.

Timber Hitch (Fig. 111). This hitch is used to secure a rope's end to a spar or bale.

Fig. 111.—Timber hitch

Timber Hitch and Half Hitch (Fig. 112). These are used to tow, hoist, or lower, a spar. If the spar is tapered it should be towed or hoisted thick end first, with the timber hitch at the thin end and the half hitch at the thick end.

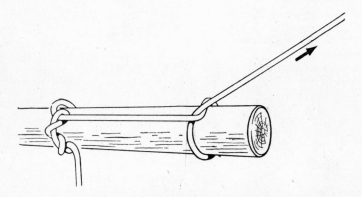

Fig. 112.—Timber hitch and half hitch

Clove Hitch (Fig. 113). A clove hitch is used to secure a rope to a spar, guard rail, or similar fitting ; also for many other purposes. It will slip along the spar or rail if subjected to a sideways pull. It can be made with the end or with the bight of the rope, as illustrated in Figures 113A and 113B respectively.

Rolling Hitch (Fig. 114). This hitch is also used for securing a rope to a spar or similar fitting, but will not slip when the pull is exerted from one side.

Round Turn and Two Half Hitches (Fig. 115). This combination is used to secure a heavy load to a spar or a ring. It will never jam and can be cast off quickly. The end should be stopped to the standing part.

Fisherman's Bend (Fig. 116). This is an alternative to a round turn and two half hitches and it is usually employed for bending a boat's cable to the ring of her anchor. It is more suitable for a jerking pull, but will jam and is not so easy to cast off. The end should be stopped to the standing part.

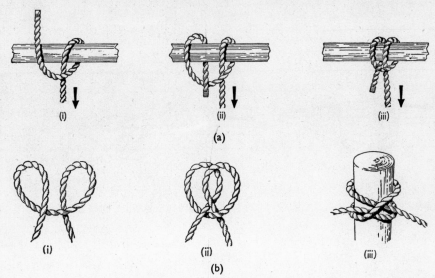

Fig. 113.—The Clove Hitch.—(*a*) Clove hitch on the end
(*b*) Clove hitch on the bight

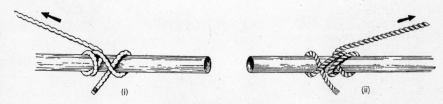

Fig. 114.—Rolling hitch

Fig. 115.—Round turn and two half hitches   Fig. 116.—Fisherman's bend

Fig. 117.—Sheet bend or swab hitch

Sheet Bend or Swab Hitch (Fig. 117). This is used to secure a rope's end to a small eye, *e.g.* the lazy painter of a boat at the lower boom to the jacob's ladder. It is also used to bend a small rope to a larger one.

Double Sheet Bend (Fig. 118). This bend is used as an alternative to the swab hitch, and is more secure.

Buntline Hitch (Fig. 119). This is used to secure a rope's end to a cringle or a small eye. It is more difficult to cast off than a sheet bend or a swab hitch.

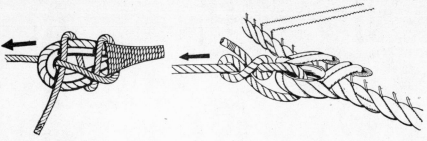

Fig. 118.—Double sheet bend   Fig. 119.—Buntline hitch

Blackwall Hitch (Fig. 120). This is used to secure a rope to a hook. It is liable to slip if subjected to more than ordinary strain.

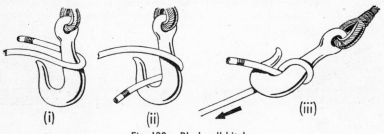

Fig. 120.—Blackwall hitch

Midshipman's Hitch (Fig. 121). This is an alternative to a Blackwall hitch. It holds better under all conditions, and especially with a greasy rope.

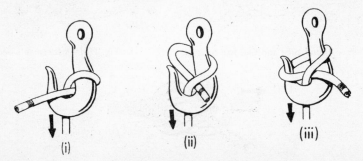

Fig. 121.—Midshipman's hitch

Double Blackwall Hitch (Fig. 122). This hitch is an alternative to both the Blackwall and midshipman's hitches. It is as secure as the midshipman's hitch.

Catspaw (Fig. 123). This is used to shorten a sling or a length of rope in the manner shown in Fig. 123 (i). It can also be used to secure a sling or the bight of a rope to a hook when the strain on both parts of the bight is approximately equal (Fig. 123 (ii)).

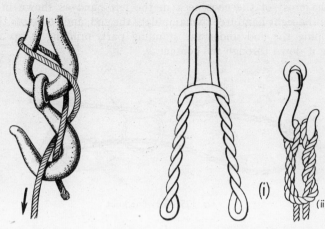

Fig. 122.—Double Blackwall hitch

Fig. 123.—Catspaw
(i) For shortening a rope
(ii) On a hook

Mousing (Fig. 124). A mousing is used to prevent a hook from unhooking; it also increases the strength of a hook.

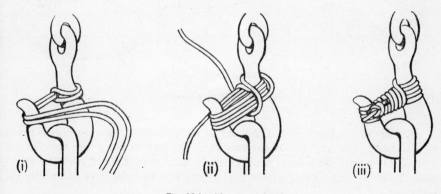

Fig. 124.—Mousing a hook

Bowline Knot (Fig. 125). This is used to make a temporary eye in the end of a rope; it is a very reliable knot and will never slip.

The bowline is usually made in the following manner, which enables it to be formed while there is a strain on the rope :—

Take the end in the right hand and the standing part in the left. Place the end over the standing part and hold the cross thus formed between the index finger and thumb of the right hand, with the thumb underneath ; the loop so formed becomes the bight of the bowline, and if required it can be formed round the body of the man making the knot. Then turn the wrist to the right, away from the body, and bring the end up through the loop so formed ; this loop is sometimes called the " gooseneck." Now take the cross of the gooseneck in the left hand as shown in Fig. 125, leaving the right hand free to manipulate the end, and complete the bowline by dipping the end under the standing part, bringing it up again, and passing it down through the gooseneck.

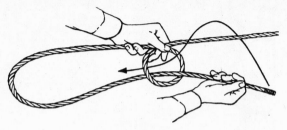

Fig. 125.—Bowline knot

Running Bowline (Fig. 126). This is used to make a running eye in the end of a rope ; it must never be placed round a man's body.

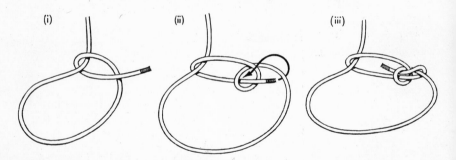

Fig. 126.—Running bowline

Bowline on the Bight (Fig. 127). As its name implies, this bowline is made on the bight, the first two operations in its formation being the same as for a simple bowline. It is used for lowering a man from aloft or over the ship's side, the short bight being placed under his arms and the long one under his buttocks.

French Bowline (Fig. 128). An alternative to the bowline on the bight, and usually more suitable, is the French bowline. It is made in a similar manner to a bowline, except that after the gooseneck has been formed and the end passed up through it the end is brought round and up through it again, so as to form a large bight which is passed under the man's armpits. The knot is then completed as for a simple bowline.

The weight of the man sitting in the main bight keeps the arm bight taut, the knot lying roughly at his breast.

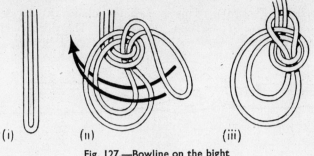

Fig. 127.—Bowline on the bight

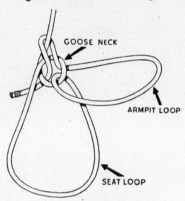

Fig. 128.—French bowline

Slip Knots (Fig. 129). The sheet bend, the bowline and the clove hitch can all be made into knots which can be released quickly by using a bight instead of an end in the last phase of making them.

Such slip knots will hold a steady strain fairly well, but can not be trusted to stand a jerking pull.

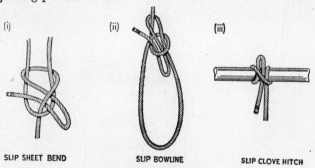

Fig. 129.—Slip knots

Fig. 130.—Hawser bend

Hawser Bend (Fig. 130). This is the common method of joining two large hawsers together. The ends should be seized to their standing parts.

Carrick Bend (Fig. 131). This is used for joining two hawsers together when the join will have to pass round the capstan. The ends should be stopped to their standing parts.

Fig. 131.—Carrick bend

Middleman and Butterfly Knots (Fig. 132). These are mountaineer's knots, but are included here because they are useful to the seaman who is employed in land operations. They are used, when men are roped together to scale a cliff, for securing the middle man or men to the bight of the rope. An overhand knot is not used for this purpose because it causes a bad nip in the rope.

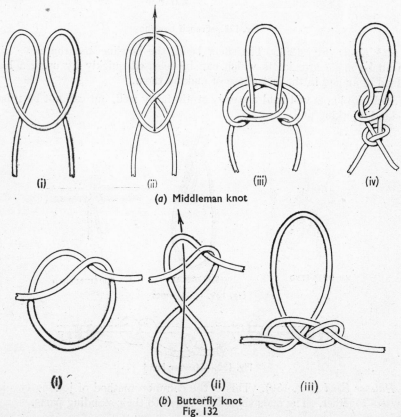

(a) Middleman knot

(b) Butterfly knot
Fig. 132

Rolling Hitch and Stop (Fig. 133). This is used to hitch a " messenger " to a hawser fitted with a hawser eye which has to be hauled through a fairlead.

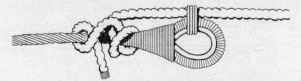

Fig. 133.—Rolling hitch and stop

Anchor Shackle and Grommet Strop (Figs. 134 and 135). Wire hawsers fitted with a hawser-eye are shackled together with an anchor shackle, which is a long shackle with a flush-ended bolt secured by a tapered pin and lead pellet through one of the lugs. A screw shackle, or one with a pin and forelock, should not be used because the bolt is apt to shake loose when moved about the deck.

Fig. 134.—Shackling wire hawsers together

If a shackle of suitable strength which will fit both eyes cannot be found, a doubled wire grommet strop can be used instead, by either of the methods shown in Fig. 135.

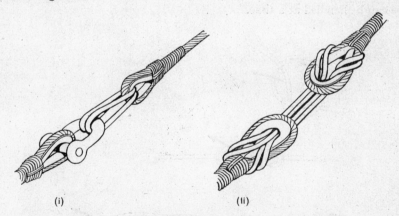

(i)   (ii)

Fig. 135.—Joining two wire hawsers with a grommet strop

Bollard Strop (Fig. 136). A wire hawser fitted with a hawser-eye is secured to a bollard with a bollard strop and an anchor shackle.

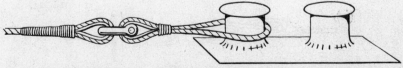

Fig. 136.—Securing a wire hawser to a bollard with a bollard strop

Sheepshank (Fig. 137). This is used to shorten the bight of a rope temporarily.

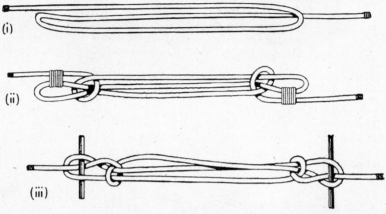

Fig. 137.—Sheepshank

The strain on the rope will usually prevent the sheepshank from slipping, but, if necessary, the loops can be stopped to the standing parts (Fig. 137 (ii)), or secured with a toggle (Fig. 137 (iii)).

Chain Shortening (Fig. 138). This series of hitches is for shortening the end of a rope ; it looks very neat, and is useful when only a short length of rope can be handled at a time.

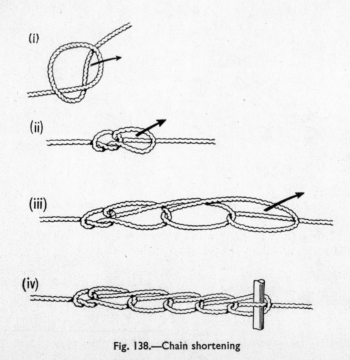

Fig. 138.—Chain shortening

It is made as follows :—

    (i) form a loop in the rope ;

    (ii) pull the bight up through the loop, thus forming another loop ;

    (iii) pull the bight through again, and repeat until the shortening is
            sufficient ;

    (iv) secure the last loop, either with a toggle or by passing the end of
            the rope through it.

Fishermen's Knots (Fig. 139). To join two lengths of line or gut of the
same size, make a loose, double, overhand knot in the end of each line so that
the bight of each knot encloses the other line, as shown in Fig. 139 (i). Haul
taut each knot separately, and then haul the two knots together.

To bend a line or a length of gut to an eyed hook, reeve the end of the
line through the eye of the hook and make a double overhand knot, with the
end round its standing part as shown in Fig. 139 (ii). Haul taut the overhand
knot, then with the standing part haul the knot to the eye of the hook.

(*Note :* Natural gut must be well soaked, and artificial gut must be
moistened, before they are manipulated.)

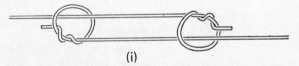

(i)

(i) Joining two lengths of line or gut together

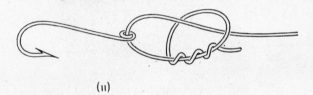

(ii)

(ii) Bending a line or length of gut to an eyed hook

Fig. 139.—Fishermen's knots

Rose Seizing (Fig. 140). This is used to secure an eye in a rope to a spar.

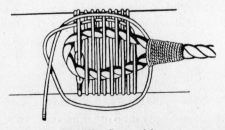

Fig. 140.—Rose seizing

Cordage Stopper.—This is a short length of fibre rope used to hold temporarily a larger fibre rope or hawser which is under strain, and it is passed by making one end fast and hitching and "dogging" the other end round the hawser. (A rope is "dogged" by twisting it spirally round another rope, either with, or against, its lay.)

To pass the stopper make a half hitch, or the first two parts of a rolling hitch, round the hawser *against its lay*, then dog *with the lay* and stop the end to the hawser. (The half hitch is less secure, but more quickly passed.)

This method is also used to clap a tail jigger to a fibre rope as illustrated in Fig. 141.

Fig. 141.—Clapping a tail jigger on a fibre rope

Chain Stopper.—This is similar to the cordage stopper, but made of chain, and it is used to hold temporarily a wire hawser.

It is passed by making a half hitch, or the first two turns of a rolling hitch, round the hawser *with its lay*, then dogging *against the lay* and stopping the end to the hawser.

This method is also used to clap a chain-tail jigger to a wire rope, as illustrated in Fig. 142.

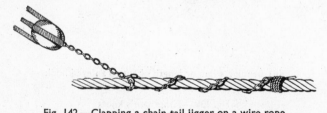

Fig. 142.—Clapping a chain-tail jigger on a wire rope

Parbuckling (Fig. 143). This is used to haul up a drum, cask, heavy spar, or other similar object.

Racking (Fig. 144). This is used to hold a tackle temporarily while the fall is being belayed if the strain is too great for this to be done by holding opposite running parts, or the running and standing parts, together with the hands. The racking turns are passed with a short length of line, the end being held in the hand or secured round the parts.

Choking the Luff. To hold a small tackle temporarily when no cleat is available its luff is "choked," as shown in Fig. 145.

The luff should be choked only if no other means are available, as it subjects the rope to undue wear.

Fig. 143.—Parbuckling

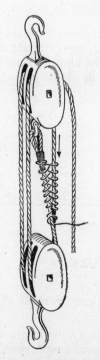

Fig. 144.—Racking a tackle

Fig. 145.—Choking the luff

Rigging Lanyards (Fig. 146). These may be used to secure the lower ends of standing rigging to the deck. Pass as many turns with the lanyard as are necessary (taking into account the strength of the lanyard and of the standing rigging) ; finish off with two half hitches around all parts below the thimble and tuck the end away.

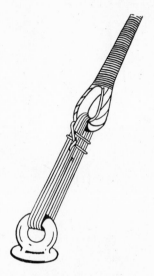

Fig. 146.—Passing a shroud lanyard

Nippers. These are used as a temporary expedient to enable one hawser to hold or haul the other. Several " nippers " (*i.e.* short strands) are necessary and each is passed as illustrated in Fig. 147. The nipper should be one-third the size of the smaller hawser, and both its ends should be tended.

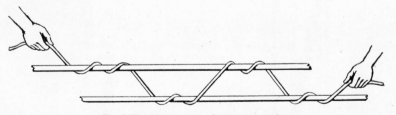

Fig. 147.—Nipping two hawsers together

GENERAL ROPE WORK

Strops

A strop is a ring of cordage or wire rope, usually made in one of the following forms :—

(*a*) *The Common Strop*, which is made from a short length with its ends bent or spliced together. It is used to pass round a rope, spar, chain cable, etc., so as to provide an eye to take a hook or shackle.

(b) *The Bale Sling Strop*, which is similar in construction to the common strop but much longer. It is primarily intended as a sling for hoisting bales, but can be used for many other purposes.

(c) *The Selvagee Strop*, which is used for purposes similar to those for the common strop but has the virtue of being able to grip the spar or other object around which it is passed more strongly so that it will withstand a sideways pull. It is made of spunyarn and thus has no specified strength.

To make a selvagee strop (Fig. 148) fix two bolts, nails, or hooks at a distance apart equal to the length of the strop required, and pass roundabout turns with a ball of spunyarn taking care to have *every* turn well taut ; when the strop is of the thickness required marl it down with a series of marling hitches.

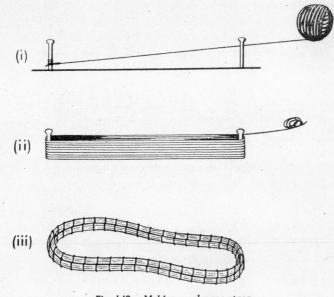

Fig. 148.—Making a selvagee strop

(d) *The Grommet Strop*, which may be long or short and differs from the common and bale sling strops only in its construction. It is formed of either one or two strands made up into a ring and laid up round their own parts.

The grommet strop made from one or two strands of wire rope is the strongest type of strop used. It is extensively used for heavy work, such as laying chain moorings, lifting heavy weights, and joining two wire hawsers together. Its construction is described in Volume II of this manual.

(e) *The Rope Grommet* (Fig. 149) is used for protecting the driving bands of projectiles from damage, and for making deck quoits and the " puck " for deck hockey. Its construction is described in Volume II of this manual.

Fig. 149.—Rope grommet

TO PUT A STROP ON A SPAR

Use a common strop, as shown in Fig. 150. If the pull is from one side, so that a strong grip is required, use a selvagee strop in a similar manner.

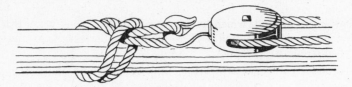

Fig. 150.—Putting a strop on a spar

TO PUT A STROP ON A ROPE

Middle a common or selvagee strop on the rope. Dog the bights opposite ways and hook the tackle on to both bights, as shown in Fig. 151.

A selvagee strop will hold on wire rope, but for a strong pull chain must be used. The chain can either be knotted into a strop and used as above, or be put on as a tail as shown in Fig. 142, page 126.

Fig. 151.—Putting a strop on a rope

Lashings

Two crossed spars can be secured together either with a " square lashing " or a " diagonal lashing." A square lashing is used when the spars are to be secured at right angles to each other, and the diagonal lashing when they are to be secured at an acute angle to each other.

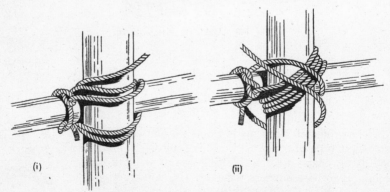

(i)   (ii)

Fig. 152.—Lashing crossed spars

(i) Square lashing   (ii) Diagonal lashing

(i) *Square Lashing* (Fig. 152 (i)). Make fast one end of the rope to one of the spars, preferably the smaller one, with a timber hitch and haul it taut. Then cross the spars with the smaller spar lying underneath.

Bring the other end of the lashing up over the larger spar, down and under the smaller, up and over the larger, and so on until sufficient turns have been taken.

To avoid riding turns the turns on the larger spar should lie in succession outside those first applied, and those on the smaller spar should lie in succession inside those first applied. Finish by taking two or three frapping turns round the parts between the spars, and make fast with a clove hitch round all parts or round one of the spars.

(ii) *Diagonal Lashing* (Fig. 152 (ii)). Make fast one end of the rope as for a square lashing, and pass as many turns as are required diagonally round both spars. Then bring the end up over one spar and take a few more turns across the opposite diagonal, finishing off as for a square lashing.

Slings and Slinging

When anything is to be hoisted, whether it is a single item or a collection of packages of stores, for example, it is attached to the hook of the hoisting rope by means of a sling, which may be formed by a strop or consist of special fittings, such as those described in Volume II of this manual. Care must always be taken when using slings as their misuse or over-loading is a frequent cause of accidents.

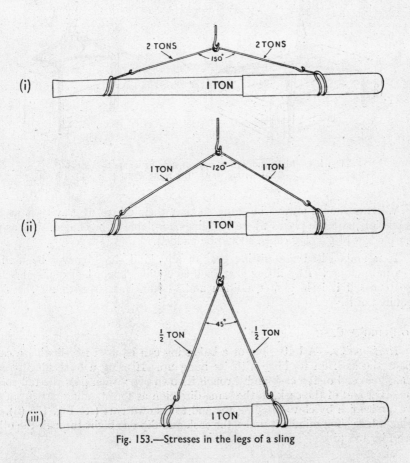

Fig. 153.—Stresses in the legs of a sling

An important principle in slinging is illustrated in the three diagrams in Fig. 153. These show an object weighing one ton slung in three different ways, with the tension in each leg of the slings marked in each method.

It will be seen that the greater the angle between the legs of the slings the greater is the tension they have to bear. For two-legged slings used in commercial practice the working load is laid down for various angles between 0° and 120°, and these slings are seldom, if ever, permitted to be used with the legs beyond this limiting angle of 120°.

There are, however, occasions when an unavoidably large angle has to be accepted, and the seaman must then take care that his sling is strong enough to take the extra strain.

The same principle applies also to simple strops, as illustrated in the two sketches (i) and (ii) in Fig. 154. In (i) the angles between the four legs of the strop are wide and each leg bears about $1\frac{1}{2}$ times the weight of the case ; in (ii) the angles between the four legs of the strop are small and each leg bears about half the weight of the case.

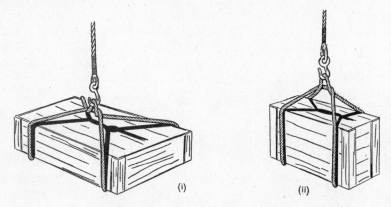

Fig. 154.—Right and wrong ways of slinging a case by a strop :
(i) wrong way   (ii) right way

Weights should always be slung so that their centre of gravity is as low as possible, and the places where the slings are liable to be chafed, such as the sharp edges of packing cases, should be padded.

It is emphasised that lifting gear of any kind should never be used in a casual manner. Any lifting gear such as a sling should be examined before use to see if it is in a fit condition and of sufficient strength for the duty required of it.

To Sling a Cask

Horizontally.—A butt sling or a bale sling can be used for slinging a cask. Place the cask on its bilge with its bung up. If using a butt sling pass it round one end of the cask and through its own eye ; then pass the tail round the other end of the cask, in the same direction as the standing part from the eye, and finish by clove-hitching the end to its own part (see Fig. 155 (i)). If using a bale sling middle it under the cask and dip one bight through the other (see Fig. 155 (ii)).

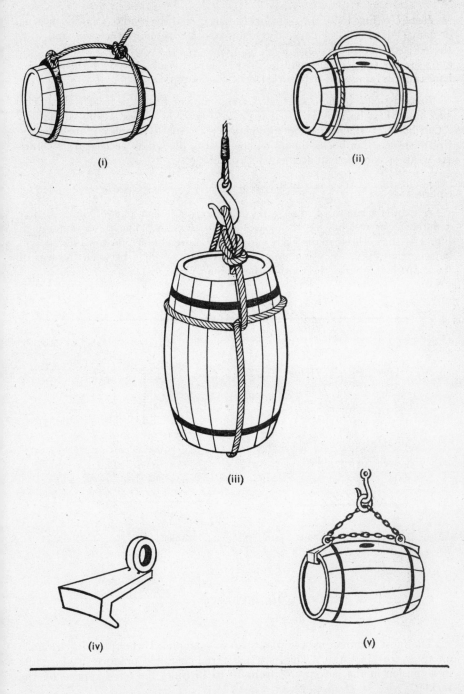

(i)

(ii)

(iii)

(iv)

(v)

Fig. 155.—Ways of slinging a cask

Head Up (Fig. 155 (iii)).—This method is used if the head of a cask is missing or damaged. Place the cask on its end, pass a rope under the cask, and with the ends make an overhand knot on the top of it ; then open out the knot and slide the two halves down the sides to a quarter of the way down the cask ; haul taut and finish off with a reef knot on the top.

Breaking bulk is the operation of removing the first cask from a tier. The cask must first be slightly lifted to make room for passing a sling around it. " Can hooks," which fit under the chines (Fig. 155 (iv) and (v)), are used for this purpose. Can hooks should not be used to lift a cask because if its chines are weak or damaged an accident will result.

Spans

A span is a length of rope, wire, or chain, made fast at two points so that a purchase or weight can be hooked on to its bight. The three sketches in Fig. 156 show three spans each supporting a weight of one ton, and it will be seen that, as when using slings, the greater the angle between the legs of the span the higher is the tension they have to bear.

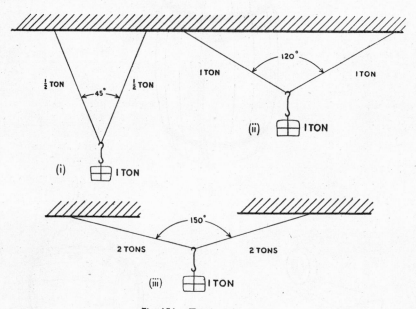

Fig. 156.—Tensions in a span

The most common misuse of a span is exemplified when hooking a tackle on to a taut jackstay. This is a most reprehensible practice as it results in a tension in the jackstay of from 10 to 15 times the force applied by the tackle.

This power is legitimately used by the seaman, however, in " swigging off " on a fall of which the hauling part is made fast (as in a halyard or a tack tackle). He hauls on the fall at right-angles to its lead, thereby exerting great force, and then recovers the slack so obtained.

The foregoing paragraphs are intended to give the seaman a rough guide as to the stresses set up in slings and spans. If required, these can be estimated accurately by using the principle of the triangle of forces, which is described in Volume II of this manual.

Whippings

Three whippings which can be used as alternatives to the common whipping described on page 94 are :—

(i) *The American Whipping* (Fig. 157). This is similar to the common whipping except that the first end of twine is left out clear between the first and second half of the turns. The two ends are secured together with a reef knot and cut off.

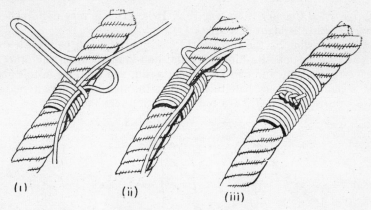

(i)   (ii)   (iii)

Fig. 157.—American whipping

(ii) *The Sailmaker's Whipping* (Fig. 158). This is the most secure ; it will not work adrift from frapping about and is therefore used for reef points, awning stops, etc.

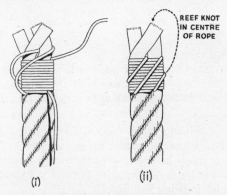

REEF KNOT
IN CENTRE
OF ROPE

(i)   (ii)

Fig. 158.—Sailmaker's whipping

To make a sailmaker's whipping, unlay the end of the rope for about 2 inches and hold it in the left hand, pointing upwards, with the middle strand furthest away. Now make a bight in the twine about 8 inches long and pass this bight over the middle strand only, with the two ends towards you. Then, with the bight of twine hanging several inches down the back of the rope and the ends pointing down in front, lay up the rope with the right hand. Leave the short end of twine where it is and, with the long end, pass the turns of the whipping, working towards the end of the rope against the lay.

When sufficient turns are on take the bight of twine, pass it up outside the whipping, following the lay of the strand around which it was originally put, and pass it over that strand where the latter comes out at the end of the rope (see Fig. 158 (i)). Now haul on the short end so as to tighten the bight, then bring this end up outside the whipping, again following the lay of the rope, and then reef knot the two ends in the middle of the rope and out of sight (see Fig. 158 (ii)).

(iii) *The West Country Whipping* (Fig. 159). This is very useful when it is required to whip the bight of a rope.

Middle the twine on the rope in the position required, pass the two ends round the rope in opposite directions and half-knot them on the other side ; now bring the ends up and half knot them again, and continue in this manner, making a half knot every half turn so that the half knots lie alternately on opposite sides of the rope. Then finish off with a reef knot.

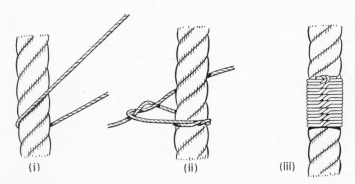

(i)   (ii)   (iii)

Fig. 159.—West Country whipping

Cordage Splicing

Splicing is a method of joining the ends of two ropes together, or of making an eye in the end of a rope, by interlocking the strands. Unless otherwise stated it should be understood that all splices *reduce the strength of the rope by one-eighth.*

Tools required for splicing are a wooden fid for opening up the strands of the standing part, and a heaving mallet for heaving tucks into place.

When reference is made in the text of this section to " the left " or " the right " of a rope the reader should imagine himself to be looking along the rope towards the end which is being handled.

Types of Splices

A *Long Splice* is used to join two ropes which are required to be rove through a block. A well made long splice does not increase the diameter of the rope and should not reduce its strength.

A Short Splice is simpler, but as the splice increases the size of the rope it cannot be rove through a block.

An Eye Splice is used to make a permanent eye in the end of a rope.

A Backsplice is used to finish the end of a rope which is not required to be rove through a block ; it prevents it from unlaying.

A Cut Splice is used to make a permanent eye in the bight of a rope.

A Chain Splice is used for splicing a rope tail into a chain which has to be led through a block or fairlead ; the earrings and outhauls for forecastle and quarterdeck awnings are examples. The chain splice is not more than two-thirds of the strength of the rope.

A Flemish Eye is an ornamental eye worked in the ends of gangway and other manropes.

The short splice, eye splice, and back splice are described in this section ; the remainder are described in Volume II of this manual.

To Make a Short Splice (Figs. 160 and 161)

The principle of the short splice lies in the tucking of each strand between those of the other rope. The strands are tucked against the lay, each being taken over the strand on its left, then under the next strand, and emerging between this and the subsequent strand ; see Fig. 160 in which the ends of the ropes are lettered A and B, and their unlayed strands lettered C, D and E, and F, G and H, respectively. (Certain whippings and stops have been omitted to show the tucking of the strands more clearly.)

Whip each rope at a distance from its end equal to five times the size of the rope (this whipping has been omitted from rope A in the illustration for the sake of clarity).

Unlay the strands to the whipping and whip their ends (these whippings have also been omitted).

Marry the two ropes so that one strand of each lies between two strands of the other (see Fig. 160 (i)). Having ensured a close marry, whip the strands strongly round the join to prevent them slipping, and stop ends C, D and E to rope B with a strong stop. (Whipping and stops have been omitted in the illustration for the sake of clarity.)

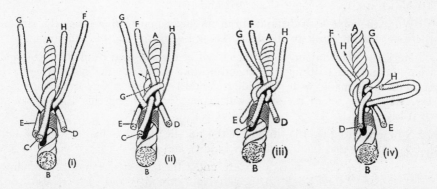

Fig. 160.—Making a short splice

Cut the whipping on A and tuck F, G, H as follows :—

> take F over C, under E, and bring it out between E and D (see Fig. 160 (ii)) ;
>
> take G over E, under D, and bring it out between D and C (see Fig. 160 (ii) and (iii)) ;
>
> take H over D, under C, and bring it out between C and E (see Fig. 160 (iii)).

Stop G, F and H to A, cut the stop and whipping on B, and tuck C, D and E in a similar manner.

Heave all six strands equally taut with a heaving mallet.

Again tuck each strand over the strand on its left and under the next one, and then repeat this operation a third time.

If the splice is not to be served (covered over with turns of spunyarn as described in Volume II of this manual) finish it off by halving the strands and " dogging " (*i.e.* whipping) each half strand to the half strand next to it (see Fig. 161). Then cut off the ends of the half strands just above the dogging.

Fig. 161.—A short splice finished by dogging the strands

If the splice is to be served taper it down after the third tuck, as follows :—

> take one third out of each strand and tuck the remaining two-thirds once, as already described ; though discarded the thirds should not be cut off until the splice is completed ;
>
> now halve the reduced strands, then tuck one half of each and leave the other ;
>
> heave all parts taut, including the discarded ends which should now be cut off.

TO MAKE AN EYE SPLICE (Figs. 162 and 164)

Whip the rope at a distance from its end equal to five times the size of the rope, then unlay it to the whipping and whip the end of each strand.

Mark the place intended for the crown of the eye, and bend the rope back from there so as to bring the unlaid strands alongside the place where the splice is to be made, with the middle strand lying on the top of the rope (see Fig. 162) ; the set of the splice will depend on selecting this middle strand correctly.

Now refer to Fig. 163, in which the middle strand is marked A, the left hand strand B, and the right hand strand C, and make the splice as follows :—

> Tuck A, from right to left, under the nearest strand of the standing part ; then bring up the left hand strand B and tuck it, also from right to left, under the next strand of the standing part.

Now turn the rope right over so as to bring the remaining strand C on the top, and then tuck C from right to left under the unoccupied strand of the standing part. Care must be taken to retain the lay of the rope in the last strand tucked as this enables it to lie closer.

Now, beginning with C, heave each strand taut with a heaving mallet. Then tuck all three strands a second and third time, and finish off either by dogging the strands or tapering them (see Fig. 164).

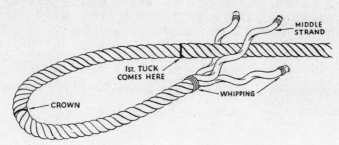

Fig. 162.—The start of an eye splice

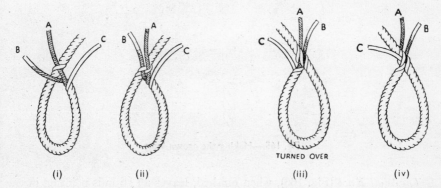

Fig. 163.—Making an eye splice

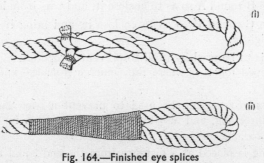

Fig. 164.—Finished eye splices
(i) Dogged
(ii) Tapered and served

Crown and Wall Knots (Figs. 165 and 167)

The crown knot forms the basis of the back splice, and with the wall knot it forms the basis of many of the knots commonly used in ropes ends and described in detail in Volume II of this manual.

The Crown Knot (Fig. 165), when finished, leaves the three strands pointing back along the rope. It is used to begin a backsplice, and in the formation of other knots, but seldom on its own.

To form a crown, whip the rope at a distance from its end equal to three to four times its size. Then unlay the strands to the whipping, whip their ends and spread them out in the form of a star, and then :—

> place strand A over B ;
>
> take strand B round A so as to enclose it, and pass it over C ;
>
> take strand C round B so as to enclose it, and pass it *down* through the bight *a*.

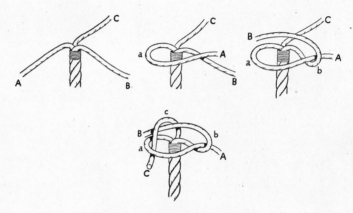

Fig. 165.—Making the crown knot

The Wall Knot (Fig. 166), when finished, leaves all strands pointing in the original direction and is merely a crown knot upside down. Prepare the rope as for a crown knot ; then :—

> take strand A and pass it under B ;
>
> take B round A so as to enclose it, and pass it under C ;
>
> take C round B so as to enclose it, and bring it *up* through the bight *a*.

If the wall is to be used by itself to prevent a rope unreeving, the strands should be whipped together where they emerge from the knot and the ends then be cut off.

The Wall and Crown can be used to prevent a rope such as a rudder lanyard from unreeving, and also to form the foundation for more advanced knots.

The whipping is placed at a distance from the end equal to six times the size of the rope, the wall being formed first and the crown made on the top of it.

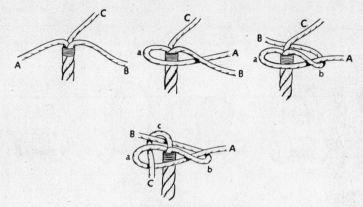

Fig. 166.—Making the wall knot

The Crown and Wall (Fig. 167) differs from the wall and crown in that the crown is made first and the wall formed under it.

It is used for finishing off the ends of seizings to prevent them from unreeving. The strands are unlaid right down to the turns of the seizings, against which the crown is formed as close as possible. The wall is then made under it and hauled taut, thus jamming the knot in tightly.

Fig. 167.—Making the crown and wall knot

To Back Splice a Rope's End (Fig. 168)

Make a crown knot, cut the whipping, and then tuck the strands back along the rope as in a short splice. Three tucks are sufficient.

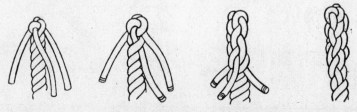

Fig. 168.—Making the back splice

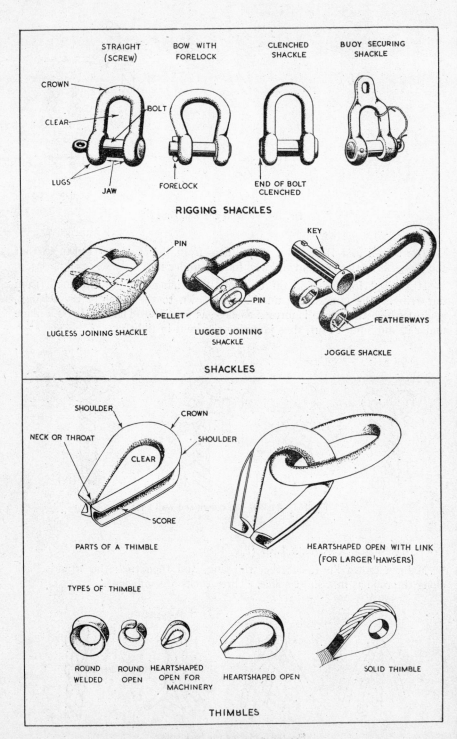

STRAIGHT
(SCREW)

BOW WITH
FORELOCK

CLENCHED
SHACKLE

BUOY SECURING
SHACKLE

CROWN

CLEAR

BOLT

LUGS

JAW

FORELOCK

END OF BOLT
CLENCHED

RIGGING SHACKLES

PIN

PELLET

LUGLESS JOINING SHACKLE

PIN

LUGGED JOINING
SHACKLE

KEY

FEATHERWAYS

JOGGLE SHACKLE

SHACKLES

SHOULDER

NECK OR THROAT

CROWN

SHOULDER

CLEAR

SCORE

PARTS OF A THIMBLE

HEARTSHAPED OPEN WITH LINK
(FOR LARGER HAWSERS)

TYPES OF THIMBLE

ROUND
WELDED

ROUND
OPEN

HEARTSHAPED
OPEN FOR
MACHINERY

HEARTSHAPED OPEN

SOLID THIMBLE

THIMBLES

Fig. 169.—Shackles and thimbles

CHAPTER VI

Rigging

RIGGING FITTINGS

VARIOUS fittings used with the standing and running rigging of a ship are illustrated in Figs. 169, 170 and 171, and briefly described below. The strengths of these fittings are dealt with in Volume II of this manual.

Shackles (Fig. 169)

These are coupling links used for joining ropes and chain together, or to some fitting, and are usually made of wrought iron or mild steel. Those which are U-shaped are called " straight shackles," and those which have curved sides are called " bow shackles " ; a bow shackle is weaker than a straight shackle.

Parts of a shackle. The ends of a shackle are called the " lugs," the space between them is called the " jaw," and the part opposite the jaw is called the " crown " ; the inside width or length of a shackle is called the " clear," thus a shackle may be described as being " long in the clear " or " wide in the clear." The jaw is closed by a removable " bolt " which passes through a hole in each lug, and a general purpose shackle is usually named by the manner in which its bolt is secured in place.

Types of shackle. In the " screw shackle " the end of the bolt is screwed into one of the lugs, and the bolt may be fitted with a flange at its head to prevent the lugs from being strained together when the bolt is screwed right home.

In the " forelock shackle " the end of the bolt projects beyond one of the lugs, and a flat tapered pin called a " forelock " is passed through a slot in the end of the bolt ; the forelock is attached to the shackle by a chain lanyard.

In a " keyed shackle " the bolt is made with two projections, called " keys," which fit into slots in the lugs called " keyways " ; when the bolt is passed through the lugs it is locked in place by turning it so that the keys and keyways are out of line with each other.

In a " joining shackle " a tapered hole is drilled through one of the lugs and the end of the bolt, and the bolt is secured in place by a similarly tapered pin being driven into this hole and held in place by a lead pellet hammered into the mouth of the hole over the head of the pin.

In the " clenched shackle " the end of the bolt is hammered over so that it cannot be removed, thus closing the shackle permanently.

Shackles for anchors and cables. Shackles used with the anchors and cables of a ship are specially named, the name usually denoting the purpose they serve. The " anchor shackle " joins the cable to the ring of the anchor ; the " buoy securing shackle " is used to join the bridle of a ship's cable to the ring of a buoy ; a " joining shackle " is used to join the lengths of a cable

143

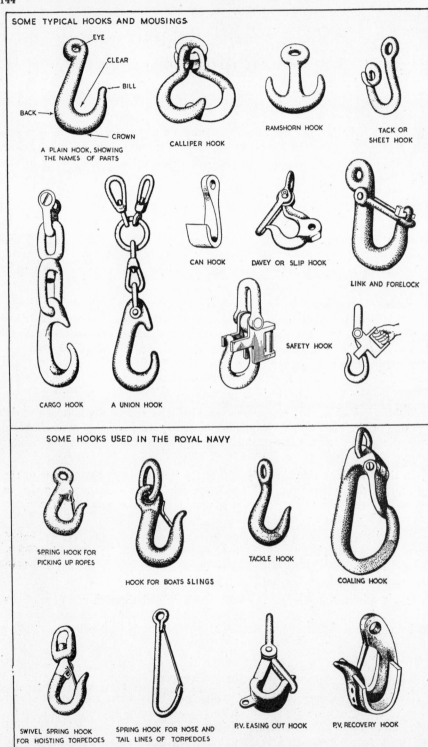

SOME TYPICAL HOOKS AND MOUSINGS

EYE
CLEAR
BILL
BACK
CROWN
A PLAIN HOOK, SHOWING
THE NAMES OF PARTS

CALLIPER HOOK

RAMSHORN HOOK

TACK OR
SHEET HOOK

CAN HOOK

DAVEY OR SLIP HOOK

LINK AND FORELOCK

SAFETY HOOK

CARGO HOOK

A UNION HOOK

SOME HOOKS USED IN THE ROYAL NAVY

SPRING HOOK FOR
PICKING UP ROPES

HOOK FOR BOATS SLINGS

TACKLE HOOK

COALING HOOK

SWIVEL SPRING HOOK
FOR HOISTING TORPEDOES

SPRING HOOK FOR NOSE AND
TAIL LINES OF TORPEDOES

P.V. EASING OUT HOOK

P.V. RECOVERY HOOK

Fig. 170.—Hooks

together ; and a " joggle shackle " is used to join a rope to a cable. The bolts of the anchor shackle and of the buoy securing shackle are secured in a similar manner to that of the joining shackle ; the joggle shackle is a keyed shackle.

An anchor shackle is longer in the clear than other shackles ; for this reason, and because its bolt is firmly secured in place with its ends flush with the lugs, it is always used to join the eyes of two wire hawsers together.

Thimbles (Fig. 169)

These are metal rings, of various shapes and sizes, made of steel or iron and grooved to fit into the eyes of fibre or wire ropes' ends so that they can be joined together by shackles ; the thimble takes the chafe of the shackle, supports the eye of the rope, and prevents a bad nip in it.

Thimbles are either " round " or " heart-shaped," and " open " or " welded." The gap in an open thimble (except the machinery type) can be widened temporarily to admit the eye of a tackle hook. The heart shape is generally preferred for thimble and hawser eyes, both in wire and fibre rope. Round, welded thimbles are used for boom gear and at the edges and corners of awnings and sails. Round, open thimbles are usually used where a hook is to be fitted into the eye : for the hook in the crown of a common stropped block, for example, and for hook ropes. The solid and machinery thimbles are designed for use when an eye is to be anchored by a bolt, as in a crane purchase, and they are shaped accordingly.

Hooks (Fig. 170)

Hooks used at sea are of many different designs and are usually made of mild galvanised steel. They are much weaker than shackles of similar size.

The point of a hook is called the " bill," the body is called the " shank," and the bottom the " crown " ; the part of the shank opposite the bill is the " back " ; the " jaw " is the space between the bill and the top of the shank, and the " clear " is the inside diameter of the crown.

The Cargo hook and Coaling hook are very similar. They are made large enough in the clear to take the four legs of a sling without jamming them against one another, and the projection fitted to the upper part of the shank acts as a guard to prevent the bill catching accidentally in a hatch coaming or some projection in its wake.

The Ram's-horn hook keeps the parts of a sling separated, and thus entirely eliminates the possibility of their jamming together.

A Calliper hook or Clip hook is used instead of a shackle in the sailing gear of some Service boats and in the rigging of signal yards. Its advantage over a shackle is that it has no bolt to rust up or get lost, but it must always be moused with spunyarn to prevent it from becoming unhooked.

Sheet hooks and Tack hooks are also used with sailing gear ; the cork-screw-shaped bill acts as a mousing to prevent accidental unhooking.

A Union hook is used in cargo work and is designed to take two whips.

Can hooks are extensively used in commercial practice, but seldom in the Royal Navy, for slinging casks and bales.

Tackle hooks are general purpose hooks made either with the eye in line with the hook, or with a " reversed eye " (*i.e.* one at right angles to the hook).

A Swivel hook is fitted with one or more swivels which prevents any twist in the whip being transmitted to the hook ; without such a fitting the load

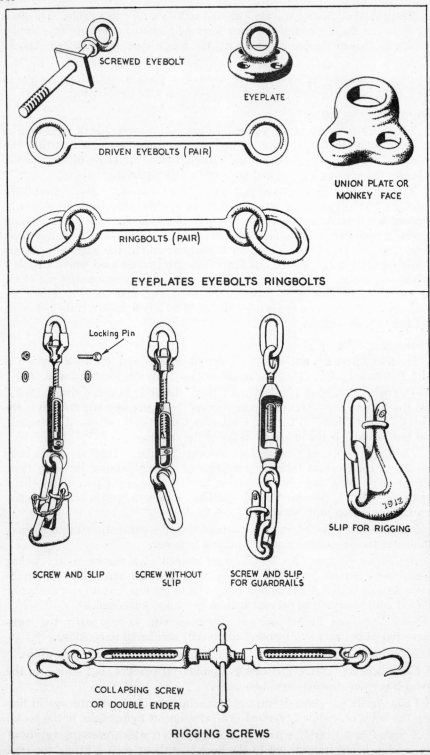

SCREWED EYEBOLT

EYEPLATE

DRIVEN EYEBOLTS (PAIR)

UNION PLATE OR
MONKEY FACE

RINGBOLTS (PAIR)

EYEPLATES EYEBOLTS RINGBOLTS

Locking Pin

SLIP FOR RIGGING

SCREW AND SLIP

SCREW WITHOUT
SLIP

SCREW AND SLIP
FOR GUARDRAILS

COLLAPSING SCREW
OR DOUBLE ENDER

RIGGING SCREWS

Fig. 171.—Rigging fittings

would spin as the whip takes the weight and this might cause the splice of the whip to draw.

A Spring hook has a mousing device, in the form of a spring-operated tongue, which prevents it from unhooking. Some other hooks have a link and forelock, for the same purpose.

A Safety hook has a handle fitted with cheeks which close the jaw of the hook when the handle falls in place. Some hooks have a mousing shackle oị prevent the hook from catching some obstruction.

Trip hooks are designed for slipping a load in mid-air, or for slipping the eye of a hawser under strain. The former type has an eye welded to the back of the hook to which a tripping line is secured ; when the line is hauled upon it upends the hook. The latter type, which is used in many tugs, is hinged at the crown and moused with a link and forelock ; when the link is knocked off the pull of the hawser opens the hook.

Eye-plates, Eye-bolts, Deck Clenches, Ring-bolts and Union Plates (Fig. 171)

Eye-plates are of stamped steel and are used for securing an eye to a metal structure ; they are either riveted or welded in place.

Eye-bolts are of wrought iron or mild steel and are used for securing an eye to a wooden structure. They are of two types, the " driven " type, which is by far the stronger of the two and in which the bolt is forced through a bored hole and held in place by a nut on its protruding end, and the " screwed " type which screws directly into the wood and is supplied with a metal plate against which its flange rests when right home. Driven eye-bolts are supplied in pairs, and must be cut and threaded as required before use.

Deck clenches are heavy metal fittings provided as anchorage points on the deck for standing rigging, hawsers, or cables which may be subjected to heavy strains. They consist of a triangular piece of metal, which is bored with a hole to take the bolt of a shackle and fixed to a base plate which is clenched through the deck by four bolts in the same manner as a driven eye-bolt.

Ring-bolts, of wrought iron or mild steel, are used wherever it is required to fit a ring to a wooden structure, usually for making fast a rope. They consist of a driven eye-bolt with a ring or a link attached. Ring-bolts are supplied in pairs, and must be cut and threaded as required before use.

Union plates are triangular or square metal plates with a hole drilled at each corner, and are used as links for shackling the ends of three or four ropes or lengths of chain together ; the triangular plates are usually known as " monkey faces " or " shamrock plates."

Rigging Screws (or Turn-buckles) and Rigging Slips (Fig. 171)

Rigging screws of various kinds are used to " set up," *i.e.* adjust for length or tension, any rigging equipment. They must not be confused with the " turning-in screw," which is used to break-in a wire rope round a thimble and which is sometimes called a rigging screw.

Rigging screws may be of any of the following types :—

 (i) a screw fitting into an internally-threaded sleeve, with a swivel eye at the head of the screw and a standing eye on the sleeve ;

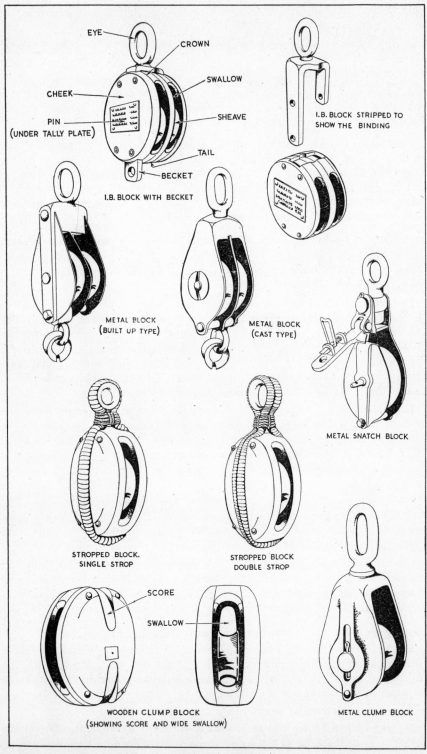

EYE

CROWN

SWALLOW

CHEEK

SHEAVE

PIN
(UNDER TALLY PLATE)

TAIL

BECKET

I.B. BLOCK WITH BECKET

I.B. BLOCK STRIPPED TO
SHOW THE BINDING

METAL BLOCK
(BUILT UP TYPE)

METAL BLOCK
(CAST TYPE)

METAL SNATCH BLOCK

STROPPED BLOCK.
SINGLE STROP

STROPPED BLOCK
DOUBLE STROP

SCORE

SWALLOW

WOODEN CLUMP BLOCK
(SHOWING SCORE AND WIDE SWALLOW)

METAL CLUMP BLOCK

Fig. 172.—Blocks

(ii) a similar assembly, but with the swivel eye on the sleeve and the standing eye on the screw ;

(iii) an internally-threaded sleeve with a right-handed screw taking into one end and a left-handed screw into the other, standing eyes being fitted at the head of each screw ;

(iv) a central screw with a threaded sleeve taking on each end, one end having a left and the other a right-handed thread, and a standing eye being fitted to each sleeve.

In (i) and (iv) the length is adjusted by turning the screw, usually with a tommy bar, and in the others by turning the sleeve ; after adjustment, simple locking devices are used to prevent the screw or sleeve from moving further.

Rigging screws issued to the Royal Navy comprise all four of these types, and they are known generally as " screws and slips," " screws without slips," or sometimes " bottle-screws " ; type (iv) is called a " double-ender," or " collapsing screw." Those issued for general purposes are of the first type described. In each type the screw is locked to the sleeve by a sliding block, and to the swivel eye at its head by a bolt taking into a slotted plate, as illustrated in Fig. 171. In addition, screws of other types are issued for special purposes such as the adjustment of guardrails, davit guys and aerials, some of which are also illustrated in Fig. 171. The collapsing screw is much more clumsy than the remainder, but can be designed with a longer travel. Bottle-screws are also used in cable work.

A *Rigging slip* is a quick-release link used for joining the end of a rope or a chain to a fitting when the end may have to be cast off frequently or rapidly. They are supplied in various sizes to the Royal Navy.

BLOCKS

A block is a portable pulley, made of wood, metal, or wood and metal ; the wooden block is slightly heavier than the all-metal block, but more comfortably handled.

Parts of a Block (Fig. 172)

The main parts of a block are illustrated in Fig. 172, and consist of : the " shell " or body ; the " sheave " or wheel over which the rope runs ; the " pin " on which the sheave turns ; and the eye, hook, strop or other fitting by which the block is secured in the required position.

The top of the block where the eye or hook is fitted is called the " crown " ; the bottom of the block is the " tail " ; the sides of the shell are the " cheeks," and the groove made in the cheeks of some blocks to take the strop is called the " score " ; the opening between the sheave and shell through which the rope passes is the " swallow " ; and the eye sometimes fitted at the tail is the " becket."

Classification of Blocks

Wooden blocks are classified by their size, which is their length from crown to tail measured round the shell ; an ordinary wooden block will take a rope one-third of its size, so that a 9-inch block, for example, would be required for a 3-inch rope. Metal blocks are classified by the size of rope for which each is designed, which is marked on a plate affixed to one cheek. Blocks may have more than one sheave ; a single block has one sheave, a double block two, a triple block three, and so on. Some details of the blocks now (1950) in use at sea are given below.

Types of Blocks

The Internal-bound (I.B.) block (Fig. 172) has a shell partly of wood and partly of metal, and is the modern type of wooden block. The metal portion consists of a fork-shaped steel fitting, called the " binding," which incorporates both the eye or hook, and the becket when fitted ; it also takes the pin of the sheave. The wooden portion, which is of elm, is really a fairing piece and takes no part of the load ; it can be replaced on board if broken. External bound blocks are used in commercial practice, but not in the Royal Navy.

Metal blocks (Fig. 172) supplied to the Royal Navy are usually built up of steel plates and fittings, and, like the I.B. blocks, their shells have a binding which supplies the strength, but the cheeks, etc., are of light plating. The simplest pattern is the " gin block," which consists of a binding carrying one large sheave, and a skeleton rope guard instead of cheeks. Some types of metal blocks, however, have their shells cast in one piece.

Metal blocks vary considerably in quality and finish, the better ones being manufactured for special purposes such as the upper blocks of boats' falls, or the blocks of engineers' tackles. Some special purpose blocks are made entirely of gunmetal or phosphor bronze, which do not corrode as easily as steel when exposed to weather and are not liable to cause sparks when working. A few of the old fashioned " malleable cast iron (M.C.I.) blocks " are still in use.

Snatch blocks (Fig. 172) are single blocks, either of metal or internal bound, in each of which part of the shell is hinged to allow a bight of rope to be inserted into the swallow from one side.

Common blocks, which are now (1950) very uncommon, have shells made entirely of elm. They are the old fashioned type of wooden block which is held in position by a strop passed round its shell and seized into a thimble-eye at the crown ; the strop thus strengthens the shell and the block.

The Clump block (Fig. 172) can be of wood or metal ; its peculiarity is that it has an exceptionally large swallow. The wooden clump block is made in a similar manner to the common block, but it will take a rope of half its own size ; a six-inch clump block, for example, will take a three-inch rope. Wooden clump blocks are used on lower booms to support the bights of the boat ropes, and metal clump blocks are usually designed to take chain.

Fiddle blocks are double blocks, usually of metal, in which the sheaves are carried one above the other instead of side by side. Though not supplied in the Royal Navy they are used in the Merchant Navy where a double block is required but where there is either insufficient lateral room for the normal type or where it is desired to separate the parts of the fall with which the block is rove.

Sheaves and Bearings

The sheaves of all wooden blocks are of phosphor bronze, and those of metal blocks are either of phosphor bronze or mild steel. Phosphor bronze sheaves are the more expensive but are desirable where the blocks are exposed to corrosion as in boats' falls and engineers' tackles, or where sparking may be dangerous as in ammunition hoists. The pins of all blocks are of steel.

The bearing between the sheaves and the pin may be of the plain, roller, or self-lubricating type. In accordance with common engineering practice a mild steel sheave with a plain bearing has a small brass bush let into its centre to form the bearing, because steel bearing on steel is liable to seize. Roller bearings are fitted in a number of special metal blocks, including most of those used for boats' falls.

Self-lubricating bearings have a perforated bronze bush next to the pin, the perforations being filled with a special lubricant. They are used in the Royal Navy for some derricks and in boat hoisting machinery.

Means of attaching

Every block, except a stropped block, has a fitting at its crown by which to secure it where required. A list of such fittings is given below :—

   (i) a standing eye in line with the sheave ;

   (ii) a standing eye at right angles to the sheave ;

   (iii) a standing eye at right angles to the sheave, with a free hook ;

   (iv) a swivel eye ;

   (v) a swivel hook ;

   (vi) a swivel eye and a free hook ;

   (vii) a jaw in line with the sheave ;

   (viii) a jaw at right angles to the sheave.

Note.—A " jaw " is a fork-shaped fitting by which a block can be suspended and at the same time kept from turning ; it is fitted to the upper blocks of some boats' falls. All blocks fitted with a swivel at the crown are called " swivel blocks."

Description

A block is fully described as follows :—

   (i) size (wooden blocks only) ;

   (ii) number of sheaves ;

   (iii) type (I.B., common, steel, etc.), with details of sheaves sometimes included ;

   (iv) size and type of fall (metal blocks only) ;

   (v) means of attachment (standing eye, swivel hook, etc.) ;

   (vi) pattern number.

Examples are :—" a 12-inch, double I.B. block, fitted with standing eye reversed (*i.e.* at right angles to sheave), and becket, pattern 131 " ; " a single steel block with mild steel sheave, for $2\frac{1}{2}$-inch fibre rope, fitted with swivel eye, free hook, and becket, pattern 5126A."

Strength of Blocks

The safe working loads of blocks are dealt with more fully in Volume II of this manual, but in general it can be said that an I.B., a metal, or a common block is stronger than the rope for which it is designed. Clump blocks and snatch blocks are much weaker ; the strength of a snatch block can be taken generally as being one-third of the strength of an I.B. block used for the same size of rope, and that of a clump block as one-quarter of the strength of such a block.

PURCHASES AND TACKLES

A purchase is a mechanical device by means of which an applied pull or force is increased ; it may be a system of levers, a system of revolving drums or wheels geared to one another, or a combination of blocks or pulleys rove with rope or chain.

A tackle (pronounced " taycle ") is a purchase consisting of a rope rove through two or more blocks in such a way that any pull applied to its hauling part is increased by an amount depending upon the number of sheaves in the blocks and the manner in which the rope is rove through them.

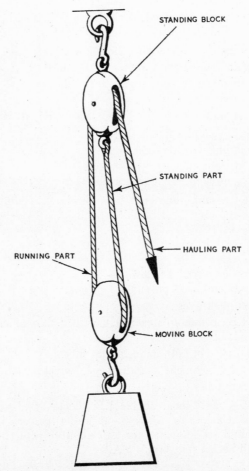

Fig. 173.—Parts of a tackle

Parts of a Tackle (Fig. 173)

The blocks of a tackle are termed the " standing block " and " moving block " ; the rope rove through them is called the " fall," which has its

" standing," " running," and " hauling parts." The size of a tackle is described by the size of its fall ; a 3-inch luff, for example, would be rove with a 3-inch fall.

Mechanical Advantage

The amount by which the pull on the hauling part is multiplied by the tackle is called its " mechanical advantage " (M.A.) and, if friction is disregarded, this is equal to the number of parts of the fall at the *moving* block. In Fig. 174, for example, there are two parts at the moving block, therefore the mechanical advantage is two ; in other words a pull on the hauling part of 1 cwt. would, if friction were disregarded, lift a weight of 2 cwt.

Friction, which occurs in the bearings of the sheaves and in the fall as it bends round the sheaves, reduces the mechanical advantage considerably ; this loss through friction is explained on page 159.

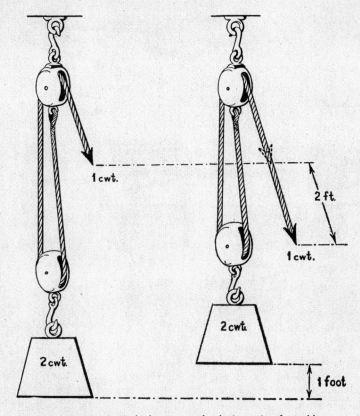

Fig. 174.—Mechanical advantage and velocity ratio of a tackle

Velocity Ratio

It should be borne in mind that mechanical advantage is gained only at the expense of the speed of working. In Fig. 174, for example, the weight will only be raised one foot for every two feet of movement of the hauling part. The ratio between the distance moved by the hauling part and that

6

moved by the moving block is known as the " velocity ratio " (V.R.) and is always equal to the number of parts of the fall at the *moving* block.

Reeving a Tackle to Advantage, and to Disadvantage

The number of parts at the moving block, and therefore the mechanical advantage, is always greater when the hauling part comes away from the moving block, and such a tackle is said to be " rove to advantage." Conversely, a tackle in which the hauling part comes away from the standing block is said to be " rove to disadvantage " (see Fig. 175). *Where practicable, therefore, rig a tackle so that the hauling part leads from the moving block, and make the block with the greater number of sheaves the moving block.*

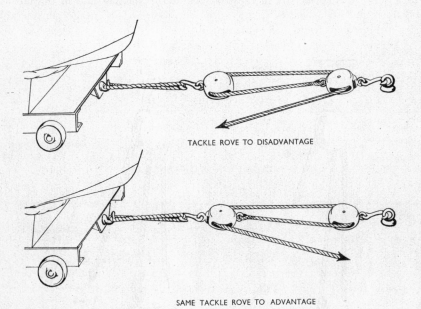

TACKLE ROVE TO DISADVANTAGE

SAME TACKLE ROVE TO ADVANTAGE

Fig. 175.—Reeving a tackle to advantage and disadvantage

Load on the Standing Block (Fig. 176)

The load on the standing block, and therefore on the fitting to which it is attached, is dependant upon the mechanical advantage of the tackle used. This load is calculated by adding the pull required on the hauling part to the weight which is being moved, and so for a given weight the greater the mechanical advantage the less will be the load on the standing block.

Examples of Tackles and Purchases

Examples of whips, tackles, and purchases used at sea, together with their velocity ratios and mechanical advantages, are given below ; in each the loss of power due to friction has been taken into account.

(1) *The Single Whip* (Fig. 177) consists of a fall rove through a single standing block ; no mechanical advantage is gained. It is used for hoisting light loads, and where speed of hoisting is an important factor.

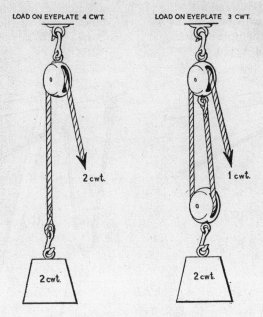

Fig. 176.—Load on the standing block

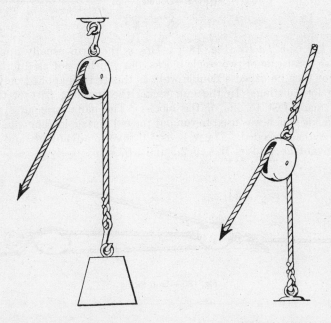

Fig. 177.—Single whip   Fig. 178.—Runner

(2) *The Runner* (Fig. 178) consists of a rope rove through a single moving block. As there are two parts of the fall in the moving block, the V.R. is 2 and its M.A. is 1·82.

(3) *The Double Whip* (Fig. 179) is a purchase used for hoisting and consists of two single blocks with the standing part of the fall made fast near, or to, the upper block, and it cannot be rove to advantage. Its V.R. is 2 and its M.A. is 1·67.

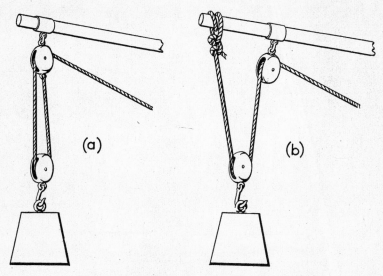

Fig. 179.—Double whips

(4) *The Gun Tackle* (Fig. 180). This is the term usually applied to a purchase consisting of two single blocks, but which is not used for hoisting; it cannot then be called a double whip as this term is applied only when it is used for hoisting. In the gun tackle the standing part of the fall is always made fast to one of the blocks. The name originates from the small tackle which was used to run out the old muzzle-loading gun carriages after they had recoiled. The V.R. is 3 if rove to advantage, and 2 if rove to disadvantage, and its M.A. is 2·5 and 1·67 respectively.

Fig. 180.—Gun tackle

(5) *A Luff* (Fig. 181) is a purchase of 3 inches in size or greater. It consists of a double and a single block, with the standing part of the fall made fast to the single block. Its V.R. is 4 if rove to advantage, and 3 if rove to disadvantage, and its M.A. is 3·08 and 2·3 respectively.

(6) *A Jigger* is similar to a luff but of from 2 to $2\frac{1}{2}$ inches in size.

(7) *A Handy Billy* is a small tackle of less than 2 inches in size ; it is usually rove as a jigger but can be rove as a small gun-tackle.

(8) *The Two-fold Purchase* (Fig. 182) consists of two double blocks and is commonly used for hoisting boats. Its V.R. is 5 if rove to advantage, and 4 if rove to disadvantage, and its M.A. is 3·57 and 2·86 respectively.

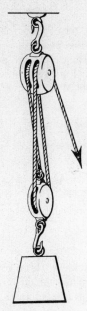

Fig. 181.—Luff

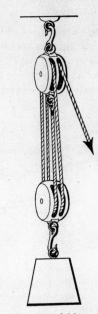

Fig. 182.—Two-fold purchase

(9) *The Three-fold Purchase* (Fig. 183) consists of two treble blocks ; its V.R. is 7 if rove to advantage, and 6 if rove to disadvantage, and its M.A. is 4·37 and 3·75 respectively.

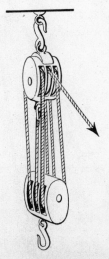

Fig. 183.—Three-fold purchase

Tackles having more than three sheaves to a block, such as the four-fold, five-fold and six-fold purchases, are not provided as upper deck tackles because they are too cumbersome to handle efficiently and because the friction in their sheaves considerably reduces their gain in mechanical advantage. If additional mechanical advantage is required it is best gained by combining two simple tackles in the manner described in paragraph (10).

(10) *Luff upon Luff* (Fig. 184) is a general term used to describe the combined use of two tackles in which the moving block of one is clapped on to the hauling part of the other ; its mechanical advantage is the product of the mechanical advantage of each tackle. Fig. 184 shows two luffs rove to advantage and as a luff upon luff whose M.A. $= 4 \times 4 = 16$.

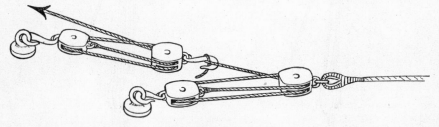

Fig. 184.—Luff upon luff

(11) *The Runner and Tackle* (Fig. 185) is a tackle with its moving block made fast to the hauling part of a runner. The velocity ratio of the runner and tackle illustrated is $2 \times 4 = 8$, and the mechanical advantage is $1 \cdot 82 \times 3 \cdot 08 = 5 \cdot 61$.

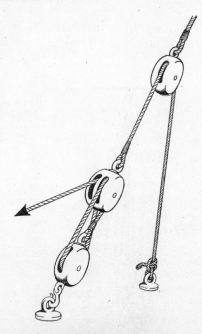

Fig. 185.—Runner and tackle

(12) *The Five-part or Three-and-two Tackle* consists of one triple and one double block, the standing part being made fast to the double block. This tackle is not usually provided in H.M. ships.

(13) *A Dutchman's Purchase* (Fig. 186) is a tackle used in reverse to take advantage of the velocity ratio of the tackle ; an example of its use is to drive a light whip at a fast speed from a slow but powerful capstan.

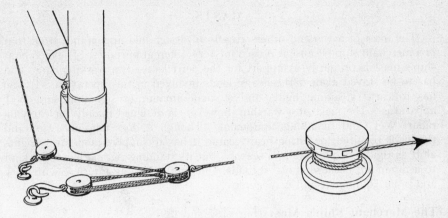

Fig. 186.—Dutchman's purchase

In the example illustrated in Fig. 186, the whip would move a distance of 5 feet for every foot travelled by the moving block. When using a tackle in this manner it should be borne in mind that the pull exerted by the capstan must be equal to the product of the weight to be hoisted, and the velocity ratio of the tackle, plus the friction in the tackle and its leading blocks ; or in this case a pull of at least $5\frac{3}{5}$ times the weight to be hoisted. Care must therefore be taken to ensure that the tackle and its pendant are strong enough for the job.

Friction in a Tackle

When a tackle is being worked considerable friction is set up, both in the bearings of the blocks and within the fall as it bends round the sheaves. This friction accounts for the difference between the velocity ratio of the tackle and its mechanical advantage, as shown in the examples of tackles already described, and the general rule for estimating the amount of such friction is to allow from one-tenth to one-eighth of the weight to be hoisted for each sheave in the tackle. For a poor quality or badly maintained tackle the allowance would be one-eighth, but for a well made tackle in good condition the allowance would be one-tenth.

To estimate the pull required on the hauling part of any tackle to hoist a given weight, divide the weight by the mechanical advantage of the tackle. Conversely, to estimate the weight which can be hoisted by a given pull on the hauling part of a tackle, multiply the pull by the mechanical advantage of the tackle ; before putting this into practice, however, take care to ensure the pull is within the working load of the fall of the tackle.

When holding or lowering a load with a tackle the friction will take part of the weight, and a lesser force is therefore required on the hauling part to hold or lower a load than to hoist it.

(*Note :* The effects of friction in tackles and purchases is more fully dealt with in Volume II of this manual, in the chapter headed " Rigging.")

MASTS

The mast of a warship differs greatly in design and appearance from that of a merchant ship because it is used for very different purposes. The merchant ship's mast is primarily a support for the derricks used in working cargo and has to be stayed against the heavy loads involved in this operation. It also has to carry steaming lights and a small amount of signalling and W/T apparatus. The mast of a warship, however, is designed mainly for carrying radar, W/T, and signalling equipment. Though it does not have to stand the loads required for lifting heavy cargo it has to support moderate weights aloft as rigidly as possible in a seaway, but its standing rigging has to be kept to a minimum because stays, shrouds, and similar rigging interfere with W/T and radar equipment and A.A. gunfire.

The Merchant Ship's Mast (Figs. 187 and 189)

The conventional form of merchant ship's mast is described first because it more nearly resembles that of the former sailing ship, to which the names of the parts and the rigging of all types of mast, and the terms used to describe their functions, owe their origin. At the start of the present century the conventional form of mast here described was almost universal, but nowadays masts vary greatly in design and rig.

Parts of a Mast and Mast Fittings

A modern mast is made in either one or two pieces ; if made in two pieces the lower one is called the " lowermast " and the upper the " topmast " ; if made in one piece the mast is called a " polemast," and if particularly tall the upper part is called the topmast and the lower part the lowermast. The top of a mast is called the " head " and the bottom is called the " heel."

A mast is said to be " stepped," *i.e.* supported, at the place where its heel rests. A polemast or a lowermast may be stepped on the ship's keelson, on one of her lower decks, or on her upper deck ; a topmast is stepped at the head of its lowermast. Where a mast passes through a deck, the deck round the " mast-hole " is strengthened by girders and beams called " mast partners," and the mast is secured in the hole by wedges. The mast-hole in the weather deck is made water-tight by a canvas cover called the " mast coat," which fits snugly round the mast and its hole.

The heel of a mast stepped on the upper deck is fitted into a box-like structure called a " tabernacle," which supports the lower part of the mast. The masts of river-going vessels which are stepped in tabernacles may be hinged so that they can be canted aft or laid on deck when the vessels have to pass under low bridges. For the same purpose a topmast is fitted so that it can be lowered and secured alongside its lowermast, in which position it is said to be " housed " ; but if it is sent right down on deck it is said to be " struck."

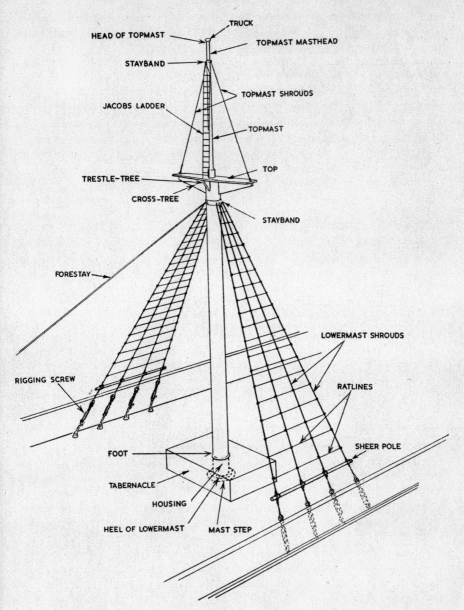

Fig. 187.—A merchant ship's mast

A mast, whether a polemast, a lowermast, or a topmast, is divided into three parts known as the " housing," the " hounding " and the " masthead." The housing of a lowermast is that part which extends from its heel to the upper deck or the top of its tabernacle ; the housing of a topmast is that part which extends from its heel to the head of its lowermast. The hounding is that part which extends from the top of the housing to a position some distance below the head where the standing rigging is secured. The masthead extends from the top of the hounding to the head of the mast, that of a lower-mast being called the " lower masthead," and that of a topmast being called the " top masthead." The lower part of the hounding of a lowermast just above the upper deck is called the " foot." In a polemast there is neither a lower masthead nor a topmast housing, the part above the position to which the topmast rigging is secured being called simply the masthead.

Where a topmast is fitted the lower ends of its standing rigging may be secured to athwartship and fore-and-aft cross pieces which are fitted to the lower masthead and called respectively " cross-trees " and " trestle-trees " ; these are supported by brackets called " cheeks," and over them is built a platform called a " top."

On the head of a lowermast is fitted a band called the " mast cap," to which is hinged a hoop called the " trunnion hoop " through which the foot of the topmast is stepped ; other fittings on the lower masthead for supporting the topmast are described later. At the upper end of the hounding of a mast is fitted a metal hoop called a " stayband," which has a number of eyes to which the upper ends of the standing rigging are shackled. A wooden disc called a " truck " is fitted to the head of a topmast or a polemast ; it is usually provided with one or two small sheaves to take signal halyards, and may have an electric signalling lantern fitted to it.

Wooden masts and yards are provided with lightning conductors consisting of copper strips running their entire length and connected to the steel hull of the ship ; special contacts between mast and mast and mast and yard are provided where necessary.

Small stump masts, called " kingposts," or " Samson posts," are fitted in some merchant ships to carry extra derricks for working cargo.

Mast Spars

A spar which is crossed horizontally athwart a mast is called a " yard," and a spar projecting aft from a mainmast and cocked up at an angle of about 45 degrees with the mast is called a " gaff " ; yards are used to carry signal halyards and wireless aerials, and a gaff is used for wearing an ensign. The booms fitted at the foot of most merchant ships' masts and used for working cargo are called " derricks " ; they are described in detail later together with yards and gaffs.

Some masts may be fitted with " spurs," which are steel arms of varying sizes projecting horizontally from the mast and used for carrying signal halyards or the gantlines for hoisting oil navigation lights and other gear into place. Brackets are provided on the foremast and the mainmast at the prescribed height above the upper deck for carrying, respectively, the fore and main electric steaming lights.

Fidded Topmast

A " fidded " topmast is illustrated in Fig. 188. It is supported at its heel by a short, stout, metal bar, called a " fid," which passes through a hole in the topmast and rests across the two arms of a bracket on the lower masthead called the " lower trestle-trees." It is steadied at the top of its housing by the trunnion hoop, which is hinged athwart the lowermast cap and lined with wood or leather to allow the topmast to slide easily within it.

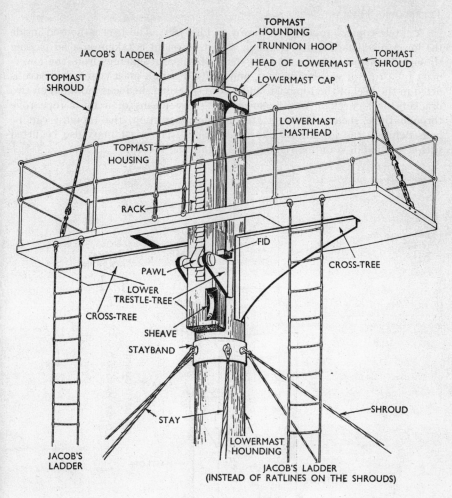

TOPMAST
HOUNDING
TRUNNION HOOP
JACOB'S LADDER
HEAD OF LOWERMAST
TOPMAST
SHROUD
TOPMAST
SHROUD
LOWERMAST CAP
LOWERMAST
MASTHEAD
TOPMAST
HOUSING
RACK
FID
CROSS-TREE
PAWL
LOWER
TRESTLE-TREE
CROSS-TREE
SHEAVE
STAYBAND
SHROUD
STAY
JACOB'S
LADDER
LOWERMAST
HOUNDING
JACOB'S LADDER
(INSTEAD OF RATLINES ON THE SHROUDS)

Fig. 188.—A fidded topmast

On the side away from the lowermast the topmast housing is fitted with
a rack, from 6 to 8 feet long, in which is engaged a pawl hinged between the
ends of the lower trestle-trees. The pawl is engaged with the rack in the
final stages of swaying a topmast into position and holds the topmast while
the holes for the fid are aligned and the fid passed through them. When the
topmast is in place the pawl does not help to support it and may therefore be
disengaged from its rack.

A vertical slot is cut diagonally across the heel of the topmast into which
is fitted a sheave, and an eye-bolt to take a corresponding sheave is fitted
to the head of the lower mast ; through these sheaves is rove the " mast rope "
used when housing or striking the topmast, or when swaying it aloft.

At the upper end of the topmast hounding is fitted a stayband to which
is shackled the topmast standing rigging. Just below this stayband a vertical
slot may be cut through the mast to take a sheave for a halyard or gantline
for hoisting a yard or other gear aloft.

TELESCOPIC TOPMAST

A " telescopic " topmast is shown in Fig. 189. The heel is housed inside the lower masthead, which is hollow, and the weight is taken on a fid passing through both masts. The mast is steadied where it emerges from the lower-mast by a ring of wooden wedges, and is fitted with a mast coat. A sheave is fitted in the heel of the topmast, and a corresponding sheave is mounted on two brackets or " cheeks " on the lowermast ; by means of a mast rope rove through these sheaves, as indicated in the illustration, the topmast can be housed inside the lowermast like a telescope. The mast may also be fitted with a stayband, standing rigging, and a gantline sheave.

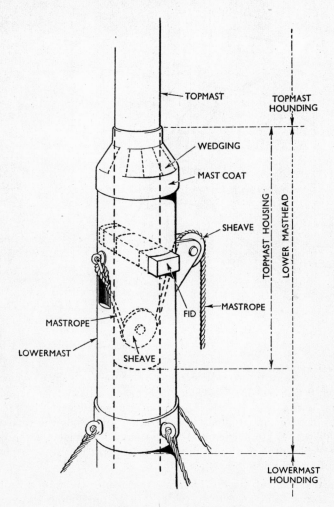

Fig. 189.—A telescopic topmast

The Warship's Mast

The masts of a modern warship are either of the " tripod " or " lattice " types, the main features of which are shown in Figs. 190 and 191 ; in both these types the lower mast needs no staying by standing rigging.

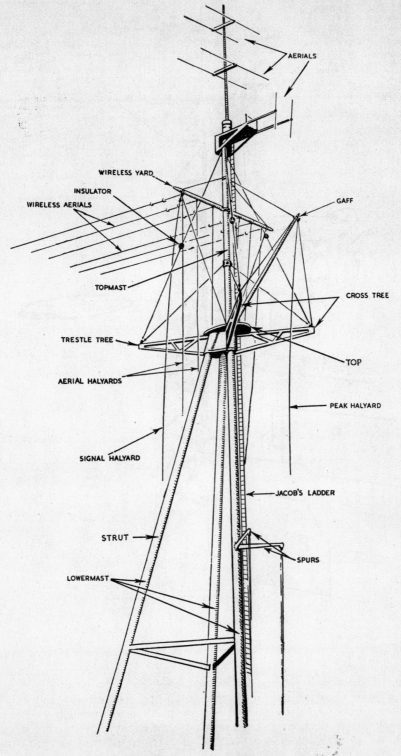

AERIALS

WIRELESS YARD

INSULATOR

WIRELESS AERIALS

GAFF

TOPMAST

CROSS TREE

TRESTLE TREE

TOP

AERIAL HALYARDS

PEAK HALYARD

SIGNAL HALYARD

JACOB'S LADDER

STRUT

SPURS

LOWERMAST

Fig. 190.—A cruiser's tripod mast

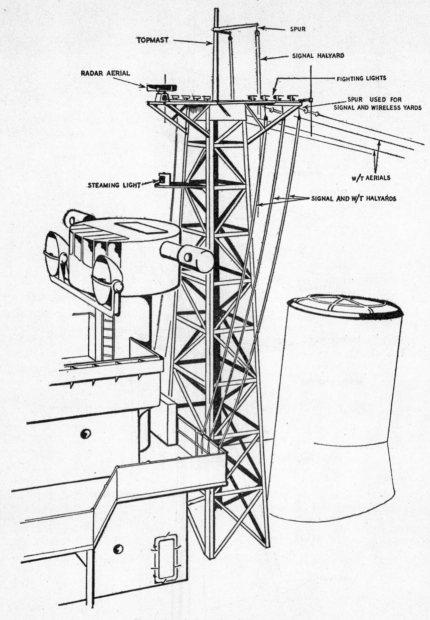

TOPMAST

RADAR AERIAL

SPUR

SIGNAL HALYARD

FIGHTING LIGHTS

SPUR USED FOR
SIGNAL AND WIRELESS YARDS

W/T AERIALS

STEAMING LIGHT

SIGNAL AND W/T HALYARDS

Fig. 191.—A destroyer's lattice mast

In the tripod type the " struts " form the lowermast, and at their upper end some form of top supported by cross-trees and trestle-trees is usually fitted. The topmast may be a continuation of one of the struts, or it may be a separate mast stepped on the top, or on a bracket below it, and secured to the lowermast head by hoops. Such a mast cannot normally be housed or struck, and it is called a " fitted topmast " ; it is stayed by standing rigging which, except in the older destroyers, is led to the trestle-trees and cross-trees of the lowermast. The lattice type of mast fitted (1950) in modern destroyers and other small warships may be provided with a small topmast to carry signal halyards, or with a telescopic topmast to carry a radar aerial ; the telescopic topmast can be housed in a similar manner to that of a merchant ship, and neither type of topmast is stayed. Jacob's ladders, or steel rungs welded to the struts, are provided on warships' masts for going aloft.

In addition to yards, gaffs, trucks, spurs, gantline sheaves, masthead signalling lanterns and brackets for navigation lights, a warship's mast carries the aerials for radar and short wave wireless installations. These are probably the most conspicuous fittings on the mast, but as their form is constantly changing with each new development it is not practicable to describe any definite layout.

The height of the lowermasts of H.M. ships is limited to 145 feet so that they can pass under the Forth Bridge. All topmasts and radar aerials extending above this height have to be designed so that they can be housed, and details of the arrangements for housing them are shown on the ship's drawings usually kept by the Engineer Officer.

Standing Rigging

A mast, except one of the tripod and lattice types, is " stayed," *i.e.* supported in position, by its " standing rigging " ; this consists of " forestays " and " backstays " which support it in a fore-and-aft direction, and " shrouds " which support it athwartships. The component parts of standing rigging are named after the mast they support, *e.g.* " fore-topmast backstay." The upper ends of the standing rigging are shackled to their stayband and the lower ends are fitted with rigging screws so that the rigging can be set up taut. Lowermast standing rigging is secured to the gunwales or the weather decks ; topmast rigging may be secured either to the cross-trees and trestle-trees of its lowermast or to the weather decks.

Insulators are fitted in all standing wire rope rigging to prevent electrical interference with W/T and radar installations. The positions of these insulators must not be altered as they are correctly determined by technical officers of the Admiralty.

The shrouds of a lowermast are led each side to the gunwales, and being led slightly abaft the mast as well as abreast it they serve to some extent as backstays. The forestay of a fore-lowermast is usually led to the eyes of the ship, and its backstays (if fitted) are led abaft the shrouds each side to the gunwales. The forestay of a main-lowermast is usually led to a position on the upper deck well before the mast and on the midship line, and the backstay is led to the stern.

The topmast is a comparatively light spar and is therefore not so heavily stayed as the lowermast. The shrouds of a topmast usually serve the double purpose of shrouds and backstays, and are led to the ends of the cross-trees. If backstays are fitted they can be led either to the deck in the same way as those of the lowermast, or to the after end of the trestle-trees. If a forestay is fitted it can be led to the deck in the same way as that of the lowermast, or to the fore end of the trestle-trees. In some modern merchant ships trestle-trees are not fitted and their topmasts have no forestays or backstays.

After the shrouds and stays have been set up taut their rigging screws are locked, packed with grease, and fitted with laced canvas covers called " gaiters."

When the ship rolls, or when a heavy weight is slung outboard from a mast derrick, the shrouds on one side may slacken owing to the mast working slightly. To support the upper ends of the rigging screws and keep them in their correct relative positions when this occurs a horizontal steel rod called a " sheerpole " is usually fitted ; it is seized to each shroud just above its rigging screw, and this serves also to keep turns out of the shrouds when the rigging screws are being set up.

Above the sheerpole, at intervals of about 15 inches, the shrouds may be joined by a number of light horizontal lines called " ratlines " ; the shrouds then form a ladder, of which the ratlines are the rungs, for use when going aloft. The operation of fitting ratlines is known as " rattling down " because originally it was begun at the masthead and continued downwards, but the modern practice is to rattle upwards from the sheerpole. In many ships no ratlines are fitted and the mast is then climbed by a Jacob's ladder leading up the mast, or by means of steel rungs fitted to the side of the mast and projecting slightly from it.

Running Rigging

In the days of sail the running rigging of a full-rigged ship was very complex and included, for example, " halyards " for hoisting and lowering the yards and sails, " sheets " for trimming the sails, " braces " for slewing the yards and " lifts " for squaring them, together with the various tackles for working them. Nowadays the running rigging on a mast is comparatively simple and consists chiefly of " signal halyards," " gantlines," and " dressing lines," which are described below, and the rigging required to work a mast derrick which is described later.

Signal halyards are made of special soft-laid rope with some of the yarns reverse spun so that the rope is very flexible and not liable to stretch or kink. They are rove through sheaves in the truck or the masthead, or through gun-metal blocks on a yard, spur or gaff, and their ends are fitted with " Inglefield clips," which are specially designed to enable flags to be quickly bent on to the halyard. A signal halyard is named from the position at which it is rove, *e.g.* " masthead halyard," and " starboard yard-arm halyard."

Gantlines are made of cordage, of small size wire rope or of chain, and are rove through blocks on the masts or funnels. They are used for hoisting gear aloft and can be kept permanently rigged, and as they often have to bear the weight of a man they must be inspected frequently. Examples of gantlines are " hammock gantlines " and " clothes lines," which are used respectively for hoisting scrubbed hammocks and washed clothes to dry, also " funnel chains " for rigging stages when painting the funnels, the " yard rope " which is used for hoisting a yard into position and for sending it down on deck, and the " mast rope " which is used for swaying a topmast aloft and for housing or striking it.

Dressing lines are used on ceremonial occasions for " dressing ship," *i.e.* for hoisting flags bent at close intervals on lines which, in a two masted ship, run from the stem to the fore-masthead, thence to the main-masthead and thence to the stern. They consist of wire rope lines to which the dressing flags are permanently bent, and are tailed with cordage whips rove through blocks at the mastheads for hoisting them into position. The foremost line is called the " fore-down," the amidships line is called the " fore-to-main," and the after one the " main-down." Ships with a single mast are fitted with a fore-down and a main-down only.

Precautions when Going Aloft

Aerials, especially radar aerials, often carry very high voltages, and it is therefore advisable to keep clear of them. An additional reason for keeping clear of radar aerials is that many of them are liable to move without warning. Permission should invariably be obtained from the Officer of the Watch before any man goes aloft, or works near an aerial. Before permission is granted, the necessary precautions are taken to ensure that all aerials are safe. In order to prevent a radio set being kept out of action unnecessarily a report should be made to the Officer of the Watch as soon as the man has returned from aloft.

SPARS

Yards

These are now used only for supporting wireless aerials and halyards for signal flags, and are called wireless or signal yards accordingly. They have been evolved from the yards of the square-rigged sailing ship, and their parts and fittings still bear the original names. The yards of a modern warship may, however, be rigidly clamped to the mast and thus dispense with some of the gear needed to hold a slung yard in position. At present (1950) signal yards in the Royal Navy are of tubular steel, and wireless yards of steel or Norway spar, but in some ships they are now replaced by spurs.

A slung yard (Fig. 192) is held athwart the mast by standing rigging, and is supported at its centre or " bunt " by a shackle called the " sling," which joins the eye of an iron band round the yard, called the " parrel band," to the eye of an iron band round the mast, called the " mast band." The yard is kept horizontal by " lifts " and is kept from slewing by " braces." The ends of the yard outside the braces and lifts are called the " yard-arms," and the parts of the yard between the bunt and the yard-arms are called the " quarters." The bunt of some slung yards may be kept close against the mast by a strop of F.S.W. rope, called a " parrel," which is passed round the mast and secured to eyes welded to the parrel band.

A " jackstay " and " footropes " are rigged along the yard to provide, respectively, hand-hold and foot-hold for men working on it, but these are not fitted on the smaller wireless yards if the lifts are within reach from the mast. The jackstay of one or $1\frac{1}{4}$-inch F.S.W. rope runs along the top of the yard from yard-arm to yard-arm, and is rove through metal eyes fitted to the yard. The footrope of $1\frac{1}{2}$-inch F.S.W. rope extends from the bunt to each yard-arm, where it is secured to an eye by a moused caliper hook, and is supported at intervals by wire rope " stirrups " which hang down from the yard. The stirrups have a soft eye in each end ; one eye is rove round the yard and the footrope is rove through the other.

In addition to blocks for the signal halyards, signal yards may be fitted with yard-arm signalling lamps, and fixed coloured lights called " fighting lights " which are used at night for identifying the ship in action.

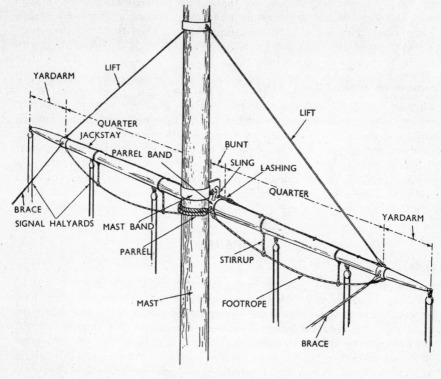

Fig. 192.—A slung yard

Wireless yards are normally fitted in pairs, the ends of the aerials being secured to one pair and the blocks for the aerial halyards to the other. Braces are fitted to one yard of each pair only, the other yard being braced by the aerials.

Gaffs

A gaff in a sailing vessel is a wooden spar used to support the head of a four-sided fore-and-aft sail; it is therefore rigged with halyards for raising and lowering it, and its lower end is fitted with jaws which fit round the mast and thus allow it to slew sideways or be topped up or down. A gaff in a steamship, however, is used only for wearing the ensign conspicuously, and is therefore rigged as a standing gaff in the manner described below and illustrated in Fig. 193.

The lower end or " throat " of the gaff is fitted with an eyed metal sleeve called a " goose-neck," which is bolted to a fork-shaped fitting pivoted at the upper end of the main-lowermast hounding; the gaff is thus supported at its throat by a joint which is hinged both horizontally and vertically. The gaff is also supported by a " standing topping lift " consisting of a pendant shackled to a " spider band " fitted round the middle of the gaff, the other end being shackled to a fitting on the after end of the main-lowermast trestle-trees; the length of the pendant is such that the gaff is held at an angle of about 45 degrees with the mast. The gaff is stayed from slewing sideways by two

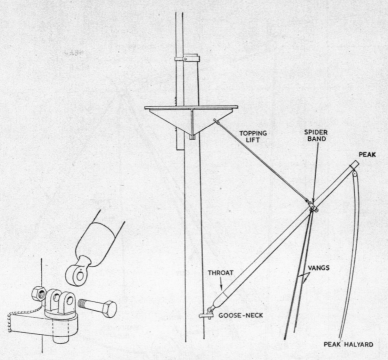

Fig. 193.—A gaff, and (inset) a gooseneck

" vangs," which are shackled to the spider band and brought down to each side of the after superstructure. To the upper end or " peak " of the gaff is fitted a gunmetal block through which is rove the peak halyard.

Derricks and their Winches

A *derrick* is a spar, made of wood or steel, rigged as a swinging boom and used for hoisting boats, stores, cargo, ammunition or gear in and out of a ship. It can be fitted to a mast or a kingpost, when it is called a " mast derrick," or to the side of a ship's superstructure, when it is called a " screen derrick." The lower end or " heel " is pivoted in a similar manner to that of the throat of a gaff, thus allowing the derrick to pivot both vertically and horizontally. The upper end or " head " is supported by a " topping lift " and stayed by " guys." The load is hoisted or lowered by a whip or a purchase, which is rove through a block at the derrick head and a leading block at the heel and then taken to a winch or brought to a motor bollard.

The rig of a derrick varies considerably in detail according to the purpose for which it is provided, the weight it is designed to hoist, and the position in which it is fitted. A simple mast derrick as fitted in merchant ships is illustrated in Fig. 194, and a screen derrick as fitted in warships is illustrated in Fig. 195. The topping lift and guys are shackled to a spider band at the derrick head. The topping lift of a mast derrick is usually led to the masthead, and that of a screen derrick to a point on the superstructure directly above the heel of the derrick ; the guys are led to positions on deck near the ship's side

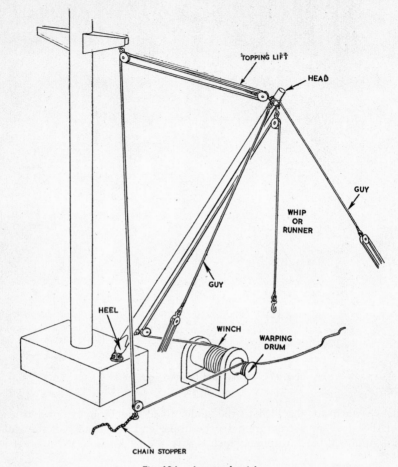

Fig. 194.—A mast derrick

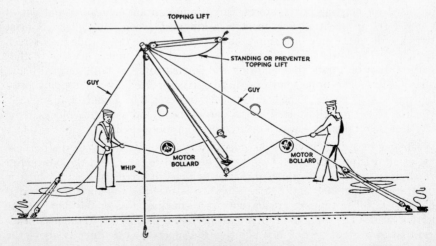

Fig. 195.—A screen derrick

and well before and abaft the heel. Topping lifts are of two main kinds, "standing" and "working," which terms are self-explanatory; a common type of working topping lift consists of a pendant tailed with a tackle, the fall being rove through a leading block aloft and a leading block at the heel of the derrick, and thence taken to a winch or brought to a motor bollard. Guys usually take the form of short pendants tailed with tackles; two are usually fitted, but heavy derricks may be fitted with as many as four; some derricks are provided with standing guys called "preventer guys," which are fitted to prevent the derrick from swinging too far in a certain direction.

Cargo derricks and methods of working them are described in more detail in Volume II of this manual.

A winch in its simplest form is a reel which can be turned in either direction by hand cranks. The mechanical advantage gained by this machine depends upon the diameter of the winch drum and the length of the crank arms, the smaller the drum and the longer the crank arm the greater will be the mechanical advantage, and this can be further increased by incorporating gearing between the cranks and the drum. The end of the winch rope is secured to one end of the drum, and the rope is wound on the drum as the latter is rotated; care should always be taken to ensure that the rope is wound on right across the drum, so that each turn lies snugly against the last one wound on. Hand winches (see Fig. 196) are always provided with a pawl and ratchet wheel on the crank shaft to prevent the winch from taking charge if the load becomes too heavy to hold by hand; the pawl should always be engaged when the winch is used for hoisting.

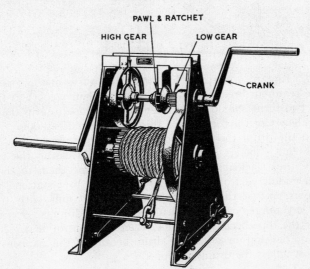

Fig. 196.—A hand winch

Power-driven winches differ widely in design, and various forms of drive, clutch and brake are fitted, depending on the use for which the winch is intended: cargo work, minesweeping, or hoisting ammunition for example. They are usually provided with two "warping drums" driven off the winch motor and fitted one on each side of the main drum; these are used for hauling ropes, hawsers and the running rigging of the derrick (see Fig. 197).

WARPING DRUMS

DERRICK WHIP

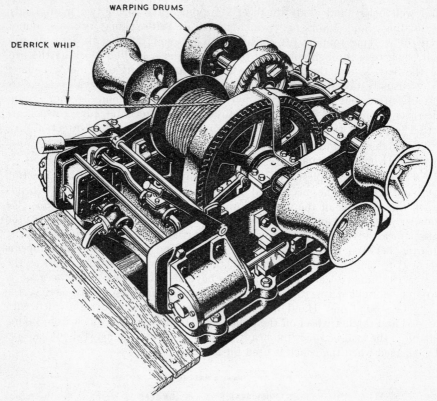

Fig. 197.—A steam winch

To bring a rope to a warping drum take two turns of the rope round the drum in the required direction and back up the hauling part as it comes off the drum ; two turns should be sufficient for the rope to grip the drum, but if the load is heavy or the rope slips a third turn should be taken. As the rope passes round the drum the turns have a tendency to ride from the middle towards one end ; this is checked by momentarily easing the pull on the hauling part, thus slackening the turns and allowing them to slide back to the narrower middle part of the drum. To hold the rope stationary while the drum is heaving in ease the pull on the hauling part sufficiently to allow the turns to slip, or " surge," round the drum ; when the drum is veering, however, do not surge the rope because you may then lose control of it. Never allow riding turns to develop on a warping drum because if this happens control of the rope is lost unless the drum is stopped.

A motor bollard is a large warping drum driven by its own motor and fitted in warships for general hauling and hoisting.

Boat Booms

A boom is any spar, except a derrick which projects horizontally from the superstructure, hull, or mast of a ship, and it may be either fixed or swinging. Boat booms project from the ship's side and are stayed in place by rigging ; they are used for making fast the ship's boats so that they lie clear of her side. A large ship may be provided with several boat booms, but a small ship usually has only one or two. The largest boat booms in a ship are usually rigged one on each side at the after end of the forecastle deck, and are called the " lower booms "* ; smaller booms called " quarter booms " may be rigged one on each quarter, and a small fixed boom rigged at the stern is called a " stern boom."

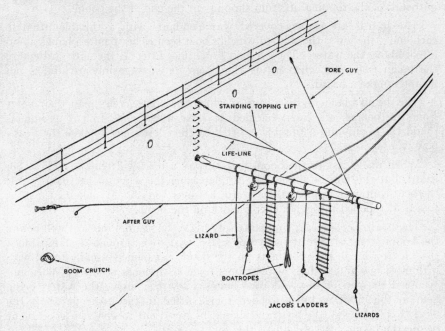

Fig. 198.—A lower boom

A lower boom (Fig. 198) and a quarter boom are rigged in much the same way as a derrick. The heel fits into a gooseneck and the boom is held horizontal and square with the ship's side by its topping lift and guys, respectively. Very occasionally a rope called a " martingale " is rigged on the under side of the boom to hold it down. When the boom is not required it is swung aft (or forward) and clamped into a crutch fixed to the ship's side about level with the heel fitting.

The guys are known as the fore guy and the after guy ; each may have a short tail spliced into its inboard end so that a runner or tackle can be clapped onto it when hauling the boom aft or forward. The booms of larger ships are fitted with standing topping lifts which are adjusted for length by means of a bottlescrew, but smaller ships usually have working topping lifts. Both guys and topping lifts are shackled to a spider band close to the end of the boom.

A stern boom is usually fitted at deck level with its heel secured to the deck by two metal clamps. It is stayed by standing guys and a standing topping lift which is usually led to the head of the ensign-staff stanchion.

---

* The term " lower boom " might infer that there is an " upper boom " but this is not so ; the name derives from the days of sail when spars called " lower studding-sail booms " were used in harbour as boat booms.

To assist boats' crews in manning their boats over the boom a small " life-line " of cordage or wire rope is rigged, waist high, between the topping lift and the ship's side or rail. At intervals along the boom are fitted a number of canvas covered grommets of wire rope into each of which a thimble is seized to take the shackles of the " lizards," Jacob's ladders, and clump blocks for " boat ropes." Thumb pieces are fitted to prevent those grommets placed outboard of the topping lift from slipping off the end of the boom.

The lizards are canvas-covered wire pendants with a thimble fitted in each end ; the lower thimble, to which a boat secures her painter, hangs about a foot above the water. The eye-bolt sometimes fitted at the outboard end of the boom is for use when lifting the boom for stowage inboard and is not meant to take a lizard.

The Jacob's ladders, by means of which the boats' crews man their boats from the booms, are each shackled at their upper ends to two grommets round the boom, and a thimble is fitted at their lower end to take the boat's lazy painter.

When made fast to the boom in a seaway a boat will tend to jerk at her lizard, but this can be minimised by increasing the scope of her painter. If the boat continues to jerk at her lizard, however, she should make fast instead to a boat rope led through a clump block on the boom.

The boatrope, which is comparatively heavy, is secured inboard well before the boom so as to give it plenty of scope, and rove through a clump block shackled to one of the grommets on the boom ; its end is usually fitted with a thimble eye and a short wire strop to which the boat secures. When un-occupied the end of the boat rope hangs a few feet above the water, being held in this position by a wooden toggle fitted in the boatrope abaft the block. In a seaway the boatrope should be eased out to give it a good bight before the boom ; the weight of this bight absorbs any tendency of the boat to jerk, and allows for the rise and fall of the boat on the waves. The heaviest boat should always take the boatrope nearest to the spider band, as this entails the least strain on the boom itself.

On arrival in harbour the booms should be swung out together, having been completely rigged beforehand with their lizards and ladders but not their boatropes. It is customary to swing out the booms as the anchor is let go, or, when securing to a buoy or jetty, by order on the pipe or bugle. Boom gear must not be allowed to show outboard while the ship is under way.

CHAPTER VII

Ships' Boats

A WARSHIP'S boats are of several different types and are employed on many different duties. In harbour they are used for embarking, disembarking or transferring mails, stores, armed parties, working parties, fire parties, libertymen, passengers and visitors; also for laying out the ship's anchors, laying down buoys for salvage work, and for recreation such as regattas or picnics. At sea they are used as life-boats in the event of shipwreck or of a man falling overboard; also for transferring men and stores to or from another ship, and for boarding a ship with an armed boarding party.

A merchant ship's boats are generally used only as life-boats, their prime function being to save the lives of the passengers and crew in the event of shipwreck or fire. Any transport facilities required by a merchant ship when in harbour are usually provided by special tenders and shore boats.

The art of handling a boat should be acquired by every seaman, and this can only be learned by study and experience. In this chapter the types and construction of boats, and the sails and rigging of sailing boats, are described. In Volume II of this manual the stowage of boats on board and their slinging, hoisting and lowering, equipment, rig, and management under oars, sail and power are described.

Types and Classes of Boats

There are three types of boat, namely: rowing boats, sailing boats and power boats. A rowing boat is propelled by oars, a sailing boat by sails, and a power boat by machinery. A boat may possess the features of all three types, but she is classified by her normal method of propulsion.

ROWING AND PULLING BOATS

A rowing boat is an open boat (*i.e.* not decked in) and is propelled by oars in one of the ways illustrated in Fig. 199. The parts of an oar and the methods by which it is pivoted in a boat are also illustrated. In all methods of rowing the oar is pivoted at about one-third of its length from the grip, and is used as a lever by dipping the blade in the water and pulling or pushing on the loom, thus driving the boat through the water.

" Sculling " defines that method of rowing in which each member of the boat's crew mans a pair of oars, and also that in which a boat is propelled by manipulating a single oar over the stern; in this latter method the loom is worked from side to side of the boat and the blade does not leave the water. Manipulation of a single oar pivoted on the gunwale by pulling or pushing on its loom is termed " rowing." Vessels such as barges or lighters may be propelled by very long oars known as " sweeps," which may either be pulled or pushed. In shallow waters boats, lighters, and other small craft may be propelled by poles pushed on the bottom, this method being called " punting " or " quanting."

(a)

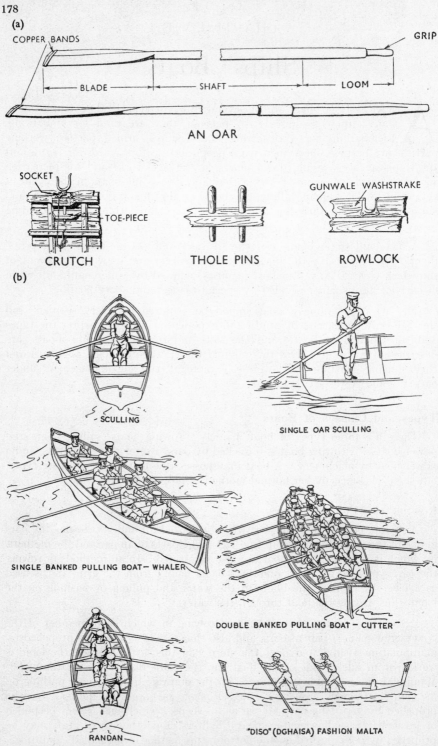

COPPER BANDS

GRIP

BLADE · SHAFT · LOOM

AN OAR

SOCKET

TOE-PIECE

GUNWALE   WASHSTRAKE

CRUTCH   THOLE PINS   ROWLOCK

(b)

SCULLING

SINGLE OAR SCULLING

SINGLE BANKED PULLING BOAT—WHALER

DOUBLE BANKED PULLING BOAT — CUTTER

RANDAN

"DISO" (DGHAISA) FASHION MALTA

Fig. 199.—(a) Parts of an oar and methods of pivoting
(b) Different ways of propelling rowing boats

In single-oared sculling, and in all methods of pushing on the loom of the oar, the crew stand up in the boat and the boat is propelled and steered by the manipulation of the oars alone. These methods are dangerous with an unskilled oarsman because he may easily lose his balance and fall overboard or capsize the boat ; they are therefore only used by skilled oarsmen and in calm weather.

The normal method of rowing a boat is to sit facing aft and pull on the looms of the oars, the boat being steered by its rudder. In the Royal Navy no one is allowed to stand up in an open boat, and, as all rowing boats are propelled by the normal method, rowing is called " pulling " and the boats are called " pulling boats." If a pulling boat is equipped with masts and sails she is known in the Navy as a " pulling and sailing boat."

Pulling boats may be " single-banked " or " double-banked." In a single-banked boat there is one oarsman to each thwart and he sits on the side furthest from the blade of his oar. In a double-banked boat two oarsmen sit on each thwart and each oarsman pulls an oar on his respective side.

The term " bank " is also used in the sense that the oars of one side of a boat are known collectively as a bank of oars, and in the sense that when two men pull a single oar that oar is said to be double-banked.

A pulling boat is named according to her type, and this name may be prefixed by her length or the number of oars with which she is equipped. Examples are : the " dory," a small flat-bottomed boat carried by fishing vessels ; the " dinghy," a small boat holding three or four people ; the " skiff," a similar small boat but used in inland waters ; the " 27-foot whaler," and the " 12-oared cutter," which are, respectively, single-banked and double-banked boats supplied to ships of the Royal Navy. The various classes of pulling, sailing, and power boats used in the Royal Navy are described in Volume II of this manual.

Sailing Boats

A sailing boat is a boat whose primary means of propulsion is by sail, but she may also be equipped for rowing, or with some form of mechanical propulsion in which case she is known as an " auxiliary sailing boat." Sailing boats are usually wholly or partly decked in. Ships do not normally carry sailing boats, their boats being primarily pulling boats which may be rigged for sailing, but the 14-ft. centre-board sailing dinghy supplied to some ships of the Royal Navy is an exception.

A sailing boat may be classified by her build, length, rig, tonnage, use and port of origin ; examples are a 5-ton yawl, 6-metre yacht, centre-board dinghy, spritsail barge, lugger, Brixham trawler, etc. Large fishing boats are generally known as " smacks."

Power Boats

Power boats are driven by steam or internal combustion engines and are usually wholly or partly decked in. They can be divided into two main classes, namely " round-bilge " and " hard-chine " boats. The former are of slow or medium speed, the fastest supplied to the Royal Navy (1950) having a maximum speed of about 13 knots. The latter are designed to plane on the surface of the water at comparatively high speeds, the fastest hard-chine

180

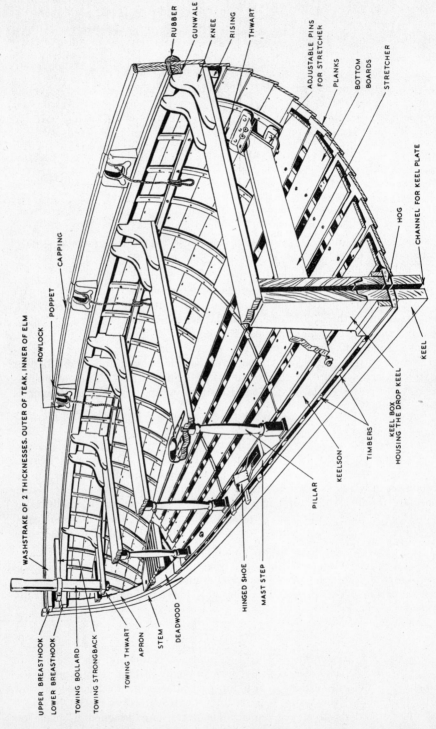

WASHSTRAKE OF 2 THICKNESSES, OUTER OF TEAK, INNER OF ELM

RUBBER
GUNWALE
KNEE
RISING
THWART

ADJUSTABLE PINS
FOR STRETCHER

PLANKS

BOTTOM
BOARDS

STRETCHER

CHANNEL FOR KEEL PLATE

HOG

KEEL

KEEL BOX
HOUSING THE DROP KEEL

TIMBERS

KEELSON

PILLAR

MAST STEP

HINGED SHOE

DEADWOOD

STEM

APRON

TOWING THWART

TOWING STRONGBACK

TOWING BOLLARD

LOWER BREASTHOOK

UPPER BREASTHOOK

ROWLOCK

POPPET

CAPPING

Fig. 200.—Clinker build

ships' boats supplied to the Royal Navy having a maximum speed of about 21 knots.   A list of the power boats carried by H.M. Ships is given in Volume II of this manual ; some are equipped with oars for use in the event of engine failure.   Some small boats, known as " outboard motor boats," are equipped with a removable power plant which is shipped over the stern.

Boat Construction

BUILDS OF BOATS

The hulls of wooden boats are usually what is called either " clinker-built " or " carvel-built."

Clinker build.   In the clinker-built boat the planks run fore-and-aft with the lower edge of one plank overlapping outboard the upper edge of the plank below it (see Fig. 200).   The planks are fastened to the timbers of the boat and to each other by copper nails, which are clenched over washers called " roves."   For single-skinned boats this is a strong and light method of construction, which is largely used for the Royal Navy's smaller boats.   A clinker-built boat is also comparatively easy to repair, because a damaged plank may be removed and replaced without unduly disturbing the adjacent planks.

Carvel build.   In a carvel-built boat the planks are placed edge to edge so that they are flush with one another, and they may either run fore-and-aft from end to end of the boat or rise diagonally from the keel to the gunwale at an angle of about 45°.

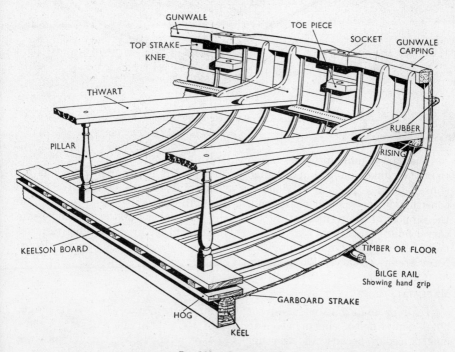

Fig. 201.—Carvel build

In single-skinned carvel-built boats the planks run fore-and-aft and are fastened to the timbers of the boat by copper nails clenched over roves (see Fig. 201). The seams may be backed by a strip of wood called an " edge strip," or be caulked with spun oakum or cotton.

In double-skinned carvel-built boats the planks of the outer skin may run fore-and-aft and those of the inner skin diagonally, or the planks of both skins may run diagonally in opposite directions, the inner skin aft and the outer skin forward, crossing each other at right angles (see Fig. 202). In both types a single thickness of calico is spread over the inner skin and then painted to make it water-tight and the two skins are clenched to each other and to the timbers of the boat.

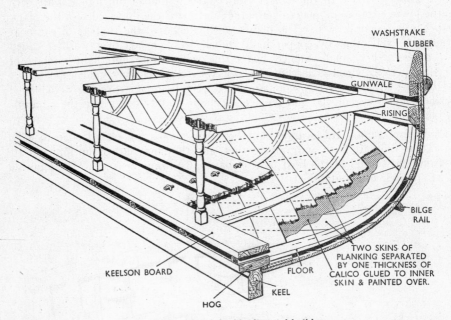

Fig. 202.—Carvel double-diagonal build

The carvel build provides a more streamlined outer surface for the hull than the clinker build, but for single-skinned boats it is not so strong as the clinker build. The carvel double-diagonal build is the strongest form of construction for wooden boats, and its strength does not depend so much on the support of the timbers of the boat as in the clinker build or the single-skin carvel build ; such boats are, however, difficult to repair if the inner skin has been holed. The largest ships' boats of wooden construction in the Royal Navy are of the carvel double-diagonal build.

MATERIALS USED

Teak or mahogany is used for the hulls of the Royal Navy's larger boats, and English elm or silver spruce for those of smaller boats. Yellow pine or cedar, because of their lightness, are often used for small pleasure craft and racing boats. The parts of a boat for which the wood selected must have grown approximately in the required shape—such as the stem, stern post, breasthook, floors and knees—are usually of oak. Canadian rock elm is generally used for the main members of the hull, such as the keel, timbers and rubber, and fir is used for other parts. Fastenings are of copper or brass throughout, and the hulls of boats built for the Surveying Service, or for use as harbour craft abroad, may be copper sheathed to protect them from damage by marine parasites such as barnacles and worms. Fittings are usually of naval brass or galvanised iron.

As elm has a tendency to absorb water, the hulls of elm-built boats are liable to become sodden unless they are carefully preserved with a good coating of paint or bottom composition.

Principal Parts of a Pulling and Sailing Boat (Figs. 200—204)

Apron. A piece of wood fitted to the after side of the stem and forward side of the stern post and extending throughout their length, to which are secured, respectively, the forward and after ends of the planks.

Backboard. A rectangular board, usually ornamented, which is shipped across the after side of the stern benches.

Benches. The seats fitted round the sides and after end of the stern sheets (see *stern sheets*).

Bilge. The space between the bottom of the boat and the floorboards.

Bilge Rails. Lengths of wood fitted along the outside of the turn of the bilge and with slots cut in them to provide a hand-hold for the crew in the event of the boat capsizing.

Bilge Stringers. Lengths of wood which run fore and aft over the timbers along the inside of the turn of each bilge. They strengthen the hull at the turn of the bilge and provide an anchorage for the outer edges of the floorboards.

Bottom Boards. Slats of wood which form the flooring of the boat ; they are secured to the timbers with eyes and wooden pins so that they can be removed if required (see also *floorboards*).

Breast Hook. A piece of wood, of the thickness of the gunwale and grown to shape, which is fitted to the curve of the gunwales in the eyes of the boat where they join the apron and so serves to strengthen the bows of the boat. In a double-ended boat a breast hook is also similarly fitted in the stern.

Buoyancy Tanks. Copper tanks fitted in the bow and stern of some boats to increase their reserve of buoyancy.

Capping. A strip of Canadian elm which is fitted to the top of the gunwale or wash strake to strengthen and protect it. At intervals it is pierced to take the sockets for the crutches or thole pins, or cut away for the rowlocks (see also *wash strake*, *sockets* and *rowlocks*).

Centre-board or Drop keel. A metal plate which can be lowered through a slot in the keel so that it projects below the boat and thus checks her leeway when under sail. It is housed in a wooden casing known as the " keel-box," the bottom of which is joined to the keel with a water-tight joint.

Counter. The overhanging part of a square-sterned boat.

184

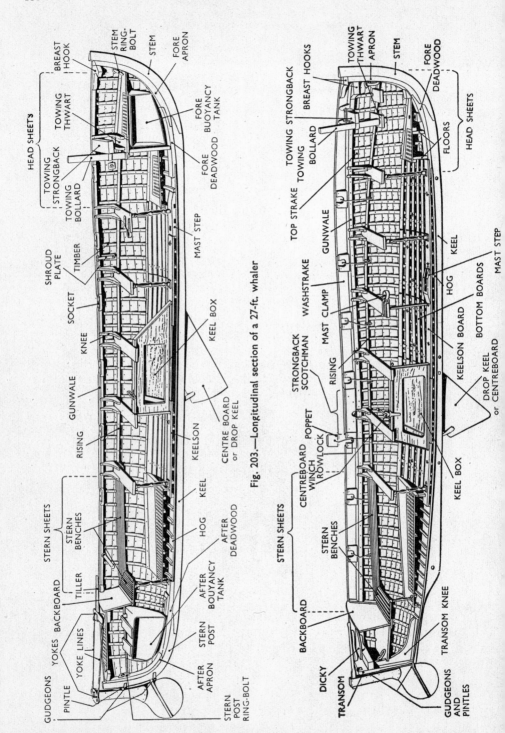

Fig. 203.—Longitudinal section of a 27-ft. whaler

Deadwood. Pieces of timber at each end of the boat which join the aprons to the hog and to which the ends of the lower planks are fastened, thus strengthening the joints of the stem and the stern post with the keel.

Dickies. Small seats, sometimes known as " quarter seats," fitted in some square-sterned boats in the angle made by the gunwale and transom, on which the coxswain sits when the boat is under oars.

Eyes. The foremost part of the boat just abaft the stem. (In ancient times, and still on the bows of some Mediterranean boats, an eye was painted on each side of the stem.)

Floors. Pieces of wood, grown to shape, which extend athwart the bottom of the boat at the bows and stern ; they serve to strengthen the bottom of the boat at her ends where the angle at which the timbers meet the keel is acute.

Floorboards. These consist of removable planks or gratings which form a platform over the bottom of the boat extending from the head sheets to the stern sheets and between the keelson board and the bilge stringers. In larger vessels this platform is known as the " ceiling."

Foot Rail. A strip of wood fitted along the top of the gunwale of decked-in boats to protect the gunwale and provide a foothold.

Garboard Strakes. The line or strake of planks which runs next to, and each side of, the keel. The inner edges of these planks are let into a groove in the side of the keel, which is called the " rabbet " of the keel.

Gudgeons and Pintles. The fittings by which the rudder is hung and pivoted to the stern post. The pintle is a vertical pin, and the gudgeon is a horizontal eye-bolt into which the pintle fits.

Gunwale. A stringer or length of wood of square cross-section which runs along the inside of the upper part of the top strake and on the top of the timbers. It strengthens the upper part of the hull (see *stringers* and *top strake*).

Head Sheets. The platform, or the space, in the bows of the boat between the stem and the bow thwart.

Hog. A length of wood fitted to the upper part of the keel and extending between the fore and after deadwoods. With the keel and deadwoods it provides the anchorage for the inner edges of the garboard strakes and the lower ends of the timbers. It also serves to strengthen the keel.

Keel. A heavy length of wood of rectangular cross-section which forms the backbone of the boat ; it runs along the fore-and-aft midship line and is joined to the foot of the stem and the foot of the stern post. The keel may be sheathed at its forward and after ends with metal strips to protect it when the boat grounds or is hauled up a beach, and in some boats it is slotted to take a centre-board.

Keelson Board. A length of wood fitted to the upper part of the hog and extending from the bows for about two-thirds of the length of the boat. It is secured to the hog by means of toggles and eyes, and sockets are cut in it to receive the mast step and the feet of the thwart pillars. The inboard edges of the floorboards are secured to it.

7

Knees. Wooden fittings which secure the thwarts to the sides of the boat. They are " grown to shape," *i.e.* cut from wood whose grain follows the curve of the knee, and then fitted and bolted or clenched to the upper strakes and gunwale, and to the upper side of the ends of the thwarts. In decked-in boats the knees are inverted, being then called " hanging knees " or " brackets," and they secure the deck beams to the timbers and the sides of the boat.

Mast Step. A piece of wood or metal shaped to take the heel of the mast and fitted in the keelson board.

Number. All boats in the Royal Navy are given a number, which is carved in two places in the boat. In double-ended boats it is carved in the stem and the stern post ; in transomed boats it is carved in the transom and in the hog just abaft the fore deadwood or just abaft the collision bulkhead. In power boats the first two figures of this number indicate the year in which the boat was built, but in pulling boats figures denoting the year are added. With the number are also carved the length of the boat, the abbreviated name of her original storing yard, and the Government broad arrow.

Pillars. Vertical supports for the thwarts ; their heels are stepped in the keelson board.

Plug. A wooden bung or screwed metal plug which fits in a hole bored in one of the garboard strakes for draining the boat when she is hoisted. The plug of a seaboat should be visible from the ship when she is hoisted at her davits so that it may be seen to be in place before she is lowered ; a starboard sea boat, for example, will have its plug in the port garboard strake.

Poppets. Pieces of wood shaped to fit into the rowlocks. They are shipped whenever the rowlocks are not being used, except when the boat is hoisted as a seaboat, and are fitted with lanyards which are secured to the risings to prevent them being lost overboard. The boat builder and the shipwright call these " shutters " and use the term poppet for the pieces of wood which support the rowlock and the wash strake.

Quarter Badges. A shaped slab of wood fitted on each quarter at the after end of the rubber for protecting the quarters of the boat from damage when lying alongside.

Rowlocks. " U "-shaped spaces cut in the washstrake to take the shafts of the oars. They are sheathed with strips of brass.

Rubbers. Strips of wood extending from the stem to the stern post or transom, and fitted to the outside of the top strakes, level with or just below the gunwale. They protect and strengthen the top strakes.

Rudder. This wood or metal fitting, which when turned to one side or the other alters the course of the boat, is hung and pivoted on the stern post ; it is also attached to the boat by a lanyard secured to a ring-bolt so that it will not break adrift when unshipped. The rudder is operated either by a tiller or a yoke and yoke lines, which are fitted to its head.

Sockets. Round holes in the gunwale, lined with metal, to take the crutches or thole pins.

Stem. The foremost vertical member of the hull, the lower end of which is scarfed to the keel. Its fore edge is usually protected with a strip of metal.

Stern Post. The aftermost vertical member of the hull, the lower end of which is joined to the keel. In boats with pointed sterns, the stern post is fitted with an apron to which the after ends of the planking are fastened. The stern post carries the rudder, which is hung from it by means of pintles and gudgeons.

Stern Sheets. The space of platform extending from the stroke thwart to the backboard, and round the sides and after end of which are built the stern benches.

Strakes. Lengths of planking which, in clinker and carvel-built boats, extend parallel with each other from stem to stern.

Stretchers. Adjustable boards or wooden bars fitted athwart the bottom boards to provide footrests for the oarsmen.

Stringers. Lengths of wood extending fore-and-aft over the timbers, to which they are fastened and which they thus brace and support. The stringers which support the ends of the thwarts are called " risings."

Strongback. A heavy baulk of timber which can be shipped athwart the boat amidships, over the gunwales or washstrakes, with its ends projecting well beyond the rubbers. It is used when a heavy weight such as a bower anchor is slung below the boat for transportation. The gunwale or washstrake is strengthened in the wake of the strongback, which is secured to the sides of the boat and to the thwart below it by fitted metal shores ; over the strong-back is rove the sling for the weight.

Tabernacle. A wooden frame, extending from the mast thwart to the mast step, for guiding the heel of the mast into position.

Thwarts. Benches fitted athwart the boat on which the oarsmen sit. The foremost thwart is called the bow thwart, and the after thwart the stroke thwart ; the intermediate thwarts are numbered consecutively from forward aft, the thwart next abaft the bow thwart being called No. 2 thwart. In cutters a spare thwart is provided which can be shipped across the stern benches abaft the stroke thwart.

Timbers. Curved pieces of wood which extend upward and outward from the keel at short intervals throughout its length and form what are virtually the ribs of the boat ; the spacing between adjacent timbers is governed by the size and build of the boat. The planking is fastened to the outboard sides of the timbers and they may be braced inboard by stringers. Timbers are sometimes called " floors."

Top Strake. The uppermost strake of a boat's planking, along the inside of which runs the gunwale.

Towing Bollard. A stout post of timber by which a boat is towed, or by which she can ride when at anchor ; it is stepped in the towing thwart in the head sheets, and clamped to a strongback shipped between the gunwales ; the tow rope or anchor cable is belayed around it.

Transom. A board which is fitted to the after side of the stern post of a square-sterned boat and extends to each side of the boat ; the after ends of the planking are fastened to it. A " false transom " in the form of a doubling is sometimes fitted over the transom to strengthen it.

Transom Knee. A piece of wood, grown to shape, which is fitted between the stern post and the hog of a square-sterned boat to support the stern post and the transom. It takes the place of the stern post apron and the after deadwood, and in some boats is incorporated in the stern post.

Wash Strake. An extra thick strake, fitted in some boats, which extends from stem to stern, and is fixed to the top of the gunwale and the top strake. It may be cut at intervals to form rowlocks for the oars, or be fitted with sockets to take crutches.

Fittings of Pulling and Sailing Boats

Barricoes (pronounced " breakers "). Small casks for drinking or ballast water, which are designated by the number of gallons they hold. They are usually stowed on racks on the bottom or floor boards.

Boat's Cable. A length of manila rope or rigging chain by which the boat rides when at anchor. It is stowed either on a reel fitted beneath a thwart, or in a cable locker built into the headsheets.

Cleats. Wood or metal fittings fitted where necessary to enable ropes to be belayed.

Centre-board winch. A small winch, rove with wire rope and fitted to the keel-box, for lowering and raising the drop keel.

Crutches. In single-banked boats these metal U-shaped fittings take the place of rowlocks. They fit into metal sockets in the gunwale and are always secured to the boat by a lanyard, but are unshipped whenever the oars are not in use except when the boat is prepared as a sea boat.

Horse. A curved bar of metal, fitted along the top of the transom, to which the after block of the mainsail sheet is shackled ; the block travels from side to side of the horse when the boat is put about.

Lazy Painter. A 4-fathom length of 1-in. or $1\frac{1}{2}$-in. cordage by means of which the boat can be hauled under the Jacob's ladder when made fast to a boom. The inboard end is secured to the ring-bolt of the foremost sling. The lazy painter should not be used for making the boat fast.

Life-line. A line fitted along each rubber so that it hangs in beckets outside the boat and thus affords a hand hold to anyone being rescued from the water. It should not be confused with the life-lines fitted to a boat's davits.

Mast Clamp. A metal clamp, fitted to the mast thwart, for clamping the mast in position.

Painter. A length of stout cordage by which the boat is towed, or by which she rides when made fast to a boom. Its length should be $1\frac{1}{2}$ times that of the boat, and its size varies with the size of the boat. One end is pointed ; the other is spliced with a $2\frac{1}{2}$ to $3\frac{1}{2}$-ft. soft eye into which are seized two thimbles, one at the throat and one at the crown, the two parts of the eye being then married and served over. The painter is shackled to the forward sling ring-bolt.

Ring-bolts. These are eyed bolts with a ring fitted through the eye. They are clenched through the stem and the stern post to take the fore and after legs of the slings.

Running Hook. A hook, fitted on each side of the bows of the boat, to which the tack of the foresail is hooked when the boat is sailing before the wind.

Sling Plates. These are metal eye-plates clenched through the keel to take the lower legs of the slings.

Slings. Two spans of chain or wire rope by which the boat is slung for hoisting. The foremost leg of the foremost sling is hooked to the ring-bolt in the stem, and the lower leg is shackled to the link of the foremost sling plate in the keel. The after leg of the after sling is hooked to the ring-bolt in the stern post, and the lower leg is shackled to the link of the after sling plate in the keel. A boat's slings should always be carried in the boat.

Steadying Spans. Short pendants of wire rope or chain which are fitted between the hooks or rings of the slings, and the gunwales. Their purpose is to prevent the boat canting to one side or the other as she is hoisted.

Stern Fast. A rope similar to the painter, but smaller and used for making fast the stern of the boat. The inboard end is shackled to the after ring-bolt.

Tack Hook. A hook fitted to the stem-head to which the tack of the foresail is hooked.

Thwart Pins. Metal pins fitted below the thwarts to which the halyards of a sailing boat are belayed.

Checking the Equipment of a Pulling Boat

Before taking away a pulling boat her coxswain should see that all her equipment is correct. The more important points requiring his attention are given below :—

The Plug should be securely inserted in its hole.

Oars. There should be a full complement and one spare ; it is particularly important that a dinghy equipped with only one pair of sculls should carry a spare oar. In double-banked boats, bow and stroke oars should be placed along the middle of the thwarts and the remainder on their respective sides, with their looms aft and all squared off ; in single banked boats the blades should be aft, and only the bow oar should be placed amidships with its blade forward.

Crutches (single-banked boats). There should be a full complement and one spare, and each should be secured by its lanyard to the boat. The lanyard may be spliced to the eye at the end of the shank, but this necessitates reeving the lanyard through the socket and toe piece before shipping the crutch. A better method is to have the lanyard spliced round the groove at the shoulders of the crutch and secured to the rising midway between two sockets ; the crutch can then easily be moved from one socket to another, or from one side of the boat to the other.

Poppets (double-banked boats). There should be one for each rowlock and its lanyard should be secured to the rising of the boat.

Stretchers. One should be fitted in place for each thwart.

The Rudder should be shipped and its lanyard be secured to the alter ring-bolt.

The Tiller or Yoke should be shipped and secured with its split pin.

The Painter should be shackled to the stem ring-bolt.

The Towing Bollard, complete with its clamp and pin, should be in the boat.

The Slings, Baler, Bucket, Anchor and Cable, Boat's Bag, Spare Tiller, Lazy Painter and Sternfast, Fenders and two Boat-hooks should all be stowed in the boat.

In addition, any of the following special stores and fittings may have to be taken away on certain occasions :—lantern and candles, sea anchor, compass, ensign and pendant staves, barricoes, strongback; spare thwart (in cutters only), life-buoy and life-belts.

BOAT'S DISTRESS SIGNAL BOX, BOAT'S BAG AND CARPENTER'S BAG

The boat's distress signal box is of metal and contains four red flares for use in distress, each of which will burn for about 30 seconds. The boat's bag and carpenter's bag are small canvas bags made up in the ship, the former with gear for the general maintenance of the boat's equipment, and the latter with materials for patching the planking if the boat springs a leak or is holed ; their contents are listed below.

Boat's Bag. Spunyarn ; tallow ; palm and needle ; marline spike ; twine ; bee's wax ; hand axe (two in a cutter) ; a 1-lb. hammer ; cold chisel ; tommy ; punch ; adjustable spanner ; spare plug ; spare crutch (single-banked boats only) ; box of matches in a water-tight tin ; electric torch ; boat's signal hook in canvas cover ; pair of hand semaphore flags ; hand answering pennant ; ensign and pendant in canvas wallet ; and boat's lead and line.

Carpenter's Bag. Spun oakum, 2 to 3 lb. for caulking ; one ball of lampwick or caulking cotton ; 8 sq. ft. of canvas, R.N. No. 1 ; $1\frac{1}{2}$ sq. ft. of sheet lead ; 6 copper tingles, varying from 6 in. sq. to 12 in. sq. in size, with nail holes punched around the edges ; one pound of tallow ; 4 sq. ft. of fearnought ; half a pound of $\frac{5}{8}$-in. copper tacks ; 60 soft-wood spills of square section and assorted sizes ; 12 tapered wood plugs, 6 inches long and from half an inch to one inch in diameter ; half a pound of 2-in. wire nails ; two beechwood wedges ; a 1-in. wood chisel, and a punch for copper tacks.

Pulling Orders

When a pulling boat is under way any order to the oarsmen except *Hold water* is obeyed on completing one full stroke after the order is given.

All such orders should be given at the moment when the blades of the oars are in the water.

On obeying a pulling order the crew take their time by the stroke oarsman, who is usually the next senior rating to the coxswain. (In the absence of the coxswain the stroke oarsman takes charge of the boat ; in double-banked boats he pulls the starboard stroke oar.)

When " port " or " starboard " is included in a pulling order, it refers to the bank of oars on the port or starboard side of the boat, respectively.

Before saluting by tossing or laying on the oars, the cautions " *Stand-by to toss oars* " or " *Stand-by for oars* " should be given.

Give Way Together is the order to start pulling, and it is obeyed together by the whole crew. If only one bank of oars is required to give way the order *Give way starboard* or *Give way port* is given.

Oars is an order to cease pulling. At this order the crew sit squarely and upright on their thwarts, with their oars horizontal and at right angles to the fore-and-aft line of the boat and with the blades " feathered," *i.e.* parallel with the water. The order *Lay on your oars* allows the crew to relax from the position of " Oars " ; they may then either rest on the looms of their oars or lay in their oars athwart the boat with the grips under the gunwale. This order is also given immediately before the order *Give Way Together*.

Back Together is the order to back water together by pushing on the looms of the oars instead of pulling. If only one bank of oars is required to back water the order *Back starboard* or *Back port* is given.

Hold Water is the order to reduce or stop the way of the boat by holding the oars at right angles to the fore-and-aft line of the boat and with their blades in the water and it should be obeyed as soon as it is given. If required to hold water with one bank of oars only, the order *Hold water* is followed by *starboard* or *port* as required.

Easy All is the order to pull less vigorously, so that the speed of the boat will be reduced. If the boat is being turned the order *Easy port* or *Easy starboard* may be given. To resume normal pulling the order *Give way together* is given.

Stroke Together is the order for all to give one stroke together. If only one bank of oars is to give a stroke the order *Stroke port* or *Stroke starboard* is given, according to which bank is required.

Way Enough is the order to stop pulling which is given when the oars are about to be boated or tossed. If the oars are not to be boated or tossed, the order *Oars* is given.

Boat Your Oars is the order to unship the oars from the rowlocks or crutches and lay them fore-and-aft in the boat on their respective sides.

Ship Your Oars is the order to place the oars in the rowlocks or crutches in readiness for pulling.

Toss Your Oars is the order to bring the oars smartly to a vertical position with the looms resting on the bottom boards and the blades fore-and-aft ; it is not given in single-banked boats or in boats fitted with crutches.

Oars Down, which is only ordered in double-banked boats when the oars are tossed, is the order to bring them down into their rowlocks ready for pulling, *i.e.* with the oars horizontal, at right angles to the fore-and-aft line, and blades fore-and-aft.

Mind Your Oars is a warning to the crew to keep the blades of their oars clear of some obstruction. If the warning concerns only one bank of oars the order *Mind your starboard oars* or *Mind your port oars* is given, as required.

Bow is the order to the bowman of a single-banked boat to boat his oar and be ready to fend off the bows of the boat with his boathook. In double-banked boats the order is *Bows*, and in obeying it the bowmen first toss their oars and " kiss " the blades together before boating them.

Bear-off the Boat is the order to thrust the boat off with the looms of the oars from the ship or landing place alongside which she is lying, or from the bottom if the boat is grounded.

Eyes in the Boat is an order to the crew to keep their gaze from wandering abroad, and to pay attention to their duties.

Pulling Drill

Getting Under Way in a Whaler

At the order " Bear off " the bowman bears off the bows of the boat and lays in his boathook, the stroke oarsman lays in his boathook and fender and springs the boat ahead, and both then sit down on their thwarts ; Nos. 2, 3 and 4 lay in the fenders on their respective sides. At the order " Ship your oars " Nos. 2 and 4 ship the crutches and oars of No. 3 and Stroke, while Stroke and No. 3 ship the crutches and oars of Nos. 4 and 2, and the bowman ships his own crutch and oar. At the order " Oars " each man grasps the loom of his oar and brings the oar to the athwartships position, with the oar and blade horizontal.

Going Alongside in a Whaler

When the boat is within about 50 yards of the accommodation ladder or landing place the order " Bow " is given. At this order the bowman lays in his oar athwartships, unships it and boats it amidships with the blade forward, and then takes his boathook and stands in the head sheets facing forward with the boathook vertical. At the same time Nos. 2, 3 and 4 and Stroke put out the fenders on their respective sides. At the order " Way enough " the crew pull one more stroke, and then, taking their time from Stroke who raises one hand, they allow their oars to swing fore-and-aft in the crutches and then fleet their looms forward. Stroke and No. 3 boat the oars of Nos. 4 and 2 and unship their crutches, and Nos. 2 and 4 boat the oars of No. 3 and Stroke and unship their crutches. Stroke then stands up ready to check the way of the boat as she goes alongside, and then holds the boat alongside either with his boathook or the manropes. Nos. 3 and 4 square off the oars on their respective sides.

Getting Under Way in a Cutter

The two bowmen and the inner stroke oarsman stand in the head and stern sheets, respectively, and hold the boat alongside. The remainder of the crew sit on their appointed thwarts and the coxswain sits on the dickie abaft the backboard. At the order " Point your oars " the remainder of the crew unship the poppets from their rowlocks, take their oars by the looms and place the blades on the wash-strake. The order " Toss your oars " is then given. At the order " Bear off " the bowmen bear the boat off and Stroke springs the boat ahead. The order " Fenders in " is then given and is followed by the order " Oars down," the oars being then lowered gently into their rowlocks and care being taken not to allow the blades to touch the water. " Give way together " is then ordered.

These orders are given in rapid sequence and are executed by the crew in precise unison. The stroke oarsman, having laid in his boathook and sprung the boat ahead, gets in his fender, ships his oar and picks up the stroke.

The bowmen, after bearing off, get in their fenders, toss their oars and " kiss " the blades together before shipping them, and then pick up the stroke.

If the boat is at the boom she is pulled to the gangway by the midship oarsmen while the coxswain reports for orders to the Officer of the Watch. The starboard stroke oarsman acts as coxswain, and the other stroke oarsman and the bowmen stand, respectively, in the stern and head sheets with their boathooks vertical.

Going Alongside in a Cutter

When the boat is within 50 yards or so of her destination, the order " Fenders out " is given, followed by the order " Bows." At this order the bowmen toss their oars, kiss the blades together and then lay them in amidships, passing the looms aft between the midship oarsmen ; they then stand in the head sheets facing forward with their boathooks vertical and stand by to fend off the bows. Then the order " Way enough " is given and the boat's crew toss their oars, taking their time from the starboard Stroke who calls out " Oars up." The inner Stroke boats his oar and stands up in the stern sheets facing outboard, with his boathook vertical, ready to fend off the boat or check her way.

When there is insufficient height alongside for the oars to remain tossed, the order " Toss and boat your oars " is given after the order " Way enough." The oars are tossed and held vertically for an instant, after which they are laid in together.

Oars are never tossed, however, when going alongside a vessel under way or going alongside a ship at anchor in a heavy sea or swell, because the blades of the oars may catch under a projection on the ship's side, or under the platform of the accommodation ladder, and so drive the looms through the bottom of the boat as she rises to sea or swell. Under such conditions the order " Way enough, boat your oars " is given, and the oars are lifted out of their rowlocks, the blades swung forward in a horizontal arc, and, as the oars are boated, the looms are fleeted aft. When leaving a vessel under these conditions the oars are first pointed forward over the gunwale and then swung outboard in a horizontal arc and shipped in their rowlocks.

Sails and Rigging of Sailing Boats

The parts of three-sided and four-sided sails are named in Fig. 205. In Fig. 206, which illustrates the rig of a 27-foot Service whaler, the details shown are common to most fore-and-aft rigged boats. Additional information about boats, sails and rigging follows.

A *boltrope* is the roping on the edge of a sail ; it is always sewn on the side of the sail which will be to port when the sail is set. The luff of a sail is always roped, the leach seldom, and the foot usually only when laced to a boom ; the sides of a sail can therefore always be identified during the day by sight, and at night by feeling them.

The trim of a sail refers to the angle between its mean plane and the fore-and-aft line of the boat, and is altered as necessary for the sail to receive the maximum wind pressure possible on the course to be steered. The sails are trimmed nearly at right angles to the fore-and-aft line if the boat is sailing with the wind directly astern, but if she is sailing as close to the wind as possible they are trimmed nearly parallel with her fore-and-aft line (see Fig. 208).

7*

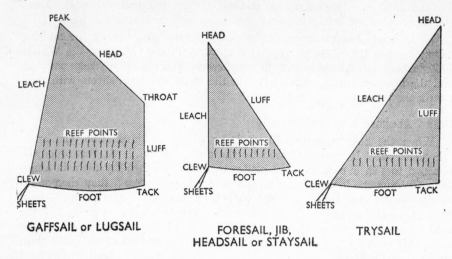

Fig. 205.—Parts of a boat's sails

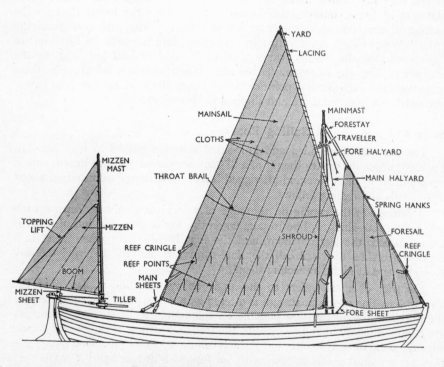

Fig. 206.—Sailing rig of a 27-ft. whaler

A sheet is a rope bent to the clew of a sail by means of which the sail is trimmed as required ; it is named after the sail to which it is bent, *e.g.* " fore sheet," " main sheet," or " mizzen sheet." To check a sheet is to ease it off so that the sail is eased out, to " aft " a sheet is to haul it in so that the clew of the sail is hauled aft, and to " let fly " a sheet is to let it run so that the sail flaps and the wind is spilled out of it.

A halyard is a rope by which a sail is hoisted and lowered, and to " settle " a halyard is to ease it away.

Cringles are eyes worked into the boltrope at the sides or corners of a sail and to which are bent or hooked the halyards, the sheets, and the tack hook.

Eyelets are the eyes worked into the head or foot of a sail for lacing it to a spar.

An earing is the lashing which secures the throat, peak, tack, or clew of a sail to a spar.

To bend on the head or foot of a sail means to secure it to a spar by its earings and lacing.

Yard and Gaff. The head of a four-sided sail is bent to and supported by either a yard or a gaff ; a yard crosses the mast, but a gaff has jaws at its throat which fit round the mast. The halyard of a gaff is bent to the gaff itself, but the halyard of a yard is bent to an iron hoop with a hook on it called a " traveller," to which the yard is hooked by means of a strop. Fig. 207 shows the difference between a yard and a gaff and their respective rigs.

A lugsail is a four-sided sail the head of which is bent to a yard.

A gaff sail is a four-sided sail the head of which is bent to a gaff.

A gaff topsail is a triangular sail set between a gaff and the masthead.

A boom is the spar to which the foot of any sail is bent.

A loose-footed sail has no boom at its foot.

Reef-points are short lengths of line secured to each side of a sail in pairs above its foot (see Fig. 205) and used for reefing it ; a sail may have one, two, or three rows of reef-points.

To reef a sail is to reduce the area it offers to the wind in order to prevent the boat from heeling over too far and being swamped or capsized. A loose-footed sail is reefed by first settling its halyard and shifting the tack-tackle and sheets to the appropriate reef cringles ; the foot of the sail is then gathered up and secured by knotting together each pair of reef points under it. (The sail is gathered, not rolled, so that water cannot lie in the foot of the sail.) A boom-footed sail is reefed by settling the halyard until the required reef cringles can be stopped down to the boom, and then knotting the reef points under the foot of the sail, but not round the boom. A sail fitted with roller reefing is reefed by revolving the boom and so rolling the sail round it until the sail-area is sufficiently reduced ; roller reefing dispenses with the need for reef points and cringles.

Stormsails are special sails for use in very strong winds instead of a boat's normal suit of sails ; they are smaller and made of heavier canvas than the normal sails.

A headsail is any sail set before the foremast, or before the mainmast if there is no foremast.

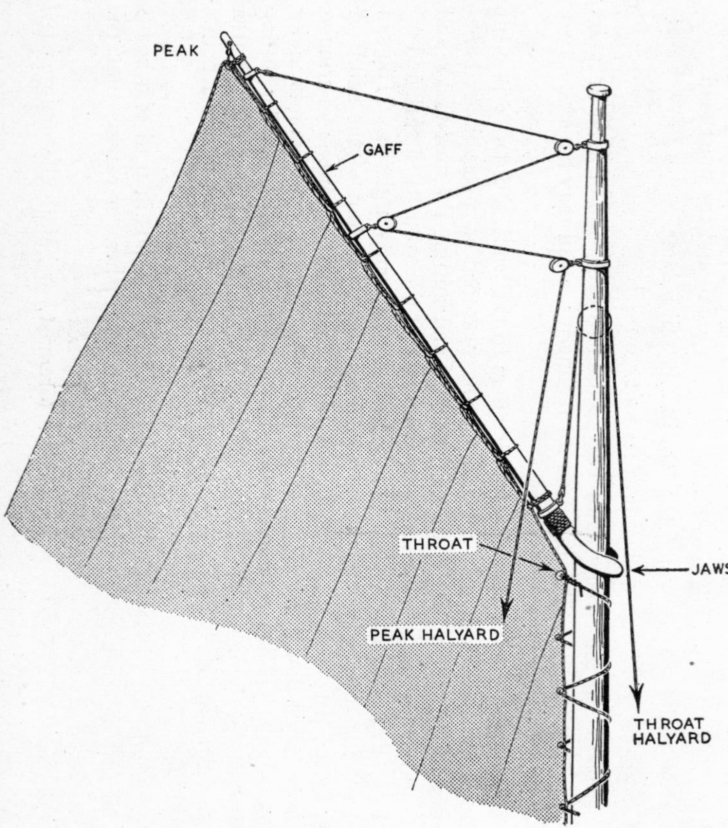

TRAVELLER

HALYARD

YARD

PEAK

STROP HOOKED TO TRAVELLER

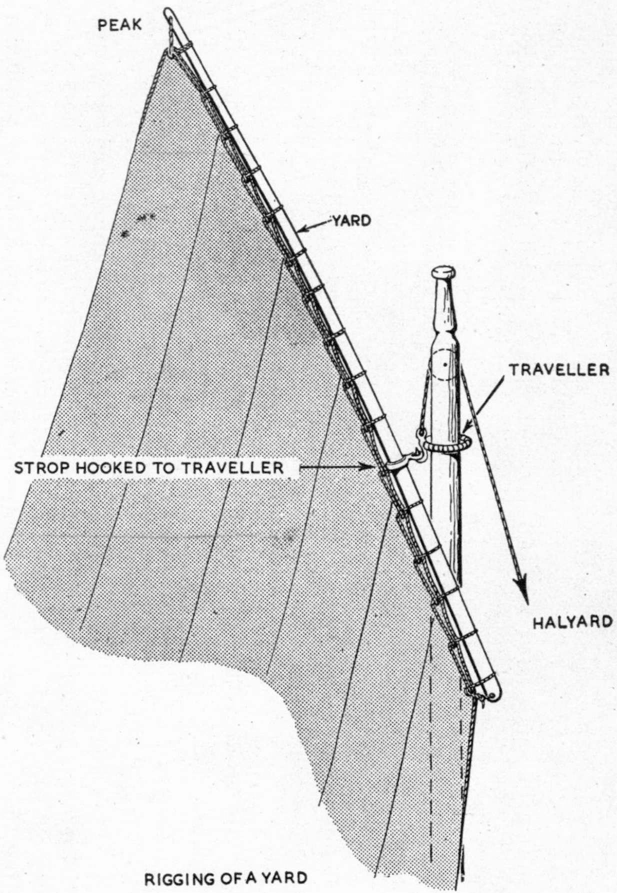

RIGGING OF A YARD

JAWS

THROAT
HALYARD

THROAT

PEAK HALYARD

GAFF

PEAK

RIGGING OF A GAFF

Fig. 207

The foresail is the sail set immediately before the foremast, or immediately before the mainmast if there is no foremast.

A jib is any headsail set before the foresail ; if there are two they are called the " inner jib " and the " outer jib," and if three the foremost one is called the " flying jib."

The mizzen is the sail set on the mizzen mast.

A trysail is any triangular sail (except the mizzen) which is set immediately abaft the foremast, or immediately abaft the main mast if there is no foremast.

A staysail is any triangular sail whose luff is supported by a stay ; its name is derived from that of the stay which supports it, *e.g.* " main topmast staysail."

A forestay is a rope leading forward from the masthead to assist in preventing the mast from falling aft ; its name is derived from that of the mast which it supports, *e.g.* " main topmast forestay."

A backstay is a rope leading aft from the masthead to assist in preventing the mast from falling forward ; its name is also derived from that of the mast it supports, *e.g.* " fore-topmast backstay."

Shrouds are ropes leading from the masthead to the sides of the boat for supporting the mast athwartships. They also are named after the mast which they support, *e.g.* " mizzen shrouds."

Standing rigging comprises all the permanently fitted and secured ropes, such as the stays and shrouds.

Running rigging comprises all the movable ropes, such as halyards and sheets.

Elementary Sailing Rules

The following rules should be complied with when sailing in open boats.

When under way the crew should sit on the bottom boards and not on the thwarts. When beating to windward, or reaching, the position of the crew should be adjusted so as to keep the boat as nearly as possible on an even keel, and the bowman should always keep a good lookout ahead and leeward under the foot of the foresail.

No one should move about the boat except when necessary, and then only quietly and carefully. No one should stand on the thwarts, or climb the rigging or the mast ; if fouled gear aloft cannot be cleared with a boathook when standing on the bottom boards the sails and mast should be lowered to clear it.

Sheets should always be kept in hand (not belayed). Oars should never be shipped or used when under sail, except that in emergency the bow oars may be used to help to put the boat about (from one tack to the other). All running rigging should always be kept clear, the ends being neatly coiled and stowed so that the ropes will run freely when required.

It is bad seamanship to drift about in a flat calm with sails set because the slatting of the sails and the swinging of the spars chafes the gear ; when the wind falls the sails should be furled, the masts lowered, the oars shipped and the boat be pulled to her destination.

198

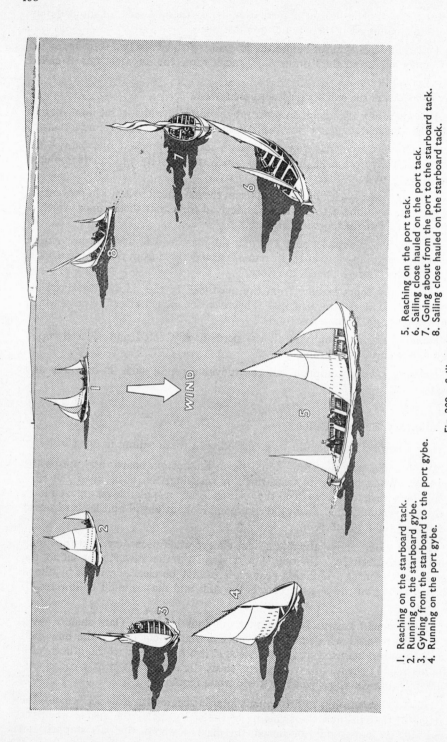

1. Reaching on the starboard tack.
2. Running on the starboard gybe.
3. Gybing from the starboard to the port gybe.
4. Running on the port gybe.
5. Reaching on the port tack.
6. Sailing close hauled on the port tack.
7. Going about from the port to the starboard tack.
8. Sailing close hauled on the starboard tack.

Fig. 208.—Sailing terms

Sailing Terms

Close Hauled (Fig. 208 (6 and 8)). Most boats cannot be sailed to windward on a course which makes a lesser angle than about 40 to 50 degrees with the direction from which the wind is blowing ; the actual angle for any particular boat depends upon her type and rig, and no Service boat other than the sailing dinghy will sail closer than about 50 degrees off the wind. A boat which is being sailed as close as possible to the wind is said to be " close hauled."

Beating. When the destination of a sailing boat lies directly up wind she gains grounds to windward by sailing close hauled on a zig-zag course, and she is then said to be " beating."

Reaching (Fig. 208 (1 and 5)). When a boat is sailing with the wind abeam, or a little before the beam, she is said to be " reaching."

Running (Fig. 208 (2 and 4)). When a boat is sailing before the wind, or with the wind abaft the beam, she is said to be " running."

Sailing Free. When a boat is reaching or running she is said to be " sailing free " (*i.e.* she can manœuvre freely on either side of her course).

Tacks and Tacking. When close hauled, or reaching, the distance sailed by a boat on any one course is called a " tack " ; when she has the wind on her starboard side she is said to be on the " starboard tack," and when on her port side she is said to be on the " port tack." When she alters course head to wind from one tack to the other she is said to " tack " or " go about " (Fig. 208 (7)). The order " Ready about " is the warning to the crew to stand by to tack.

Wearing. When a boat changes from one tack to the other by altering course stern to wind (*i.e.* the opposite to tacking) she is said to " wear."

Gybing and Gybes. As the boat's stern passes through the wind when wearing, the mainsail will be blown from one side to the other, and the boat is then said to " gybe " (Fig. 208 (3)). When running with the wind on her starboard quarter a boat is said to be on the " starboard gybe " (Fig. 208 (2)), and when running with the wind on her port quarter she is said to be on the " port gybe " (Fig. 208 (4)).

CHAPTER VIII

Anchors and Cables

Methods of Securing a Ship to the Bottom

WHEN in sufficiently shallow water a ship can be secured to the sea bottom by means of her ground tackle, *i.e.* her anchors and cables. This can be done either with a single anchor or with two anchors, and in the latter case she is said to be " moored." In ports and most large harbours a ship can also be secured to the bottom by unshackling one of her cables from its anchor and shackling it on to a mooring buoy, which is secured to the bottom by its own permanently laid down anchors and cables.

ANCHORING

Letting go a single anchor is the simplest method, and if the holding ground is good and sufficient cable is veered the ship will ride easily to her anchor in bad weather. The disadvantage of this method is that the ship will take up a large amount of sea room in swinging around her anchor with the wind and tidal stream (see Fig. 209 (i)).

MOORING SHIP

The object of mooring with two anchors is usually to reduce the sea room required by the ship for swinging. The anchors are let go at some distance apart from each other and the ship is then secured midway between them so that she swings almost around her stem (see Fig. 209 (ii)). In the Royal

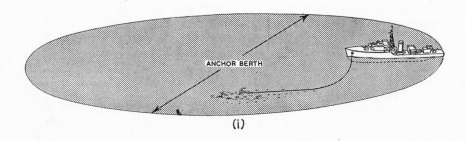

(i)

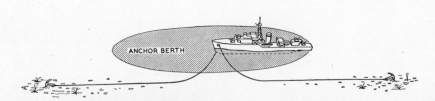

Fig. 209.—(i) A ship at single anchor   (ii) A ship moored

Navy this is known as "mooring ship," though in earlier times it was more precisely called "mooring a cable each way" to distinguish it from other methods of anchoring with two anchors. A ship thus moored rides in safety if the directions of the wind and current and tidal stream lie approximately along the line of the anchors, but if she rides at a large angle with this line the cables form a taut span and the resulting heavy stress in them may cause the anchors to drag. When mooring the two anchors should therefore be let go in the line of the prevailing wind, current, or tidal stream, whichever is usually the stronger. When a ship lies athwart the line of her anchors, she is said to lie at "open hawse."

To prevent turns forming in the cables as the ship swings with wind and tide a swivel is inserted between the cables and then veered outboard, but as it takes some time to unshackle this "mooring swivel" from the cables it is seldom used if the ship is likely to have to leave harbour at short notice.

A ship may also be moored with the object of enabling her to ride out a gale with less likelihood of dragging her anchors. The anchors are then let go so that the ship lies with an angle between her cables of less than 20°; this helps to keep the ship from yawing and divides the weight of the ship between the two anchors.

SECURING TO A BUOY

In harbours with inadequate space for anchoring it is usual for ships to secure to a permanent mooring. This consists of two or more anchors laid on the bottom and connected by heavy ground chains to a central ring which lies on the bottom (see Fig. 210). To the central ring is attached a single length of cable called the "buoy pendant," the upper end of which passes through, and is supported by, a "mooring buoy." To the upper end of the buoy pendant is fitted a large shackle, known as the "ring of the buoy," to which the ship secures her own cable; swivels are fitted in the buoy pendant to

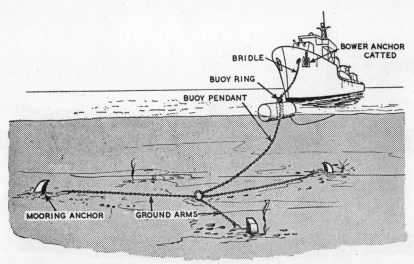

Fig. 210.—A ship secured to a buoy

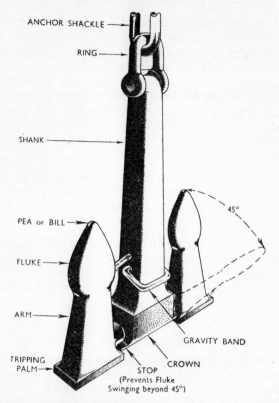

ANCHOR SHACKLE

RING

SHANK

PEA or BILL

FLUKE

ARM

TRIPPING PALM

GRAVITY BAND

STOP
(Prevents Fluke
Swinging beyond 45°)

CROWN

45°

Fig. 211.—Parts of an anchor

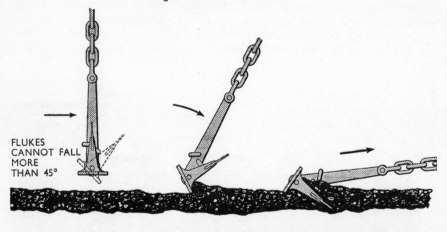

FLUKES
CANNOT FALL
MORE
THAN 45°

Fig. 212.—How an anchor holds

prevent it from becoming twisted as the ship swings. The purpose of the buoy is to keep the ring of the buoy above the water when the moorings are not in use, but, for the sake of brevity, a ship riding to a permanent mooring is said to be " secured to a buoy." The length of cable between the ship and the mooring buoy is called the " bridle."

In naval ports permanent moorings may be of six numbered classes these being numbered according to the maximum size of ship for which they are intended, a Class 1 Mooring being the heaviest. To the rings of the buoys of Class 1 and Class 2 Moorings are usually attached two smaller links, called " reducing links," to which smaller ships secure because their " buoy securing shackles " are too small to fit the ring itself. (For a detailed description of permanent moorings see Volume III of this manual.)

Because of the good hold of their anchors and the heavy gear employed, permanent moorings usually afford the safest method of securing a ship. Although the anchors of these moorings are permanently bedded, and have exceptionally heavy cables, they must be correctly laid in the first place and then inspected at regular and frequent intervals.

Parts of an Anchor

Fig. 211 shows a typical anchor. It should be noted that the arms can move through an angle of 45° each side of the shank.

How an Anchor holds

Fig. 212 shows how an anchor beds itself in the bottom when it is let go and the weight of the ship is taken by the anchors and cable.

When let go the anchor lies flat on the bottom until the pull of the ship on the cable drags the anchor along the bottom and thus causes the tripping palms to tilt the arms so that the flukes dig themselves in and give the anchor a hold; in soft holding ground the anchor may completely embed itself. For the anchor to maintain its hold it is essential that the pull of the cable on it should be horizontal, and sufficient cable must therefore always be veered to ensure that the part next to the anchor lies on the bottom. The length of cable between the anchor and the ship also acts as a spring in preventing the anchor from being jerked out of the ground when the ship is yawing or pitching.

The amount of cable which should be veered depends on the depth of the water, the weather expected, and the nature of the bottom. Clay and mud afford good holding ground, also chalk if it is soft enough for the flukes of the anchor to embed themselves in it; shingle, shells and rock afford bad holding ground. With wrought-iron cable and fair holding ground the amount of cable should be from four to six times the depth of water; but with the modern forged steel cable, which is much lighter, the amount should be increased to six to eight times the depth of water.

When the anchor is weighed the upward pull of the cable breaks the flukes out of the bottom. If the flukes have caught under a rock it may be necessary to weigh the anchor by attaching a cable or wire hawser to its gravity band and then heaving in on it in a reverse direction to that in which the anchor was laid.

A Ship's Anchors

Bower and Sheet Anchors. A ship's largest anchors are called her " bower anchors." They are used for anchoring or mooring the ship and are stowed one on each bow in a " hawsepipe."

A spare bower anchor, called the " sheet anchor," is carried in some larger ships for use in emergency. It is usually stowed in a hawsepipe on the starboard bow, just abaft the starboard bower anchor.

The Stream Anchor is smaller than the bower anchor and is carried by some larger ships for use as a stern anchor. It is stowed either in a stern hawsepipe or on deck under a suitable davit. A wire hawser with a swivel shackled on to the anchor is used in place of a chain cable, and the anchor is weighed by the after capstan, a Carpenter's stopper being provided to hold the hawser.

Kedge Anchors are smaller and handier, and are normally used for pointing the ship in some required direction ; for example, a kedge anchor is often used for hauling and holding the stern of an anchored ship against wind and tide to keep her clear of a regatta course. A kedge anchor is laid out and let go from a boat, a small wire hawser being used as its cable, and it is therefore usually stowed near a convenient davit, ready for hoisting it out to a boat. In former days ships were often moved in harbour by laying out anchors ahead successively and " kedging " up to them, but this is seldom done nowadays.

A *Killick* is any small anchor used for general purposes.

Arrangement of Anchors and Cables

(i) *In a Large Warship.* Fig. 213 shows a typical arrangement of the machinery and gear for working anchors and cables in a cruiser. In the illustration the ship is riding to her starboard anchor, and her port anchor is stowed in its hawsepipe. From the hawsepipe each cable leads aft to its " cable holder," thence forward to its " navel pipe," and down this pipe to its " cable locker " which is situated in the bottom of the ship. On the fore-and-aft line is the " capstan," which is used primarily for working hawsers but can also be used for working cable should the necessity arise.

On the deck below the forecastle is the capstan engine, which can be made to revolve in either direction at varying speeds, its operation being controlled by a handwheel situated amidships abaft the cable holders. The capstan engine drives the spindles of the capstan and the cable holders by means of worm and rod gearing. The spindle of the capstan can be disconnected from the engine to enable the capstan to be worked by hand in ships provided with capstan bars.

Each cable holder can be connected to or disconnected from its spindle by a dog clutch, which is operated by revolving a plate on the head of the cable holder. Thus cable can be hove in or veered under power by connecting up its cable holder and setting the capstan engine in motion in the required direction ; or cable can be allowed to run out freely by disconnecting its cable holder from its spindle. When both cables are being worked this arrangement enables both of them to be hove in, or veered under power, simultaneously ; it also allows of either cable being run out freely, and enables one cable to be hove in while the other is veered under power.

Each cable holder is fitted with a band brake, operated by a handwheel just abaft the cable holder. This brake controls the speed at which cable is

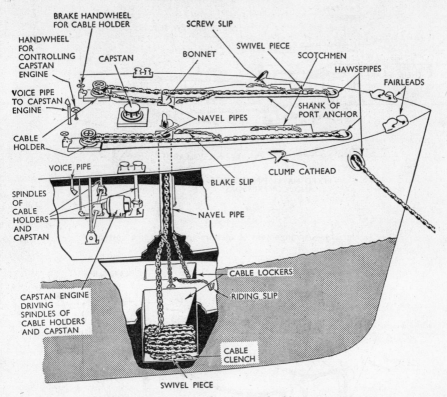

Fig. 213.—Arrangement of anchors and cables in a cruiser

allowed to run out when the cable holder is disconnected; it also holds the cable holder fast when the ship is riding at anchor or made fast to a buoy.

The cable can be stoppered (*i.e.* held temporarily) by means of chain slips. Abaft each hawsepipe is a " screw slip," used for heaving the anchor close home in its hawsepipe. Abaft each screw slip is a " Blake slip," used for holding the cable temporarily while handling its inboard part. At the top of each cable locker is a " riding slip," which is put on the cable when the ship is at anchor or secured to a buoy, and acts as a " preventer " should the brake of the cable holder fail to hold the cable.

A removable " bonnet " is clamped over each navel pipe to prevent water on the forecastle from running down the navel pipe. On each bow is a " clump cathead " from which the anchor is hung when its hawsepipe is required for the bridles of cable for securing the ship to a buoy. Each cable is provided with two " swivel pieces," one next the anchor and one on the inboard end ; the inboard swivel piece is shackled to a " cable clench " at the bottom of the cable locker. The forecastle deck in the wake of each cable is strengthened and protected by a strip of steel plating called a " Scotchman."

If a sheet anchor is provided its cable has a cable holder, navel pipe, cable locker, swivel pieces, Blake screw slip and riding slip, but its cable holder spindle cannot be connected to the capstan engine and so its cable has to be hove in by the capstan or by one of the other cable holders.

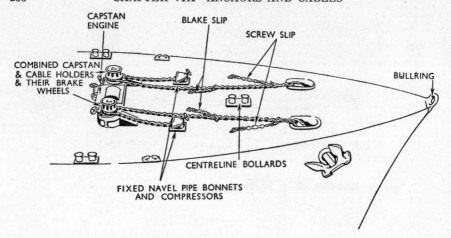

Fig. 214.—Arrangement of anchors and cables in a destroyer

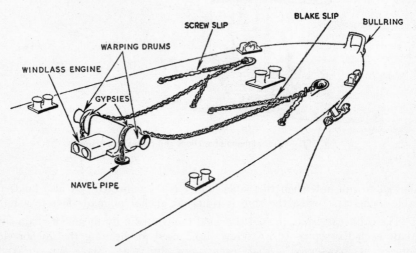

Fig. 215.—Arrangement of anchors and cables in a small warship

(ii) *In a Destroyer.* A different arrangement of cable gear is provided for destroyers (see Fig. 214). On the stem head is a " bullring " through which the bridles are led when the ship makes fast to a buoy, and clump cat-heads are not provided because there is no need to cat either bower anchor. A pair of centre-line bollards is provided abaft the hawsepipes ; these are used for towing and for securing the second bridle when the ship is made fast to a buoy. Each cable is provided with a Blake slip and screw slip, and each is worked by a combined capstan and cable holder, which is driven by an electric or steam capstan engine situated on or under the forecastle deck. Each capstan is keyed to its spindle, and each cable holder can be connected to, or disconnected from, its capstan by means of a dog clutch. The method of operating the cable holders is similar to that in a cruiser. The bonnets of the navel pipes are fixtures and in each is incorporated a " compressor " which takes the place of the riding slip. When the hand wheel on the forward side of the compressor is turned, a spade-shaped wedge of steel is moved across the mouth of the navel pipe until it nips a link of the cable against the lip of the navel pipe and so holds the cable fast. The remainder of the cable gear is similar to that of a cruiser.

(iii) *In Small Warships*. The forecastle arrangement in these vessels is shown in Fig. 215. The capstans and cable holders are replaced by a " windlass," which revolves on a horizontal shaft driven by a reversible steam or electric engine situated just abaft it on the forecastle deck. Two " gypsies," which take the place of cable holders, are mounted on the shaft and each is provided with a band brake. As in a cable holder each gypsy can be connected to, or disconnected from, the shaft by a clutch. " Warping drums," which take the place of a capstan, are keyed one to each end of the shaft and revolve with it. A compressor or a riding slip is not normally provided and the vessel usually rides on the brake of the windlass with the Blake slip on and acting as a preventer. In other respects the cable gear is similar to that of a destroyer.

(iv) *In a Merchant Ship*. A merchant ship's anchor and cable arrangements, except those of the largest liners, are very similar to those of a small warship equipped with a windlass.

CHAPTER IX

The Mariner's Compass

Direction

A COMPASS is an instrument which indicates the direction of north, and by means of which any other direction can be obtained.

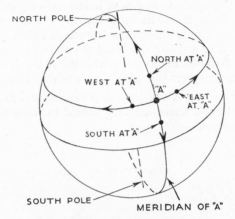

NORTH POLE

NORTH AT "A"

WEST AT "A"

"A"

EAST AT "A"

SOUTH AT "A"

SOUTH POLE

MERIDIAN OF "A"

Fig. 216.—Direction on the Earth's surface

The ends of the axis about which the Earth rotates are known as the " geographical " or " true," North and South Poles. Any imaginary line which joins the geographical poles by the shortest route over the Earth's surface is called a " meridian," and will run due north and south. Any such line passing through a place is known as the meridian of that place.

The direction in which the Earth rotates is known as " eastward " and the opposite direction is known as " westward." A line drawn due east or due west from any place is always exactly at right angles to the meridian of that place.

If the direction of north from any place is known, then any other direction can be described by angular measurement relative to the direction of north. A man looking towards the North Pole is said to be facing due north ; if he turns to his right through an angle of ninety degrees he will face due east ; if he turns a further ninety degrees (180° in all), he will face due south ; if he turns another ninety degrees to his right (270° in all) he will face due west ; and by turning yet another ninety degrees he will once more face due north. He will thus have turned through 360° in a clockwise direction and will have faced in turn the " cardinal points " of the compass, namely north (000°), east (090°), south (180°) and west (270°).

Compass Cards and their Graduation

These directions, and any intermediate directions, can be marked round the edge of a circular card which, when mounted on a compass, is known as the " compass card." There are three methods by which a compass card is graduated to indicate direction and these are now described.

(1) *The Three-figure method* (Fig. 217). By this method the compass card is graduated in degrees, clockwise from 000 (north) to 359, as illustrated in Fig. 217. With this method a direction is always described in terms of three figures ; the direction of north for example is described as " zero-zero-zero " and written 000°, and the direction of east is called ". zero-nine-zero," and written 090°. With this method of graduation a direction can be described simply and accurately, and it is the usual method used at sea.

Fig. 217.—A three-figure compass card

(2) *The Point method* (Figs. 218 and 219). In this method the compass card is graduated in 32 named " points," as illustrated in Fig. 218. Of these, north, east, south, and west form what are known as the four " cardinal " points.

By halving the right-angles between these cardinal points, four other points are obtained, which are known as " half-cardinal " points. These are :—north-east (N.E.), south-east (S.E.), south-west (S.W.), and north-west (N.W.) (see Fig. 219 (*a*)).

By halving the angles between the cardinal and half-cardinal points a further series of points are obtained which are known as " three-letter " points. There are eight of these, and they are named from their nearest cardinal point thus :—north-north-east (N.N.E.), east-north-east (E.N.E.), east-south-east (E.S.E.), south-south-east (S.S.E.), south-south-west (S.S.W.), west-south-west (W.S.W.), west-north-west (W.N.W.), and north-north-west (N.N.W.) (see Fig. 219 (*b*)).

These cardinal, half-cardinal and three-letter points together form the 16 points of the compass which the seaman is required to know, and by which he may describe direction in a general sense ; a wind, for example, may be described as blowing from south-south-east.

The remaining sixteen points are obtained by halving the angles once more (see Fig. 218), and they are termed " by-points " because they are named " by "

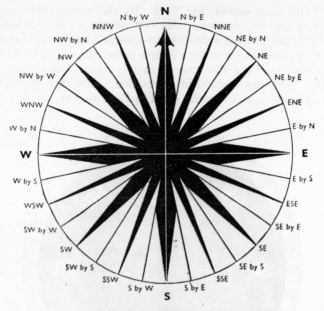

"POINT" COMPASS CARD

Fig. 218.—A " point " compass card

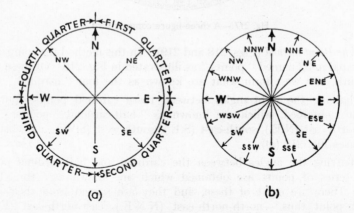

(a)   (b)

Fig. 219.—Method of " halving "

their nearest cardinal or half-cardinal points, thus :—north-by-east (N. by E.), north-east-by-north (N.E. by N.), north-east-by-east (N.E. by E.), east-by-north (E. by N.) and so on through the second, third and fourth quarters of the compass.

The term " point " is also used to describe the angle between any two successive points of the compass, which is $11\frac{1}{4}$ degrees; 2 points thus equal an angle of $22\frac{1}{2}°$, 4 points an angle of 45°, 8 points an angle of 90°, and 16 points an angle of 180°. This method of describing an angle or direction is usually used in a relative sense; the direction of an object may, for example, be described as "two points abaft the beam," *i.e.* red or green $112\frac{1}{2}°$.

"Boxing the compass" means naming the points of the compass in succession, clockwise, through the four quarters of the compass. The seaman, when boxing the compass, is required to name only the cardinal, half-cardinal and three-letter points.

(3) *The Quadrantal method* (Fig. 220). Another method by which the compass card is graduated is a combination of the three-figure and the point methods, and is known as the "quadrantal method." This method is becoming obsolete in the Royal Navy, but it is still found on most of the old fashioned magnetic compass cards.

Fig. 220.—A quadrantal compass card

Here the four quarters or "quadrants" of the compass card are each graduated into ninety degrees, with zero at north and south and 90 at east and west. By this method the directions of the cardinal points are named simply north, east, south and west, while intermediate directions are named in degrees *from* north or south *towards* east or west. The direction of south-west for example would be described as "south-forty-five west," and written S.45° W.

COMPARISON OF GRADUATIONS BY THE THREE METHODS

The following table gives a comparison of graduations by the Three-figure Point and Quadrantal methods.

Three-figure method	Point method	Quadrantal method
000°	N.	North.
022½°	N.N.E.	N. 22½° E.
045°	N.E.	N. 45° E.
067½°	E.N.E.	N. 67½° E.
090°	E.	East.
112½°	E.S.E.	S. 67½° E.
135°	S.E.	S. 45° E.
157½°	S.S.E.	S. 22½° E.
180°	S.	South.
202½°	S.S.W.	S. 22½° W.
225°	S.W.	S. 45° W.
247½°	W.S.W.	S. 67½° W.
270°	W.	West.
292½°	W.N.W.	N. 67½° W.
315°	N.W.	N. 45° W.
337½°	N.N.W.	N. 22½° W.

Applications of Direction

Direction is referred to in different ways for different purposes, the following being the more common :—

The Ship's Head, which describes the direction in which the ship is pointing.

The Course, which describes the direction in which the ship is steered.

The Track, which describes the path along which the ship has moved, or the path along which it is desired she should move (the track may differ from the course owing to the effects of wind or current).

A Bearing, which is the direction of one position from another position.

Ship's Compasses

Two types of compass are used at sea, namely the " gyro-compass " and the " magnetic compass," and the principles on which they work are entirely different.

The gyro-compass is mechanically and electrically operated by the ship's electric power supplies ; it is very accurate, but its accuracy depends upon skilled maintenance and the provision of electric power.

The magnetic compass is operated by the magnetism of the earth ; it is not affected by any mechanical or electrical breakdown in the ship, but is not nearly so accurate as the gyro-compass. For this reason the magnetic compass is no longer being fitted as the standard compass of the ship in large modern warships carrying more than two gyro-compasses.

The gyro-compass indicates the direction of the geographical or true North Pole of the Earth, while the magnetic compass indicates a direction known as " magnetic north," the difference between these two directions is known as " variation," which is described in Volume II of this manual.

THE GYRO-COMPASS

Fig. 221 shows a typical ship's compass of the gyro-repeater type. The compass card is pivoted in a bowl and is rotated by an electrical mechanism within the bowl so that it will take up a position with its zero mark pointing to true north. Around the edge of the compass card is a ring, called the " relative bearing ring," which is fixed to the inside of the bowl. On this ring, at the forward side of the compass, is a pointer called the " lubber's line," and the bowl and ring are mounted in the compass stand so that a straight line from the centre of the compass card to the lubber's line lies parallel with the fore-and-aft line of the ship ; the graduation mark on the compass card which coincides with the lubber's line will therefore indicate the direction of the ship's head. It is important to remember that as the ship turns from one course to another, the compass card will remain steady pointing to north while the lubber's line, being fixed to the ship, will turn round the card.

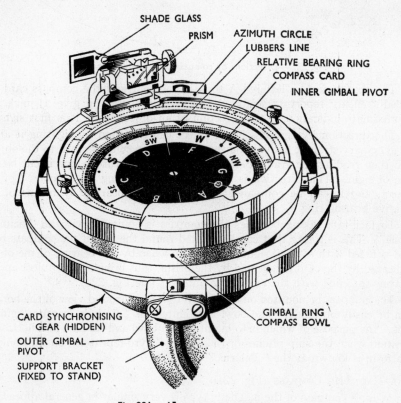

Fig. 221.—A gyro-compass repeater

The relative bearing ring is graduated in degrees either side from the lubber's line, from zero (right ahead), through abeam on either side (90°), to right astern (180°). The relative bearing ring will therefore indicate the direction of an object from the ship relatively to the fore-and-aft line of the ship. Such directions are known as " relative bearings," and those to starboard are prefixed by " green " and those to port by " red " ; for example, the relative bearing of an object which is abeam to starboard would be described as " green 90," and that of an object abeam to port as " red 90 " (see Fig. 222).

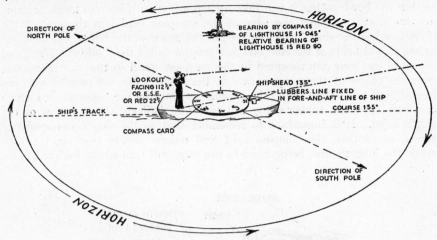

Fig. 222.—Directions by compass and relative directions

The six 60° sectors lettered A to G in the centre of the compass card are called " enemy reporting sectors " and they are used to give a quick but approximate indication of the direction of an object when it is first sighted.

The direction by compass of an object can be found by sighting it along an imaginary straight line joining the centre of the compass card to the object, and then reading the graduation on the edge of the card which is cut by the line of sight. This direction is known as the " bearing by compass " of the object, and it can be compared with its relative bearing by means of the relative bearing ring.

To facilitate taking bearings the compass is equipped with an " azimuth circle." This is a ring that can be rotated round the top of the compass bowl and is fitted with a " V " sight and a prism whereby the bearing of the object indicated by the card is reflected by the prism, thus bringing the object and its bearing into line with the eye of the observer (see Fig. 223).

The compass is mounted on a stand so that an all-round view of the horizon can be easily obtained. The bowl is mounted on " gimbals " and a " gimbal ring," the purpose of which is to maintain the bowl and its card in a horizontal position when the ship pitches or rolls. The " gyro-repeater " on the compass platform is known as the " Pelorus."

THE MAGNETIC COMPASS (Fig. 224)

A ship's compass of the magnetic type is very similar in general appearance to the gyro-repeater type. Its compass card is mounted on a number of magnetic needles, which are mounted on a central pivot within a " float." The bowl is completely filled with a liquid in which the compass card floats, thus reducing friction between card and pivot to a minimum and damping down any tendency of the card to oscillate.

The liquid in the bowl is a mixture of alcohol and water," doctored " to make it unfit for drinking. This liquid may begin to evaporate, in which case a bubble will appear in the bowl ; the bubble can be removed by inverting the bowl, removing the drain plug, and " topping up " the liquid with distilled water.

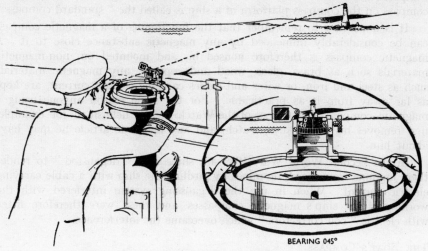

Fig. 223.—Taking a bearing

Magnetic compasses are affected by the magnetism of the ship, which causes errors in the compass readings known as " deviation." The deviation of any particular magnetic compass is reduced to a minimum by fitting small corrector magnets below, and close to, the bowl. In addition, soft iron spheres

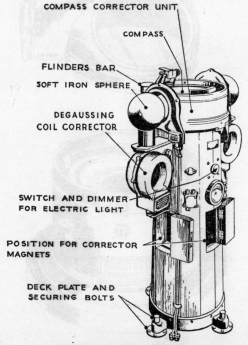

COMPASS CORRECTOR UNIT

COMPASS

FLINDERS BAR

SOFT IRON SPHERE

DEGAUSSING
COIL CORRECTOR

SWITCH AND DIMMER
FOR ELECTRIC LIGHT

POSITION FOR CORRECTOR
MAGNETS

DECK PLATE AND
SECURING BOLTS

Fig. 224.—A magnetic compass

and soft iron bars (known as " Flinders' bars ") are fitted in close proximity to the compass. These correctors are placed within, or mounted on, the compass stand, which is known as the " binnacle " (see Fig. 224). The magnetic compass on the compass platform of a ship is called the " standard compass."

It is important to remember that the functioning of a magnetic compass can be considerably influenced by any magnetic substance close to it. A magnetic compass is therefore housed in, and mounted on, non-magnetic materials such as brass, glass, wood and copper ; any magnetic materials such as steel and iron, or wires and cables carrying electric current, are kept as far away from it as practicable. For the same reason anyone using a magnetic compass, the Officer-of-the-Watch or the helmsman for example, first removes his knife, keys, watch, and any magnetic article he may have about him.

In the Second World War (1939–45) ships were " degaussed " to render them immune from magnetic mines by girdling the ship with a cable carrying electric current. When in use the degaussing system interfered with the working of the ship's magnetic compasses, and these were therefore fitted with electric " coil correctors " which overcame the interference.

THE BOAT'S COMPASS

This is a small, portable, magnetic compass of the liquid type, mounted on gimbals in a small hooded binnacle. Being portable, and because it may

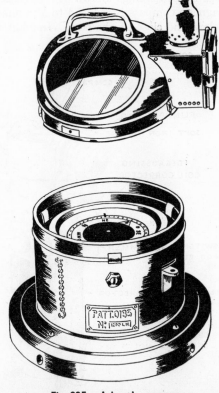

Fig. 225.—A boat's compass

therefore be changed from one boat to another, it is not corrected for deviation. It may, however, be used as a fixed compass, and so a small " corrector box " is provided in the binnacle in which small corrector magnets may be placed for adjusting the compass for deviation. An azimuth circle is also provided, for use when the compass is fixed.

When used in a boat the compass should be placed with its lubber's line in the fore-and-aft line of the boat and as far as practicable from anything magnetic such as the boat's engine.

Using a Boat's Compass.—It should be borne in mind that the compass will not point to true north because of the errors of variation and deviation ; also that quite apart from the effects of wind and current, the boat's return course will not be the exact opposite of her outward course, owing to the deviation error of the compass. Whenever a course is steered by eye the corresponding compass course should therefore be noted and recorded, due allowance being made for the effect of any wind or current, so that in the event of fog or bad visibility a correct course may be steered by compass. The best way to take a bearing of an object from a boat is to point the boat at the object, taking care to have sufficient room to manœuvre.

8

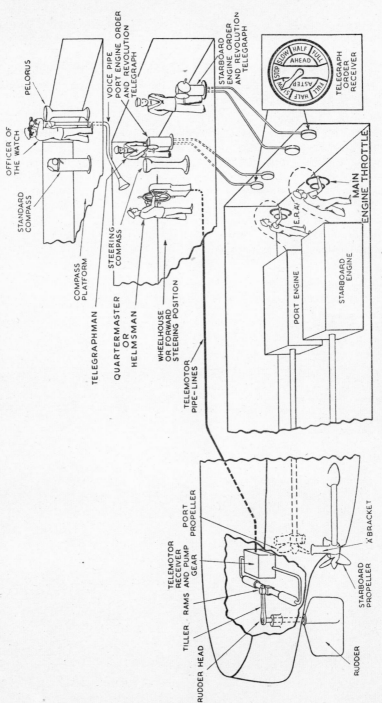

PELORUS

OFFICER OF
THE WATCH

STANDARD
COMPASS

VOICE PIPE
PORT ENGINE ORDER
AND REVOLUTION
TELEGRAPH

STARBOARD
ENGINE ORDER
AND REVOLUTION
TELEGRAPH

HALF FULL
SLOW AHEAD
STOP
SLOW FULL HALF
ASTER

TELEGRAPH
ORDER
RECEIVER

COMPASS
PLATFORM

STEERING
COMPASS

TELEGRAPHMAN

QUARTERMASTER
OR
HELMSMAN

WHEELHOUSE
OR FORWARD
STEERING POSITION

TELEMOTOR
PIPE-LINES

E.R.R.

MAIN
ENGINE THROTTLE

PORT ENGINE

STARBOARD
ENGINE

Fig. 226.—How conning orders are obeyed

TELEMOTOR
RECEIVER

PORT
PROPELLER

TILLER RAMS AND PUMP
GEAR

RUDDER HEAD

STARBOARD
PROPELLER

'A' BRACKET

RUDDER

CHAPTER X

Conning and Steering

CONNING

G IVING orders for the course and speed of the ship, as directed by her Captain, is known as " conning " the ship.

The orders are given by the Officer of the Watch, or by the Navigating Officer, from the primary conning position of the ship, which, in a warship, is known as the " compass platform " and situated on the bridge.

The compass platform is one of the main nerve centres of the ship, and on it are the standard compass (if fitted), the gyro-compass repeaters, and most of the instruments necessary for navigating and conning the ship and for checking her course and speed.

A " secondary conning position," situated aft, is provided in most ships. It is manned in action, but only used if the compass platform has been put out of action.

How Conning Orders are Obeyed (Fig. 226)

All conning orders from the compass platform are passed by word of mouth or by instrument to the " steering position," which is manned by the " quartermaster," " helmsman " and " telegraphmen."

The rating detailed as helmsman steers the ship under the supervision of the quartermaster, who is responsible to the Officer of the Watch that all orders affecting the wheel and engines are promptly and correctly carried out. When the ship is manœuvring the quartermaster usually takes the wheel himself.

Ratings detailed as telegraphmen man the " engine order telegraphs " and " revolution telegraphs." They repeat all orders received from the Officer of the Watch, and transmit them to the engine-room by moving their telegraph pointers to " slow," " half " or " full speed," " ahead " or " astern," as ordered. Below, the engine-room staff see these orders repeated on their " telegraph order receivers," and obey them as required by means of the engine throttles or the reversing gear.

HOW A SHIP IS STEERED (Fig. 227)

One of the most important duties of a seaman is to be able to steer well, either by sight on the object ordered, or by compass. This ability can only be acquired by careful attention to details and by experience.

The movement of the steering wheel sets the steering mechanism in motion, which turns the rudder. When the ship is moving ahead the rudder turns the ship by swinging her stern away from, and her bows towards, the direction desired ; it has the opposite effect when the ship is moving astern. When moving ahead the ship's head always pays off in the same direction as the top spokes of the wheel, so that if you wish the ship's head to go to port the top

219

spokes of the wheel must be moved to the left, and if to starboard the top
spokes of the wheel must be moved to the right. When moving astern the
stern always pays off in the same direction in which the top spokes of the
wheel are moved.

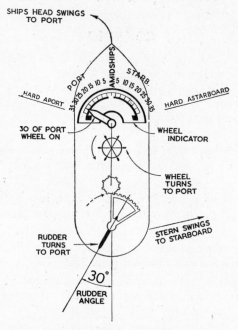

Fig. 227.—" Port thirty "

Rudder Angle

Within the limits of the movement of the rudder the greater the angle
between the rudder and the fore-and-aft line of the ship the quicker she will
swing and the smaller will be her turning circle. A ship is usually designed to
allow for a maximum rudder angle of 35 degrees each side of the " midships "
position.

Putting on and Taking off Rudder

The wheel should always be turned steadily by its spokes, without using
undue speed or force, until the required rudder angle has been put on. It
should not be started or brought up suddenly, or the steering engine may be
damaged. With " telemotor " steering gear the wheel should not be allowed
to fly back to amidships too quickly. If there is any tendency for the wheel
to jam, the fact should at once be reported. Any desired rudder angle can
be put on up to the maximum of 35 degrees, when the wheel and rudder are
each said to be " hard over " ; this rudder angle is usually put on in steps
of 5 degrees. With the wheel and rudder hard over there is a tendency for
the steering mechanism to be strained or become jammed, and for normal
purposes the largest rudder angle used is therefore 30 degrees. The amount
of wheel required for any desired rudder angle is shown by a pointer, known
as the " wheel indicator," which is geared to the wheel and moves over a
graduated scale situated in front of it.

Steering Orders

It is most important that all steering orders should be given clearly and in the standard form. It is equally important that they should be acknowledged in the standard form and obeyed correctly and in orderly fashion.

Altering Course

Orders for an alteration of course always start with the direction and are immediately followed by the rudder angle, *e.g.* " Starboard twenty." This is repeated by the helmsman, who puts the wheel over until the desired rudder angle is obtained, when he reports " Twenty of starboard wheel on, Sir." As the ship's head approaches the new course the rate of swing may require to be reduced, in which case an order to ease the wheel may be given, *e.g.* " Ease to ten." The helmsman repeats the order and moves the wheel to port until the wheel indicator shows 10 degrees of starboard wheel, when he reports " Ten of starboard wheel on, Sir." When the ship's head is near her new course this wheel must be taken off, and so the order " Midships " is given, which should be repeated and obeyed by the helmsman as in previous cases. Shortly after this the swing will require to be countered and the order " Port ten " will therefore usually be given. The order is repeated and the rudder put over to the required angle, the helmsman reporting " Ten of port wheel on, Sir." When the ship's head is within a degree or two of the new course the order " Midships " will be given.

Whenever the order " Midships " is received it cancels any previous wheel order, and the wheel should be placed in the midships position and kept there until a fresh order is received. If it is observed that the wheel has been put the wrong way, it is good practice to order " Midships " before ordering the required wheel.

Steering by Compass

When the helmsman is required to steer a course by compass the ship is conned as described above until her head is on the required course, when the order " Steady " will be given. Immediately he hears this order the helmsman notes exactly which degree of the compass card coincides with the lubber's line, repeats the order and reports the course as indicated by his steering compass, *e.g.* " Steady, course zero-five-seven, Sir." If the ship's head pays off on either side of the new course immediately after the order " Steady " is given, the helmsman moves his wheel in the direction required to return the ship to that course, and when her head is again on the correct course he makes his report " Course, Sir, zero-five-seven." The Officer of the Watch checks the reported course with the " Pelorus " or the " standard compass " and, if he is satisfied, he will say " Very good " and the helmsman will continue to steer that course without further orders. If the helmsman's reported course is incorrect, or if his compass is registering deviation or a small gyro error, he will be ordered to steer another course, perhaps within a degree or two of his reported course, *e.g.* " Steer zero-five-eight." This order is repeated and the wheel moved accordingly, and when the ship's head is on the new course the report is made " Course, Sir, zero-five-eight." The helmsman then steers the ship on this course.

The following example shows the orders, replies, and reports for an alteration of course from 008° to 306° :—

Order	Reply	Report
" Midships."	" Midships, Sir."	" Wheel's a'midships, Sir."
" Port thirty."	" Port thirty, Sir."	" Thirty of port wheel on, Sir."
" Ease to fifteen."	" Ease to fifteen, Sir."	" Fifteen of port wheel on, Sir."
" Midships."	" Midships, Sir."	" Wheel's a'midships, Sir."
"Starboard, ten,"	" Starboard ten, Sir."	" Ten of starboard wheel on Sir."
" Midships."	" Midships, Sir."	" Wheel's a'midships, Sir."
" Steady."	" Steady, course three-zero-seven, Sir."	—
" Steer three-zero-six."	" Steer three-zero-six, Sir."	" Course, Sir, three-zero-six." (When the ship is on her course.)

Immediately before another alteration of course is made the order " Midships " is usually given. This serves the double purpose of ensuring that any rudder angle which may be on is taken off, and of warning the helmsman that an alteration of course is coming.

STEERING BY EYE

In ships where the helmsman can see ahead from the steering position he may be required to steer on a ship ahead or on a distant object. If so, the ship will be steadied as nearly as possible on the desired course by conning, and, after the order " Midships," the helmsman will be given such orders as " Steady on the lighthouse," or " Follow the next ahead." In the former example he then steers the ship by keeping the lighthouse in line with the jackstaff and the centre of the wheel ; in the latter he follows in the wake of the ship next ahead, keeping her masts and funnels in line dead ahead and turning astern of her in her wake if she alters course. When turning in the wake of the ship next ahead he should endeavour to keep the stem inside the line between the smooth and broken water on the outside edge of the wake. It should be noted, however, that only in small vessels is the helmsman ordered to steer in the wake of the next ahead ; in larger ships the Officer of the Watch cons the ship for all alterations of course.

The helmsman should always be ready to revert to steering by compass as soon as this is indicated by the order " Steady."

In small vessels a helmsman may be required to steer by eye when his ship is making stern way. It is best then to face aft, imagine the stern to be the bows, and work the wheel in the same manner as when going ahead.

Hints on Steering

USE OF THE WHEEL

Remember that the " lubber's line " is fixed in the fore-and-aft line of the ship and represents the ship's head, and that the compass card remains steady while the ship swings round it. The direction of the ship's head is read off the compass card against the lubber's line. To keep the ship on a given compass course the lubber's line must be kept constantly opposite the correct degree marked on the compass card by turning the wheel to port or starboard to move the lubber's line as required. If the lubber's line wanders off to the right the top spokes of the wheel must be turned to the left to bring it back into place ; similarly, if the lubber's line moves to the left the top spokes of the wheel must be turned to the right.

When the wheel of a large ship is put over the ship does not begin to swing for some time. If, as sometimes occurs, the ship is swinging in the opposite direction at the time of putting the wheel over, she will take longer to answer the rudder than had she been steady.

When a large ship has begun to swing it takes a certain amount of opposite rudder to stop her again. It is important to lose no time in " getting the feel " of the ship, which, like a horse or a dog, may show a tendency to assert a will of her own. This tendency must be anticipated and forestalled.

The art of steering consists largely in watching the lubber's line very closely and putting the wheel over the instant the ship *starts* to swing off her course instead of waiting until she has actually swung off. The wheel must be eased again immediately the swing is checked, and opposite rudder be used if she starts to swing in the opposite direction. The amount of rudder to be used depends upon the ship, her speed, and the weather, but *success lies largely in using as little as possible, and the higher the speed of the ship the less rudder she requires.*

MAKING GOOD THE COURSE

In a seaway the ship cannot always be kept exactly on her course, but when she swings off it the man at the wheel should endeavour to swing her back an equal amount *to the other side,* and he should not allow her to swing more to one side than the other ; otherwise the mean course steered will not be the correct one.

CARRYING RUDDER

Unless wind and sea are right ahead, if the rudder of a ship is kept amidships she will usually wander off her course owing to the pressure of the wind on her superstructure or the force of the waves on either end of her hull. In most warships the ship's head tends to come up into the wind because their pivoting point is well forward ; in some merchant ships, however, whose pivoting point lies further aft, it may tend to fall off to leeward.

To counteract this tendency the helmsman may have to keep a small angle on the rudder, and the ship is then said to be " carrying rudder." Ships which require rudder to keep them from paying off from the wind are said to carry " weather rudder " ; and ships which, under the same conditions of wind and sea, require rudder to keep them from flying up into the wind are said to carry " lee rudder " (Fig. 228).

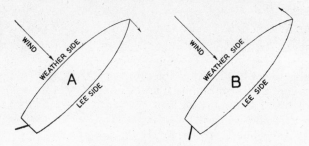

Fig. 228.—Carrying rudder :—

A—weather rudder

B—lee rudder

Orders for Helmsmen and Quartermasters

A helmsman is always given orders as exactly as possible. He should not be ordered to steer more than five degrees either side of his reported course, any larger alterations being carried out by conning until the desired course is achieved.

On being relieved the helmsman must always turn over to his relief the course and the amount of rudder which the ship is carrying, e.g. " Course 040, ship carrying five degrees of port wheel." The helmsman should never turn over to his relief during an alteration of course, but should wait until the ship is once more on a steady course.

The quartermaster is responsible for seeing that all wheel and engine orders are obeyed correctly. Whenever the ship is manœuvring (i.e. in confined waters, crowded shipping lanes, or in company with other ships) he should take the wheel himself. Before turning over the wheel to a helmsman he should first ask permission of the Officer of the Watch.

At the change of the watch the new quartermaster should report to the Officer of the Watch—" Quartermaster relieved, Sir. Course (so and so), telegraphs at (so and so), revolutions (so and so), quartermaster (or helmsman) at the wheel."

ORDERS FOR REGULATING THE SPEED AND MOVEMENT OF THE ENGINES

Telegraph Orders

The wording of engine orders from the compass platform to the telegraphmen has been standardised for the sake of uniformity and the avoidance of phonetic errors such as confusion between the words " port " and " both." The underlying principle is that the word " engines " is always used in conjunction with the words " both " or " all," but on no other occasion.

If it is observed that the engine or engines has been put the wrong way, it is good practice to order " Stop " before ordering it or them in the required direction.

Examples :—

   (i) Applicable to ships with two or four propeller shafts—

      " Half ahead (or astern) both engines."
      " Stop both engines."
      " Half ahead port."
      " Slow astern starboard."
      " Stop port."

  (ii) Applicable to ships with three shafts—

      " Half ahead (or astern) all engines."
      " Stop all engines."
      " Half ahead port and starboard."
      " Stop port and centre."
      " Full ahead port."
      " Stop starboard."

The telegraphmen should always repeat any such order given *word for word* before they transmit them to the engine-room, and a further report should be made when they have been acknowledged by the engine-room staff.

Example :—

Order	Reply	Report
" Stop both engines."	" Stop both engines, Sir."	" Both telegraphs repeated stop, Sir."
" Half ahead port."	" Half ahead port, Sir."	" Port telegraph repeated half ahead, Sir."

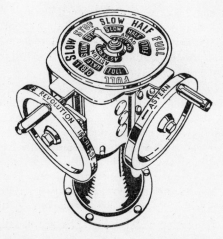

Fig. 229.—Combined engine order and revolution order telegraph

Engine Order Telegraphs (Fig. 229)

These spoken orders are transmitted mechanically to the engine-room from the steering position by means of " engine order telegraphs." These telegraphs are fitted in the primary steering position, one for each propeller shaft in single, twin, and triple-screw ships, and one for each pair of shafts in quadruple-screw ships ; they are usually connected to their repeaters in the engine-room by rod gearing.

The dial of each telegraph and repeater is graduated for the orders " Full," " Half," and " Slow," for both " Ahead " and " Astern," and it is also graduated for " Stop." The order " Stand-by " is sometimes included as well. When the hand-wheel is turned to transmit an order a pointer moves over the face of the dial indicating the order transmitted. The hand-wheel has to be moved through one complete revolution for each step in the range of orders.

As each order is transmitted a bell (which is incorporated with the repeater) rings in the engine-room to draw attention to the order. The tones of these bells are different for port and starboard repeaters.

Each order is acknowledged from the engine-room by means of a " reply gong " situated in the steering position. The code used is as follows :—

Slow Ahead or Astern	...	1 stroke of the gong.
Half Ahead or Astern	...	2 strokes ,, ,, ,,
Full Ahead or Astern	...	3 ,, ,, ,, ,,
Stop		4 ,, ,, ,, ,, with a pause between the first two and the last two.

A differently toned gong is used for port and starboard.

The direction of movement of the propeller shafts, ahead or astern, is indicated by the electrically worked " tell tales " situated on the compass platform.

Revolution Order Telegraphs (Fig. 229)

A warship possesses a comparatively large range of speed which must be adjustable to within narrow limits (usually half a knot) to enable her to manœuvre in close company with other ships. Orders for her engines must therefore be qualified by the number of revolutions which correspond with the speed required.

This is done by means of the " revolution order telegraph," which transmits the number of revolutions required on each shaft to the engine-room, where it is repeated on a " revolution order repeater." The method of transmission is by hand-wheel and rod gearing, in steps of one, two, or three revolutions at a time, one turn of the hand-wheel being required for each step. Whenever the revolutions are altered a warning bell with a different tone to that of the engine order telegraphs rings in the engine-room. Revolution orders are acknowledged from the engine-room by one or two strokes of the associated reply gong, which also has a different tone from the reply gongs of the telegraphs.

The engine and revolution order telegraphs are usually combined in one instrument, as shown in Fig. 229.

In H.M. ships the revolutions per minute at which the engines are to be worked at the different speeds ordered are as follows :—

SLOW (AHEAD or ASTERN)   ... A pre-determined number of revolutions sufficient to give the ship steerage way—usually about 5 knots.

HALF (AHEAD or ASTERN)   ... As indicated on the revolution order telegraph.

FULL (AHEAD or ASTERN)   ... *EMERGENCY*—Maximum revolutions possible with the power available.

Merchant ships are not provided with revolution order telegraphs because they do not normally travel in company, and so their speed need not be adjustable to within narrow limits. They normally proceed at their economical speed, which is usually within a knot or two of their maximum full speed, and, except when manœuvring in confined waters, the normal position of their telegraphs while on passage is " Full Ahead." " Emergency full speed " (*i.e.* speed employing the utmost power available) is indicated by moving the telegraphs from " Full Speed " to " Stop " and back to " Full Speed " twice in quick succession.

Logging Engine Orders

All orders transmitted to the engine-room for movement of the engines are logged in a register by the engine-room staff.

CHAPTER XI

Sounding by Lead and Line

A MEASUREMENT of the depth of water is called a " sounding," and it is measured in feet, or fathoms, or in a combination of both. A fathom measures 6 feet. Soundings are taken by a "lead and line," as described in this chapter, or by a " sounding machine " or by " echo sounding," as described in Volume II of this manual.

The simplest method of taking a sounding in shallow water is with a pole, and for this reason barge poles, the bearing-off spars of craft working in shallow waters, and the boat-hook staves of ship's boats, should be marked off in feet.

Boats' Lead and Line (Fig. 230)

In less shallow water harbour craft and boats use a " boats' lead and line " for sounding. It consists of a weighted line marked at intervals along its length. The weight or " lead " is of leg-of-mutton shape and weighs 7 pounds, and the " line " consists of 14 fathoms of $2\frac{1}{2}$-pound line.

The first three fathoms of the line are marked respectively with 1, 2 and 3 strips of leather, and each of these fathoms is marked in feet by 1, 2, 3, 4 and 5 knots. Thereafter, up to 13 fathoms, the line is marked in the same way as a hand lead and line, which is described below.

When soundings are taken due allowance must be made for the speed of the boat through the water. This is done by heaving the lead ahead of the boat and reading off the sounding when the line is vertically up and down with the lead on the bottom ; it must also be done when the boat is stationary but stemming a tidal stream.

Hand Lead and Line (Fig. 230)

This is used in ships for sounding up to a depth of 20 fathoms, and at speeds not exceeding 10 knots ; sounding is usually carried out by this method when entering or leaving harbours. The lead consists of a tapered bar of lead, weighing from 10 to 14 pounds, to which is bent a 25-fathom length of $1\frac{1}{8}$-inch special lead-line. The base of the lead is hollowed out to receive tallow, and the head is shaped into an eye through which is rove a hide becket. Placing tallow in the base of a lead is called " arming " it, and its purpose is to pick up a sample of the sea bed for examination if required.

The lead-line has a long eye splice at one end, and a back splice at the other. It is bent to the lead by reeving the eye splice through the hide becket and passing the lead through the eye, thus forming a cow hitch between the eye and the becket.

Markings

The hand lead-line is marked as follows :—

2 fathoms	...	*two* strips of *leather*.
3 fathoms	...	*three* strips of *leather*.
5 fathoms	...	a piece of *white duck*.

7 fathoms	...	a piece of *red bunting*.
10 fathoms	...	a piece of *leather* with a *hole* in it.
13 fathoms	...	1 piece of *blue serge*.
15 fathoms	...	a piece of *white duck*.
17 fathoms	...	a piece of *red bunting*.
20 fathoms	...	*two knots*.

The three different materials, serge, duck and bunting, are used so that the markings can be distinguished from one another in the dark by the feel of their texture, either with the fingers or the lips.

When using a longer line than 25 fathoms successive tens of fathoms after 20 are marked by an additional knot, and every intervening 5 fathoms is marked by a single knot.

Marking the Line

Before fitting a new lead-line it should be stretched thoroughly by towing it astern, and it should then be accurately measured off and marked while wet as it will lengthen when dry and so be inaccurate when in use. The markings are measured from the end of the eye splice (thus giving a sounding " the benefit of the lead ") against previously marked off lengths on the deck. Knots are made in mackerel line which, as with the material for the other marks, is tucked securely around two of the strands of the lead-line.

Calling the Soundings

The correct sounding is shown where the water level cuts the line when the line is up and down with the lead on the bottom, and the leadsman calls the sounding in accordance with the following practice :—

Marks.—All the fathom soundings which are marked, *i.e.* 2, 3, 5, 7, 10, 13, 15, 17, 20 fathoms (and 25, 30, 35, 40 fathoms, etc., when using a long line), are called " marks."

Deeps.—All the intervening fathoms, which are not marked, *i.e.* 4, 6, 8, 9, 11, 12, 14, 16, 18, 19, etc., are called " deeps."

The leadsman therefore calls, for example, " By the mark seven," and " Deep nine."

To assist in gauging the deeps they are sometimes indicated by a length of mackerel line tucked between the strands of the lead-line. Fractions of fathoms are measured by the quarter and the half, *i.e.* 1 ft. 6 in. and 3 ft. respectively, and because of the possibility of confusion between the call of " a quarter " and " three-quarters " the latter is not used, but is called as a " quarter less " the next highest mark or deep. Examples of the calls for fractions are :—

" And a quarter six " for $6\frac{1}{4}$ fathoms ;

" And a half six " for $6\frac{1}{2}$ fathoms ;

" A quarter less seven " for $6\frac{3}{4}$ fathoms.

Heaving the Lead

When a sounding is required while a ship is making way through the water the lead must be hove sufficiently far ahead to allow time for it to reach the bottom before the leadsman is directly above it. The faster the ship is moving, or the deeper the water, the farther ahead therefore must the lead be hove.

9

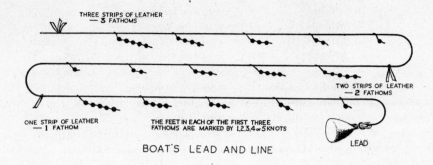

THREE STRIPS OF LEATHER
— 3 FATHOMS

TWO STRIPS OF LEATHER
— 2 FATHOMS

ONE STRIP OF LEATHER
— 1 FATHOM

THE FEET IN EACH OF THE FIRST THREE
FATHOMS ARE MARKED BY 1,2,3,4 or 5 KNOTS

LEAD

BOAT'S LEAD AND LINE

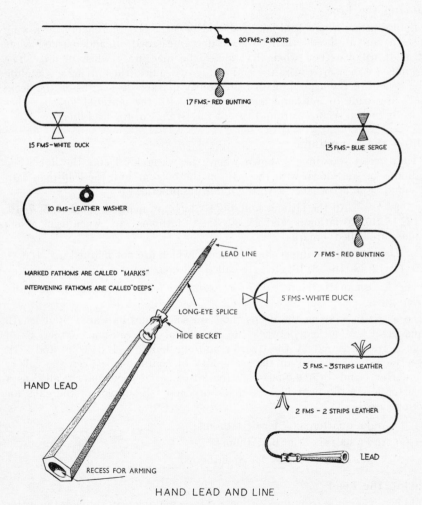

20 FMS.- 2 KNOTS

17 FMS.- RED BUNTING

15 FMS - WHITE DUCK

13 FMS.- BLUE SERGE

10 FMS - LEATHER WASHER

LEAD LINE

7 FMS - RED BUNTING

MARKED FATHOMS ARE CALLED "MARKS"

INTERVENING FATHOMS ARE CALLED "DEEPS"

5 FMS - WHITE DUCK

LONG-EYE SPLICE

HIDE BECKET

3 FMS. – 3 STRIPS LEATHER

HAND LEAD

2 FMS – 2 STRIPS LEATHER

RECESS FOR ARMING

LEAD

HAND LEAD AND LINE

Fig. 230.—Lead-lines

(i)

(ii)

Fig. 231.—(i) Old fashioned chains   (ii) Modern chains

Ships are usually fitted with two small hinged platforms, situated one each side well forward on the forecastle deck, which project from the ship's side when let down and on which the leadsman stands. These platforms are called " chains," because, in the days of sail, the platform outside the bulwarks to which the mast shrouds were secured was called " the chains," and the fore-chains provided a convenient stand for the leadsman (Fig. 231 (i)).

Fig. 231 (ii) shows a modern ship's chains. Before entering the chains, the leadsman should :—

    (i) remove his knife and lanyard ;
    (ii) see that the breast-rope and apron are properly secured ;
    (iii) see that the end of the lead-line is made fast ;
    (iv) see that the becket is in good condition ;
    (v) see that the line is clear.

The lead is eased down towards the water for a distance of 2 fathoms and the line is held in the outboard hand when facing forward, a round turn being taken around the hand (see inset on Fig. 231). A sufficient amount of line for the scope of the throw required is coiled in the left hand. The lead is then swung pendulum fashion and with increasing impetus until it reaches just above the horizontal on the forward swing, at which point it is let go. Then, immediately the lead strikes the water, any slack in the line is quickly taken up with both hands, and the sounding is taken when the line is taut and directly up and down. The sounding is then called to the bridge, loudly and clearly to avoid any possibility of its being misunderstood or not heard. If no sounding is obtained, the call should be : " No bottom at 20 fathoms," or at whatever length of line was used.

The lead can be hove to a greater distance by swinging it overhead in a circle two or three times before letting it go. To swing the lead overhead a sharp pull should be given to the line as it reaches the horizontal, by bending the arm smartly in at the elbow and bringing the hand to the shoulder. When the lead has passed overhead the arm should be straightened to take the pull as it descends, and the process be repeated until sufficient impetus has been imparted to the lead.

As soon as a sounding has been taken the leadsman's mate (called the " lazy leadsman ") hauls in the line, while the leadsman coils it right hand under the left hand over to make a right-handed coil and thus prevent kinking.

There is an art in heaving the lead and obtaining accurate soundings which can only be acquired by practice.

When gauging a sounding it is better to underestimate it than to over-estimate it. In other words, if in any doubt it is better to call a lesser sounding than that actually indicated.

Sounding at Night

When sounding at night marks can be identified by the feel of their texture instead of by their colour. The sounding is estimated by identifying the mark nearest inboard from the hand and deducting its distance from the water level. This distance is called the " drift."

Calling the Ship's Movement

When a ship is getting under way, or coming to an anchor, and has little or no way upon her, it is important that the bridge should know whether she is moving and in what direction. On such occasions the leadsman should allow the lead to rest on the bottom with the line kept just taut, and he can then tell if the ship is drifting or moving, and in what direction, by seeing if the line " grows " away from him instead of remaining vertically up and down. If the line grows forward his report will be " Ship's going astern, Sir ! " ; if it grows under the ship from the starboard chains his report will be " Ship's going to starboard, Sir ! "and so on.

Sounding by Sounding Machine, and Echo Sounding

The normal method of sounding at sea is now (1950) by " echo sounding," and sometimes by sounding machine. Both of these are fully described in Volume II of this manual.

CHAPTER XII

Charts; Buoyage; Lights

CHARTS

A CHART is virtually a contour map of the sea bed and its surrounding coast line, but whereas a map gives the height and contours of the land above sea level a chart gives the depth of the bottom below sea level.

The level of the sea is constantly changing owing to the rise and fall of the tide, and this has to be taken into account when drawing a map or a chart. The heights marked on a map are heights above " mean sea level," which is the average level of the surface of the sea calculated from observations taken over a long period of time ; but the depths shown on a chart are related to an arbitrary level of the sea called the " chart datum," which is a low-water level below which the tide will seldom fall in the area covered by the chart. The depths indicated on a chart are therefore almost the minimum depths experienced, and the height of the tide must be added to them to obtain the estimated depth at any particular time. The actual depth obtained by sounding will therefore be greater than the charted depth by an amount equivalent to the height of the tide at the time (see Fig. 232).

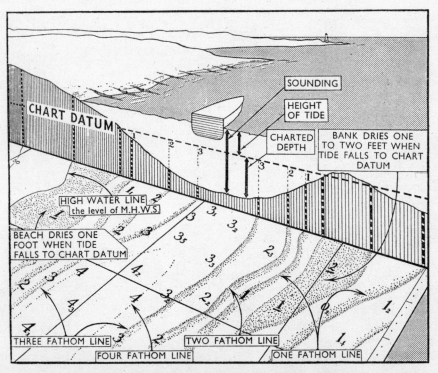

Fig. 232.—Relation between charted depths and soundings

The depths shown on a chart are usually in fathoms, but where a depth is under eleven fathoms it is indicated in fathoms and feet ; 8_5 on the chart would therefore represent a depth of 8 fathoms and 5 feet.

The height of a beach, bank, rock, or other feature which is periodically covered and uncovered by the rise and fall of the tide is given in feet above the chart datum, the figure being underlined, *e.g.* $\underline{3}$, to distinguish it from a depth. For isolated reefs or rocks this height may be written *dries three feet* to distinguish it from a rock which is always covered.

The heights of all those features which are always uncovered, or only covered by exceptional tides, are given in relation to a level known as " mean high water springs " (M. H. W. S.), which is the mean level of the spring tides at that locality. The heights of these features are therefore indicated when nearly at their minimum.

The nature of the bottom is indicated on most charts by the initial letter, or a contraction, of the term describing its consistency ; thus Ck is chalk, Co is coral, Cy is clay, G is gravel, Gd is ground, M is mud, R is rock, S is sand, Sh is shells, Sn is shingle, and St is stones. Such knowledge of the nature of the bottom is required when anchoring a vessel because different types of bottom have different holding properties. Clay and mud afford good holding ground, but shingle, shell and rock are bad. Chalk affords good holding ground if sufficiently soft for the flukes of the anchor to bed themselves in it.

There are various conventional markings and signs on a chart to indicate the different features of the shores and coasts which are of value and interest to the seaman. The more common of these, together with the symbols used for buoys, beacons and other aids to navigation, are illustrated in Volume II of this manual.

BUOYAGE

A navigator finds his way in the open sea by taking observations of the sun, moon, planets, and stars, also by radio aids such as wireless bearings where available. When in sight of land he finds his way by taking bearings of salient coastal features such as headlands, points and conspicuous buildings, and by taking soundings ; he may also be aided by radar. When making port he finds his way up the channels and fairways, past rocks and shoals, by the aid of " landmarks " such as lighthouses and beacons, and by " sea-marks " such as lightships and buoys of which the more common are described below.

Buoys

Buoys are floating structures moored to the bottom, and are used to mark shoals, banks, rocks, wrecks, or other dangers to navigation ; they are also used to mark the edges of channels and fairways. The shape and colour of a buoy, also its " top-mark " when fitted, indicate its purpose, and they are made as distinctive as possible so that they can be easily recognised from a distance.

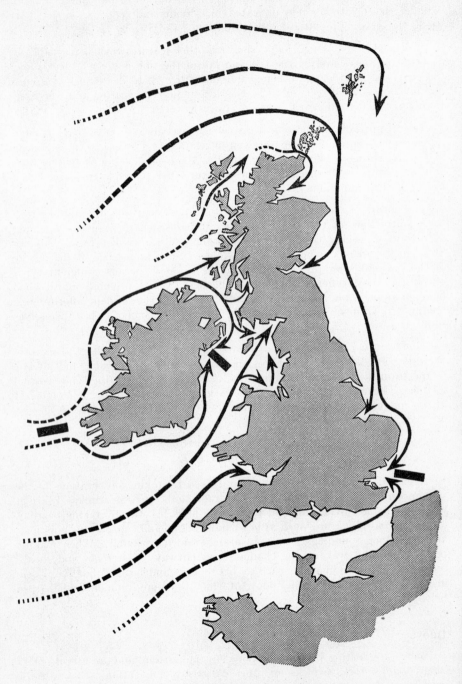

Fig. 233.—Direction of the main flood stream round the British Isles

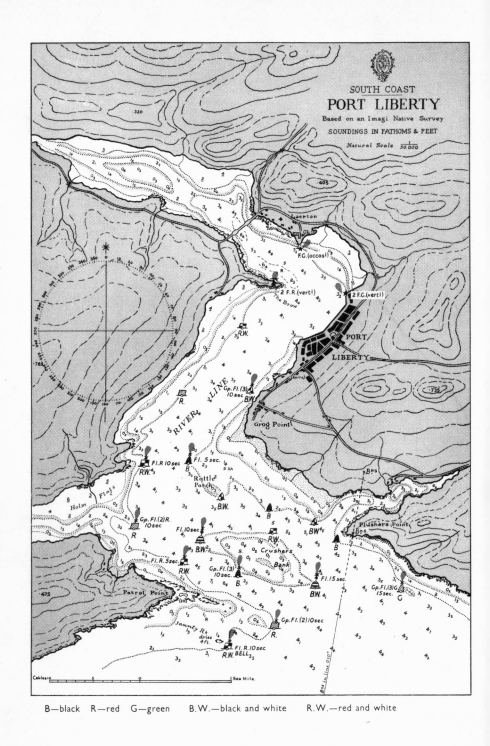

B—black   R—red   G—green   B.W.—black and white   R.W.—red and white

Fig. 234. Chart of Port Liberty

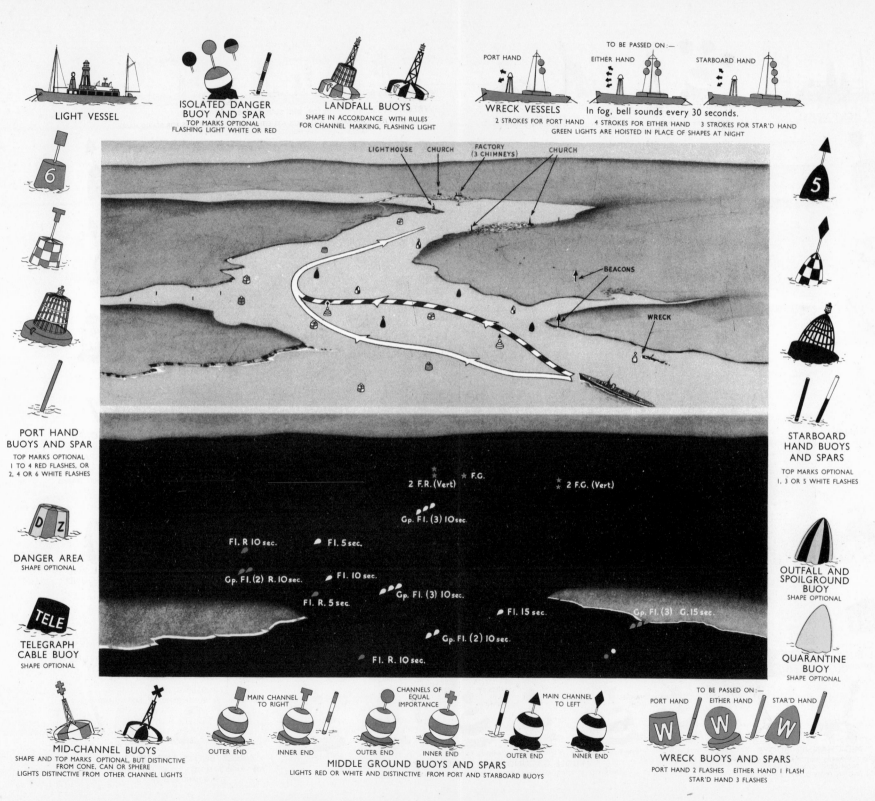

LIGHT VESSEL

ISOLATED DANGER
BUOY AND SPAR
TOP MARKS OPTIONAL
FLASHING LIGHT WHITE OR RED

LANDFALL BUOYS
SHAPE IN ACCORDANCE WITH RULES
FOR CHANNEL MARKING, FLASHING LIGHT

WRECK VESSELS
2 STROKES FOR PORT HAND   4 STROKES FOR EITHER HAND   3 STROKES FOR STAR'D HAND
GREEN LIGHTS ARE HOISTED IN PLACE OF SHAPES AT NIGHT
TO BE PASSED ON:—
PORT HAND   EITHER HAND   STARBOARD HAND
In fog, bell sounds every 30 seconds.

PORT HAND
BUOYS AND SPAR
TOP MARKS OPTIONAL
1 TO 4 RED FLASHES, OR
2, 4 OR 6 WHITE FLASHES

DANGER AREA
SHAPE OPTIONAL

TELEGRAPH
CABLE BUOY
SHAPE OPTIONAL

LIGHTHOUSE   CHURCH   FACTORY
(3 CHIMNEYS)   CHURCH

BEACONS

WRECK

2 F.R. (Vert)   F.G.   2 F.G. (Vert.)

Gp. Fl. (3) 10 sec.

Fl. R 10 sec.   Fl. 5 sec.

Gp. Fl. (2) R. 10 sec.   Fl. 10 sec.

Fl. R. 5 sec.   Gp. Fl. (3) 10 sec.

Fl. 15 sec.   Gp. Fl. (3) G. 15 sec.

Gp. Fl. (2) 10 sec.

Fl. R. 10 sec.

STARBOARD
HAND BUOYS
AND SPARS
TOP MARKS OPTIONAL
1, 3 OR 5 WHITE FLASHES

OUTFALL AND
SPOILGROUND
BUOY
SHAPE OPTIONAL

QUARANTINE
BUOY
SHAPE OPTIONAL

MID-CHANNEL BUOYS
SHAPE AND TOP MARKS OPTIONAL, BUT DISTINCTIVE
FROM CONE, CAN OR SPHERE
LIGHTS DISTINCTIVE FROM OTHER CHANNEL LIGHTS

MIDDLE GROUND BUOYS AND SPARS
LIGHTS RED OR WHITE AND DISTINCTIVE FROM PORT AND STARBOARD BUOYS
OUTER END   INNER END   OUTER END   INNER END   OUTER END   INNER END
MAIN CHANNEL
TO RIGHT
CHANNELS OF
EQUAL
IMPORTANCE
MAIN CHANNEL
TO LEFT

WRECK BUOYS AND SPARS
PORT HAND 2 FLASHES   EITHER HAND 1 FLASH
STAR'D HAND 3 FLASHES
TO BE PASSED ON:—
PORT HAND   EITHER HAND   STAR'D HAND

Fig. 235. Types of Buoys and Buoyage of Port Liberty

A buoy may be provided with a light to indicate its position in darkness, or with a bell or whistle to indicate its position in low visibility. Such a buoy is usually larger than an unlighted buoy and has a cage-work structure built up on the body of the buoy. Some buoys may also carry a radar or other reflector superimposed on their superstructures.

A buoy should not be used as a mark by which to fix the ship's position when other more reliable marks are available, because it is liable to drag from its position in bad weather and may be moved at short notice by the harbour authorities.

The types of buoys and marks used off the coasts of the British Isles are illustrated in Fig. 235, which shows the entrance to an imaginary port (" Port Liberty ") as viewed from seaward, and illustrates the method of buoyage. Opposite this illustration is a chart of the same port (Fig. 234), and if this is compared with Fig. 235 little difficulty should be experienced in understanding the system.

The buoyage illustrated conforms with the " lateral system " agreed to internationally in 1937, and it may be encountered in all parts of the world ; but it should be borne in mind that many other systems of buoyage are used by foreign countries which have not subscribed to the international agreement, or in places where the agreement has not yet been put into effect.

Chapter I of each volume of the *Admiralty Sailing Directions* contains a description of the buoyage systems in use in the area covered by the particular volume.

Starboard and port-hand buoys define the respective sides of a channel or fairway, and they are also used to mark a rock or a shoal which may be passed only on one side.

The starboard hand of a channel or fairway is that side which is on your right hand when going with the main flood stream, or when approaching a harbour, river, or estuary, from seaward ; the port hand is that side which is then on your left hand (the direction of the main flood stream around the British Isles is shown in Fig. 233). A ship should therefore leave a starboard-hand buoy on her starboard hand when entering a port or proceeding up a channel, and should leave it on her port hand when leaving the port or proceeding down a channel.

To differentiate a sequence or group of starboard and port-hand buoys they may be lettered or numbered consecutively from seaward ; when numbered, odd numbers only are used for starboard-hand buoys, and even numbers only for port-hand buoys.

Middle-ground buoys mark the outer and inner ends of a shoal or other obstruction which lies in a channel and can be passed in safety on either side. Where the main traffic route passes on one side of the shoal and the secondary traffic route on the other this fact is indicated by the top-mark of the buoy. Middle-ground buoys may also mark the junction of two or more channels.

Mid-channel buoys may be used to indicate the middle of a main deepwater channel or fairway, and, in conformity with the rule that a vessel should always keep to the right-hand side of a channel where it is used for two way traffic, they should always be left on the port hand of a vessel whether she is going up or down channel.

Other buoys or marks used in coastal waters and harbours are described briefly below.

Quarantine buoys mark the anchorage for shipping awaiting " pratique " (*i.e.* permission from the Port Authorities for a ship to proceed to her allotted berth up harbour).

Outfall buoys mark the position where a sewage or other pipe discharges into the sea.

Spoil-ground buoys mark the areas where dredgers and refuse barges may dump their spoil.

Cable buoys mark the position of telegraph and other submarine cables in the vicinity of which anchoring is prohibited.

Special mark-buoys mark areas allocated to military authorities for purposes such as practice firing or bombing.

Dan-buoys out at sea may mark the limits of fishing grounds where submerged nets may be encountered, and also the limits of mine-sweeping areas.

Mooring-buoys, of many sizes and usually cylindrical in shape, may be found in any harbour or anchorage.

Landmarks and Leading Marks

Beacons, and other conspicuous landmarks such as lighthouses, factory chimneys and church spires, may provide marks for leading ships up a channel clear of navigational dangers, and are then termed " leading-marks."

Stakes close inshore may mark the limits of inshore fishing grounds where submerged nets may be encountered.

Stakes, large branches of trees, or spars sometimes called " withys," may mark the sides of the channel in small rivers.

Wreck-marking Vessels and Buoys

Wrecks which constitute a danger to shipping in the vicinity of channels or fairways may be marked by wreck-marking vessels or by wreck-buoys. The side on which the wreck-marking vessel may be passed is indicated by shapes or lights hoisted at her yard arm ; the shape of the wreck-buoy (either can, conical or spherical) indicates on which hand it should be left.

Landfall Marks

Landfall marks such as lightships or buoys with tall superstructures may be used to indicate the seaward approach to a harbour, river or estuary. Many such marks display their names painted conspicuously in white letters.

Lightships

A lightship is used instead of a light-buoy where it is necessary for the mark or light to be seen from a greater distance ; unlike the light-buoy, its light is " watched " by the crew, and is therefore more reliable. Lightships are usually painted red or black, with their name painted in white letters on the hull, and they usually carry a " daymark " and their light on a mast or similar structure.

LIGHTS

A navigational mark such as a lighthouse, lightship, or buoy which exhibits a light during the hours of darkness is marked on a chart by a small purple splash of colour over the star or dot indicating its position.

The colour of a light may be white, red, green, blue, orange, or violet, and it may show all round the horizon as one colour or may be split into sectors of different colours ; also, the light may show over certain areas only, in which case a sector of some particular colour may indicate a fairway or an area of danger.

Characteristics

The nature of the beam exhibited by a light is known as its " characteristic," of which there are four main types, namely :—" fixed," " flashing," " occulting " and " alternating."

A *fixed light* shows a steady beam.   There are comparatively few fixed lights because they might occasionally be mistaken for shore lights or the lights of a ship.

A *flashing light* shows a regular series of flashes, the intervening periods of darkness being always longer than the periods of light.

A *fixed and flashing light* shows a steady beam, varied at regular intervals by a single flash of relatively greater brilliance.

An *occulting light* appears as a fixed light broken at regular intervals by short periods of darkness called " eclipses."

An *alternating light* shows two or more colours successively, which may or may not be separated by periods of darkness.   When thus separated, if the periods of darkness are more than those of light the light is known as " alternating flashing," but if the periods of light are greater than those of darkness the light is known as " alternating occulting."

Group flashing and group occulting lights.   A further method of differentiating one light from another is known as " grouping," in which a series of flashes or a series of eclipses is separated by intervals of darkness or light.   Thus, a " group flashing " light would show at regular intervals a group of two or more flashes, a " group occulting " light would show a steady light broken at regular intervals by a group of two or more sudden eclipses, and a " fixed and group flashing " light would show a steady beam, varied at regular intervals by a group of two or more flashes of relatively greater brilliance.

Quick flashing lights.   Yet another method is really a modification of the flashing and group flashing systems and comprises a light which flashes rapidly at a greater rate than once a second ; thus there are " quick flashing " lights (Qk. Fl.), " interrupted quick flashing " lights (Int. Qk. Fl.), and " group interrupted quick flashing " lights (Gp. Int. Qk. Fl.).

Diagrammatic examples of light characteristics, together with their abbreviations as marked on charts, are given in Fig. 236.

Period

The time shown on a chart or in the *Admiralty Lists of Lights* against the characteristic of a flashing light indicates the interval between the beginning of one flash and the beginning of the succeeding flash ; for occulting, alternating, group flashing, or group occulting lights the time shown indicates the interval of time occupied by one complete cycle.   This interval is known as the " period " of the light.

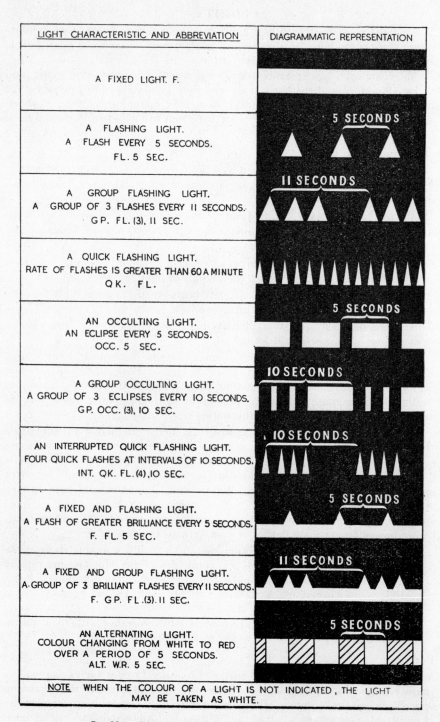

LIGHT CHARACTERISTIC AND ABBREVIATION	DIAGRAMMATIC REPRESENTATION
A FIXED LIGHT. F.	
A FLASHING LIGHT. A FLASH EVERY 5 SECONDS. FL. 5 SEC.	
A GROUP FLASHING LIGHT. A GROUP OF 3 FLASHES EVERY 11 SECONDS. GP. FL. (3), 11 SEC.	
A QUICK FLASHING LIGHT. RATE OF FLASHES IS GREATER THAN 60 A MINUTE QK. FL.	
AN OCCULTING LIGHT. AN ECLIPSE EVERY 5 SECONDS. OCC. 5 SEC.	
A GROUP OCCULTING LIGHT. A GROUP OF 3 ECLIPSES EVERY 10 SECONDS. GP. OCC. (3), 10 SEC.	
AN INTERRUPTED QUICK FLASHING LIGHT. FOUR QUICK FLASHES AT INTERVALS OF 10 SECONDS. INT. QK. FL. (4), 10 SEC.	
A FIXED AND FLASHING LIGHT. A FLASH OF GREATER BRILLIANCE EVERY 5 SECONDS. F. FL. 5 SEC.	
A FIXED AND GROUP FLASHING LIGHT. A GROUP OF 3 BRILLIANT FLASHES EVERY 11 SECONDS. F. GP. FL. (3). 11 SEC.	
AN ALTERNATING LIGHT. COLOUR CHANGING FROM WHITE TO RED OVER A PERIOD OF 5 SECONDS. ALT. W.R. 5 SEC.	

NOTE   WHEN THE COLOUR OF A LIGHT IS NOT INDICATED, THE LIGHT MAY BE TAKEN AS WHITE.

Fig. 236.—Diagrammatic examples of light characteristics

Chart Indications for Lights

The distance at which a light can be seen in clear weather by an observer 15 feet above sea level is shown against most lights (but not against those of buoys), the visibility distance of the light depending upon its brilliance and its height above sea level. Most coastal lights in the British Isles and elsewhere are exhibited from sunset to sunrise, but a light marked " occasl." or " irreg." is only exhibited on certain occasions. A light marked " (U) " indicates that it is " unwatched " and that implicit reliance must therefore not be placed upon it. Buoys are, of course, always unwatched lights, although the symbol (U) is not marked against them on the charts.

Admiralty Publications on Lights

Details of all lights *except those of buoys and wreck marking vessels* are contained in the *Admiralty List of Lights*, which is published annually in 12 volumes, each volume covering a certain area of the world. Full instructions for interpreting these lists are contained in the foreword to each volume. Details of light-buoys are given in the appropriate volume of the *Sailing Directions*, and on the largest scale chart of each area.

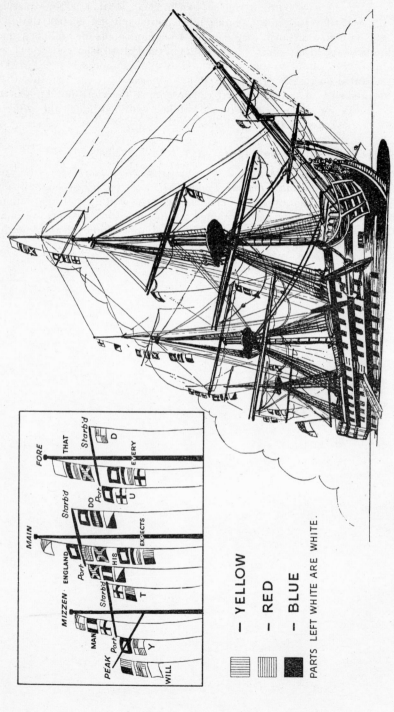

Fig. 237.—H.M.S. "Victory" flying the famous signal made by Lord Nelson at Trafalgar

CHAPTER XIII

Naval Communications

HISTORICAL BACKGROUND

THE history of naval signalling goes back many hundreds of years, but the methods of signalling used today are nearly all of much more recent origin.

Until the Napoleonic wars signalling was mostly carried out by means of sail movements, the firing of guns, and the display of flags in various positions to convey different meanings, the codes used having been privately compiled and printed, and being limited both in scope and use.

In 1780 Admiral Kempenfelt devised a code (subsequently revised and elaborated by Lord Howe in 1790), consisting of numeral flags and a small number of special flags and pennants, by which several hundreds of different signals could be made. This code was basically the same as that used by Lieutenant Pasco to make Nelson's famous signal at Trafalgar (see Fig. 237), but the significations of the flags had been changed owing to the capture of the signal book by the French in 1804. A revised signal code containing much more detail was produced as the result of research by Admiral Home Popham, who, for a number of years, had devoted much of his time to this subject.

Semaphore signalling was adopted in 1795 from a system devised by the Reverend Lord George Murray, which at first consisted of a screen containing six shutters which could be operated to give numerous combinations. This system was used by the Admiralty for communicating with the Nore and Portsmouth Commands, the signals being relayed by a chain of signal stations situated within sight of each other on convenient hills. It was extended later to Plymouth, and an improved semaphore was adopted which was devised by Sir Home Popham, in 1816, and consisted of two movable arms lit by lanterns at night and operated so as to form different angles. It is claimed that in clear weather a signal could be transmitted by this system from London to Portsmouth in ten minutes although it had to pass through ten different stations in transit. These land stations were finally closed down in 1848 after the invention of the electric telegraph, but the system is commemorated to this day by many of the original sites of these stations being known locally as " Telegraph Hill."

The Morse code, so named after its American inventor Samuel Morse, revolutionised signalling on land with the introduction of the " Electro-magnetic Recording Telegraph." The use of this instrument was first demonstrated by the transmission of a message over a line from Baltimore to Washington on May 24, 1844. The wide possibilities of this system were quickly recognised, and in 1865, as a result of experiments and trials carried out by Captain Philip Colomb, Royal Navy, and Captain Bolton of the 12th Regiment, the Royal Navy adopted the " flashing system " in which shutters and flags were used by day and lamps by night for transmitting signals in the Morse code.

Visual signalling held complete sway afloat until 1905, when wireless telegraphy emerged from its early experimental stage into practical use and further development.   The revolution in naval communications brought about by the advent of wireless can be easily appreciated when it is realised that before 1905 a naval unit, when at sea and outside visual range, was entirely cut off from all outside communication except by despatch vessel.

The world-wide naval organisation and control achieved in recent years, and particularly during the Second World War (1939–1945), was made possible only by the communication " network " which was perfected as a result of the rapid progress in the development of wireless and other signalling systems.

SYSTEMS OF COMMUNICATION AND THEIR USE

The various systems of communication are complementary to each other, and although in certain circumstances one particular system may be quicker or more suitable than another, all are so organised that together they provide a network of communications to meet the varied requirements of the whole Naval Service.   A message on its transmission route between originator and final addressee may therefore be " handled " by one, several, or all of the various systems.

Abbreviations Employed for the Different Communication Systems

VS   ...   ...   Visual and sound signalling.

SST   ...   ...   Supersonic telegraphy.

Wireless   ...   Wireless telegraphy (W/T), Voice, Radio, Teleprinter (RTP).

LT   ...   ...   Line telecommunications—Teleprinter (TP), Telephone (PN), Cable.

Mail   ...   ...   Airmail and surface mail—Airgram (AG) and Postagram (PG).

Hand   ...   ...   Despatch—By boat, messenger, or despatch rider.

WaT   ...   ...   Warning telephone—Internal broadcasting system.

The Different Systems and their Use

Visual signalling (VS) embraces all methods of signalling by direct sight or sound, and includes flags, flashing, semaphore, siren, whistle and foghorn.

Flag signalling provides a rapid means during daylight of passing manœuvring and other signals of an urgent nature between ships in close company ; the codes used are so designed that the more common requirements can be signalled in one " hoist," or by a combination of short hoists making one " display."   For harbour purposes in particular, single flags and pennants are generally used to signal routine requirements or indicate the performance of certain functions ; *e.g.* :—

" Fresh water boat required " ;
" Have divers down alongside or in close vicinity."

Flashing, by means of " directional " lights to individual ships and " non-directional " lights to several ships simultaneously, is used both by day and night, the morse code being used for this purpose. Under war conditions the use of lights during darkness or in low visibility is either prohibited, or restricted to directional lanterns of the lowest brilliancy, because unrestricted use of lights may disclose the position of our forces to the enemy.

Semaphore signalling is carried out by forming the various letters and signs with hand-flags; it is used during daylight only and is particularly suitable for harbour signal traffic. With well trained operators it is the most rapid visual method available for inter-communication between ships in close company. One or two operators suitably placed can transmit simultaneously to a large number of ships, and semaphore can be read equally well either from the front or rear of the sender, the " Direction " sign being the guide to the direction in which he is facing.

Sound. This includes siren, foghorn and whistle, the Morse code being employed. The use of sound is restricted to emergencies, usually between ships or boats, when other systems are not suitable or desirable ; *e.g.* U ($\cdot$ $\cdot$ —) " You are standing into danger."

Supersonic Telegraphy (*SST*) is the transmission of messages through the water by morse code using " sonic " equipment.

Wireless Telegraphy (*W/T*) is the communication of a message by electro-magnetic waves passed in the Morse code, and it should never be called " radio " which is a general term for wireless and radar. It can be used for either short or long range working. For inter-ship working the messages are usually keyed by hand, " but broadcasts from shore to ships at sea are usually transmitted automatically from a previously prepared tape."

Voice is the communication of a message by electro-magnetic waves using speech. It is particularly suitable for short-range tactical communications. The operating procedure must be understood by all seamen and is therefore fully explained in Volume II of the manual.

Radio Teleprinter (*RTP*) is the transmission of teleprinter signals by wireless, and it is the main method of communication between shore stations. The operators need only be trained typists.

Line Telecommunications (*LT*) includes telephony, telegraphy and teleprinter, and is used extensively to relieve congestion on Wireless and other communication systems between shore authorities. It is also used directly between ships, or ship and shore, when ships are secured alongside or to buoys connected with the shore by telephone or telegraph cable.

Teleprinter (TP) provides a means by which messages are transmitted over a land line or cable by using a typewriter keyboard and special apparatus. It is used extensively in the United Kingdom by all three Services, and in certain areas abroad. A simple procedure is used which can be easily learned by any person who is proficient at typing.

Telephone (PN) is used primarily for conversations. Telephone connection from ships to a shore exchange are often available for ships alongside or at a buoy.

10

Hand Message. The transmission of messages by boat or despatch service is used, both at sea and in harbour, to relieve other signalling systems, or for transmitting important orders and information when circumstances do not permit of other methods being employed. Hand messages must be clearly marked so that they are easily recognisable by boats crews and orderlies ; they are therefore enclosed in an envelope marked :—

ON HER MAJESTY'S SERVICE

HAND MESSAGE

The Main Signal Office,

H.M.S.............................

All envelopes so marked must be delivered to the M.S.O. (Main Signal Office) of the ship addressed without delay.

When a large number of ships are present it is usually necessary to run a special Despatch Boat service in addition to the normal Duty Boat routine. At sea such messages are transferred between ships by means of a heaving line, or " messenger."

Mail.—Airmail-airgram (AG), and Surface Mail—postagram (PG). These are written or typed in message form by the communication department and enclosed in envelopes clearly marked " airgram " or " postagram " which are then handed to the secretariat for despatch by the appropriate route. On reaching their destination they are handed to the communication department for distribution, and their marking ensures that they are handled with a higher degree of priority than ordinary air or surface mail. This system is usually used for the transmission of non-urgent messages, and to relieve other methods of communication from congestion.

Use of Precedence and Security Classifications

PRECEDENCE

The handling of a message may be expedited or retarded, according to its degree of urgency, by the use of a " precedence indication " by the originator. The more common indications are *Operational Immediate, Priority, Routine,* and *Deferred.*

Any message bearing the precedence indication *Operational Immediate,* or *Priority,* must be handled as expeditiously as possible, and in that relative sequence.

SECURITY

Every message is given one of the following security classifications :—

    (i) *Top Secret ;*   (iv) *Restricted ;*

    (ii) *Secret ;*   (v) *Unclassified.*

    (iii) *Confidential ;*

Messages of the " top-secret " category are handled by officers throughout. " Secret " and " confidential " messages are handled by communication ratings for some of the distribution process and by officers for the rest. The remaining types of messages are handled by ratings. The contents of all messages of a security classification of " restricted " and higher are never to be divulged to " non-Service " persons. The classification " unclassified " confers no degree of security on the contents of a message.

FLAG SIGNALLING

The flags and pennants used in Naval signalling comprise :—

(i) alphabetical flags, numbered pennants, and substitutes. } the same as the International Code (*see* Figs. 239 and 240) ;

(ii) numeral flags, special flags, and special pennants, and the fourth substitute } of special design and used exclusively by ships and shore stations of the Royal Navy (these are illustrated in Volume II of this manual).

Construction of Flag Codes

Each flag or pennant may have one or more meanings when hoisted in different positions or in different circumstances ; and similarly, groups of two or more flags may signify other meanings. This combination of flags and hoists, together with their different significations, is known as a " signal code."

A flag signal may therefore consist of :—

(i) a single flag or pennant ;

(ii) a combination of flags and/or pennants in one hoist ;

(iii) several hoists flying simultaneously, which are read in their relative sequence ;

(iv) several " displays," each of one or more hoists, the displays being hoisted consecutively.

In certain cases additional meanings may be conveyed by hoisting a flag signal " at the dip," *i.e.* at a position two-thirds of the full distance up the halyards.

Notes on Learning the Colours and Meanings

The best method of learning these is to memorise with certainty the designs and meanings of four or five flags at a time before proceeding to the next group. A set of cards, home made, to represent the different flags and pennants and then played as a card game, is a great aid in learning the flag code.

THE MORSE CODE

The principal methods used for transmission of messages by the Morse code are :—

(i) flashing light ;

(ii) wireless telegraphy ;

    (iii) line telegraph ;

    (iv) buzzer ;

    (v) siren, whistle, or foghorn.

Construction of the Morse Code

Symbols of the Morse code are expressed by two elements called a *dot* (or a *short*), and a *dash* (or a *long*), signalled either single as in letters " E " (· one dot) and " T " (— one dash), or in combination, as in letters " L " (. — . .) and "A" (. —).

The two elements can be signalled in various ways. In visual signalling it is done by the motion of any single object which is made to appear and disappear for long and short periods of time (*e.g.* flash of a lamp or projector) ; sound signalling, by short and long blasts on a siren, whistle, or foghorn ; in telegraphy by the short and long aural sounds of a buzzer, or by short and long periods of silence between the clicks of a sounder, or by the left and right deflections of a pointer as in the needle instrument.

Alphabet

A	● ▬	J	● ▬ ▬ ▬	R	● ▬ ●
B	▬ ● ● ●	K	▬ ● ▬	S	● ● ●
C	▬ ● ▬ ●	L	● ▬ ● ●	T	▬
D	▬ ● ●	M	▬ ▬	U	● ● ▬
E	●	N	▬ ●	V	● ● ● ▬
F	● ● ▬ ●	O	▬ ▬ ▬	W	● ▬ ▬
G	▬ ▬ ●	P	● ▬ ▬ ●	X	▬ ● ● ▬
H	● ● ● ●	Q	▬ ▬ ● ▬	Y	▬ ● ▬ ▬
I	● ●			Z	▬ ▬ ● ●

It will be observed that no letter consists of more than four elements. Those letters which occur most frequently in the English language are given the shortest symbols ; for example, in ordinary composition the letter " E " (·) appears about 120 times for every time that the letter " Q " (— — · —) appears.

Numerals

1	● ▬ ▬ ▬ ▬	6	▬ ● ● ● ●
2	● ● ▬ ▬ ▬	7	▬ ▬ ● ● ●
3	● ● ● ▬ ▬	8	▬ ▬ ▬ ● ●
4	● ● ● ● ▬	9	▬ ▬ ▬ ▬ ●
5	● ● ● ● ●	Ө	▬ ▬ ▬ ▬ ▬

The symbols for figures always conform to the following limitations :—

(i) each consists of five elements (dots or dashes) ;

(ii) dots and dashes are not sandwiched ; each sign begins either with one or more dots or with one or more dashes.

Special Signs

ALL SHIP CALL 2, 2, 2, 2 • • — — —		The " call up," by flashing, for all ships and stations. An all-round light must be used for this purpose.
LONG BREAK — • • • —	$\overline{BT}$	Precedes and follows the " text " portion of a message ; written thus : =
ENDING — • —	K	The " end of transmission " sign used when a receipt to the message is required. It is also used by the addressee, in answer to a call, to mean " I am ready to receive your message."
RECEIPT • — •	R	Means " message received " ; it is made to the originator of the message by the recipient in reply to the " end of transmission " sign K.
ENDING • — • — •	$\overline{AR}$	The " end of transmission " sign used when no receipt is required.
PERIOD • — • — • —	AAA	A punctuation mark in plain language ; written thus : ⊙
ERROR • • • • • • • • (eight or more)	EEEEEE	Means " erase the portion of the message just transmitted ; the corrected portion will follow " ; or, if followed by the message ending sign $\overline{AR}$, means " erase the whole of this message, which is cancelled."
REPEAT • • — — • •	$\overline{IMI}$	Made by the recipient, to the originator. If made alone it means " repeat all of your last transmission." If the sign is followed by the letters AA (all after), AB (all before), WA (word after) or WB (word before) followed by a word, then it means " repeat only that portion of the message so indicated." It is used by the originator to precede the second transmission of the whole or a portion of the message.

Some of the signs, except the single letter ones, are composed of two or more alphabetical symbols made as one, and they are always written with a bar above the letters, for example, $\overline{AR}$. These signs are only some of the special ones used when transmitting messages in Morse Code ; other signs are given in Volume II of this Manual. A line over two or more letters indicates that they are to be transmitted as a single character, *i.e.* without pause.

Spacing

Correct spacing is essential. The dots and dashes and the spaces between them should always bear a constant ratio to one another, as described below, in which the dot is taken as the unit.

A dash is equivalent to three units. This ratio of the dash to the dot gives the required " rhythm " to the code and must not be varied, whatever the speed of transmission.

The space of time between any two elements of a letter or sign is equal to one unit ; that between two complete letters or signs is three units ; and that between two words or groups is five units.

In order to slow down the speed for training purposes, or when operators are not proficient, a longer pause must be allowed between symbols and, proportionately, between words or groups.

Teaching Method

Experience has shown that the best method of learning the Morse alphabet is to take the symbols in their alphabetical sequence and thoroughly master a few at a time. The beginner may therefore divide the alphabet into portions containing about six letters for each lesson, the first being from A to F inclusive. When those letters have been thoroughly mastered the next six should be learned, and so on. No new series of letters should be tackled until the whole of the preceding letters have been thoroughly learned.

Training in both transmitting and receiving are equally necessary. For early training a buzzer is the best medium, because the ear becomes quickly attuned to recognise the rhythm of the various signs. A flashing light should be introduced as soon as the signs have been memorised.

In the naval schools of signalling it has been found best for beginners to be taught to transmit and receive correctly groups of letters (which do not spell sense) before allowing them to read or make plain language. If the beginner starts his Morse training with plain language he is apt to get into the habit of guessing.

A useful " test message " can be given by mixing letters and figures in the ratio 2 to 1, and dividing the result into groups of four ; each group is then equal in length to one average word of plain language (five letters). By this means proficiency can be tested at a given rate by timing the transmission ; e.g. six groups transmitted in one minute represents a speed or rate of six words a minute. An example of such a test message is given below.

Q U 1 F	N S 8 Z	M 4 O 8	9 G 4 J
9 M I Y	2 K 7 A	T V X 0	E S L 3
J 0 P C	V 3 5 D	C E 7 R	W H 6 B

THE SEMAPHORE CODE

The different semaphore signs are made by moving one or two handflags so that they form various angles with the perpendicular. It is essential that each angle be formed correctly, as good communication depends upon accuracy in this respect.

Alphabet and Special Signs

The alphabet and the special signs used are shown in Fig. 238. It will be noticed that, with few exceptions, the letters follow round in succeeding circles, differing from each other by angles of 45 degrees.

Method of Instruction

Semaphore can be learned by using the arms only, but practice with the handflags is also necessary to ensure that the correct angle is formed with their staves. When making a sign with handflags the line between the shoulder and the point of the handflag stave must be absolutely straight, as shown in the diagrams.

The simplest method of memorising the signs is to take them in a series of circles, thus :—

1st circle :	A to G (single arm signs) ;
2nd circle :	H to N (omitting J) ;
3rd circle :	O to S ;
4th circle :	T, U, Y ;
5th circle :	Numeral sign, J and V ;
to complete :	W, X and Z.

In the first circle the letters A to C inclusive are made with the right arm, E to G with the left, and D with whichever arm is most convenient to the sender. In the second circle the right arm should be kept stationary at letter A, the left arm being used for completing the sign ; the letter L is therefore made with the right arm at letter A, and the left at E. Similarly, in the remaining circles the right arm is kept at the standing position peculiar to the circle, while the left arm completes the sign.

The arms are moved from sign to sign by the shortest route. The tendency to bend the elbow is most conducive to bad signalling and must be carefully guarded against. The handflags should be kept clear, and held accurately at the proper angle. In changing from one sign to another the arms should be kept straight, and be swung through a vertical plane. Both feet should always be kept firmly on the deck, about fifteen inches apart ; this will provide a firm stance and check any tendency to swing the body with the arms, which is fatal to good signalling.

The most common faults are holding the arms too close to the body for A and G, not accurately horizontal for B and F, not exactly midway between the vertical and horizontal for C and E, and not exactly vertical from the shoulder blade for D.

As each circle is mastered the beginner should be practiced in making the letters out of their alphabetical order ; he should thoroughly master the letters in this manner (without having to pause to think) before learning the letters in the next circle.

When transmitting to another station the sender must always get into a conspicuous position and choose a background which is as far away as possible. A skyline affords the best possible background.

It is better to transmit slowly and accurately ; undue hurry in forming the letters will only result in bad transmission and mistakes. A semaphore message made at six words a minute and correctly read the first time is far better than one which has to be repeated because the sender transmitted it at such a speed that he could not form the letters correctly.

The *direction sign* (J) shows from which side the letters are to be read.   It is often necessary to transmit in an opposite direction to that of the reader ; the latter must therefore be careful to observe in which direction the sender is facing by noting in which direction the horizontal arm of this sign is extended, bearing in mind that this is always the sender's *left* arm.

The signs for *long break* (BT), *period* (AAA), and *repeat* (IMI) are used in a similar manner to those of the Morse code.   Other signs used in Semaphore signalling are given in Volume II of this manual.

SEMAPHORE CODE

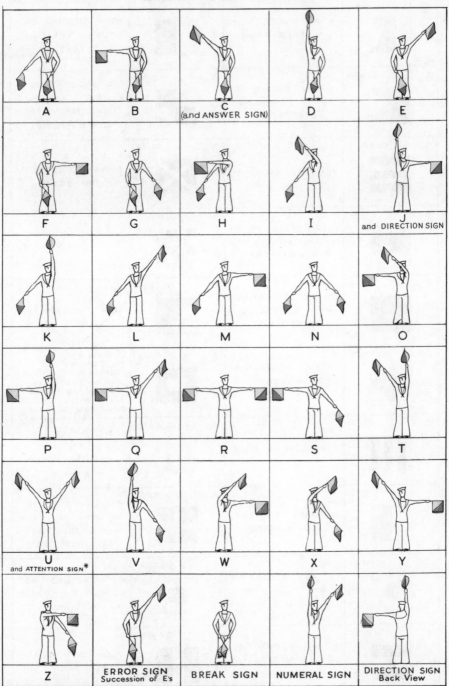

Fig. 238

NAVAL AND INTERNATIONAL CODES ALPHABETICAL FLAGS
The meanings given are those of the International Code only

A ALFA 		I AM UNDERGOING A SPEED TRIAL	**K** KILO 		✳ YOU SHOULD STOP YOUR VESSEL INSTANTLY
B BRAVO 		I AM TAKING IN OR DISCHARGING EXPLOSIVES	**L** LIMA 		✳ YOU SHOULD STOP — I HAVE SOMETHING IMPORTANT TO COMMUNICATE
C CHARLIE 		YES (AFFIRMATIVE)	**M** MIKE 		I HAVE A DOCTOR ON BOARD
D DELTA		KEEP CLEAR OF ME — I AM MANOEUVRING WITH DIFFICULTY	**N** NOVEMBER 		NO (NEGATIVE)
E ECHO 		I AM DIRECTING MY COURSE TO STARBOARD	**O** OSCAR 		✳ MAN OVERBOARD
F FOXTROT 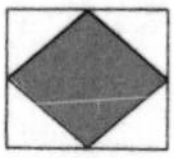		✳ I AM DISABLED — COMMUNICATE WITH ME	**P** PAPA 		IN HARBOUR :- ✳ ALL PERSONS ARE TO REPAIR ON BOARD AS THE VESSEL IS ABOUT TO PROCEED TO SEA. AT SEA :- ✳ YOUR LIGHTS ARE OUT OR BURNING BADLY.
G GOLF 		I REQUIRE A PILOT	**Q** QUEBEC 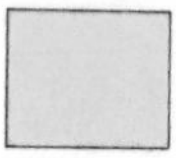		MY VESSEL IS HEALTHY, AND I REQUIRE FREE PRATIQUE
H HOTEL 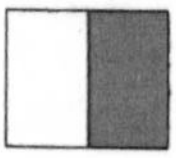		I HAVE A PILOT ON BOARD	**R** ROMEO 		✳ THE WAY IS OFF MY SHIP — YOU MAY FEEL YOUR WAY PAST ME
I INDIA 		I AM DIRECTING MY COURSE TO PORT	**S** SIERRA 		MY ENGINES ARE GOING FULL SPEED ASTERN
J JULIET 		I AM GOING TO SEND A MESSAGE BY SEMAPHORE	**T** TANGO 		DO NOT PASS AHEAD OF ME

NOTE :- (1) ONLY THOSE LETTERS AND MEANINGS MARKED ✳ MAY BE INDICATED BY THE MORSE CODE EITHER BY SOUND OR BY FLASHING
(2) OTHER FLAGS, OF THE NAVAL CODE ONLY, ARE GIVEN IN VOLUME II.

Fig. 239

NAVAL AND INTERNATIONAL CODES (CONTINUED)

ALPHABETICAL FLAGS AND SUBSTITUTES		NUMBERED PENNANTS	
U UNIFORM 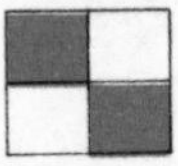 ✳	YOU ARE STANDING INTO DANGER	ONE	 USED ON ALL OCCASIONS WHEN IT IS REQUIRED TO REPRESENT NUMBERS IN FLAG SIGNALLING.
V VICTOR  ✳	I REQUIRE ASSISTANCE	TWO	
W WHISKEY  ✳	I REQUIRE MEDICAL ASSISTANCE	THREE	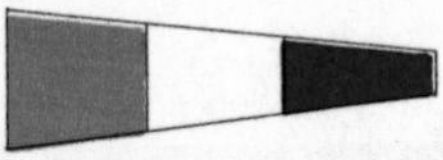
X X-RAY 	STOP CARRYING OUT INTENTIONS AND WATCH FOR MY SIGNALS	FOUR	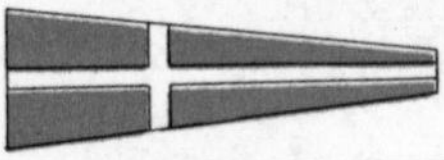
Y YANKEE 	I AM CARRYING MAILS	FIVE	
Z ZULU  ✳	TO BE USED TO ADDRESS OR CALL SHORE STATIONS	SIX	
1ST SUBSTITUTE	 USED TO REPEAT THE FIRST FLAG OR PENNANT IN THE SAME HOIST	SEVEN	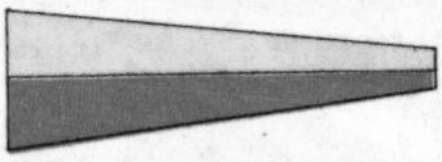
2ND SUBSTITUTE	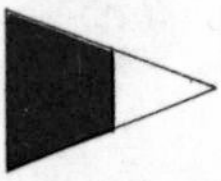 USED TO REPEAT THE SECOND FLAG OR PENNANT IN THE SAME HOIST	EIGHT	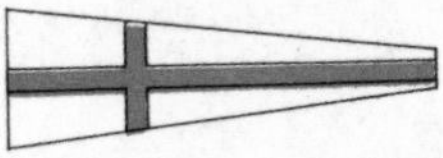
3RD SUBSTITUTE	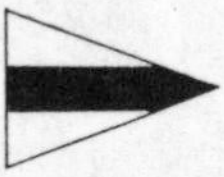 USED TO REPEAT THE THIRD FLAG OR PENNANT IN THE SAME HOIST	NINE	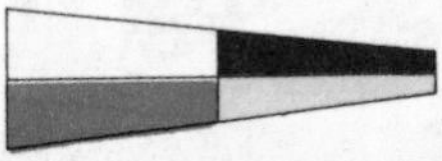
CODE AND ANSWER	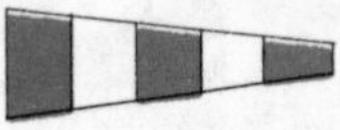 USED TO ACKNOWLEDGE A SIGNAL. ALSO FLOWN BY A WARSHIP WHEN MAKING A FLAG SIGNAL FROM THE INTERNATIONAL CODE TO DISTINGUISH IT FROM THE NAVAL CODE	ZERO	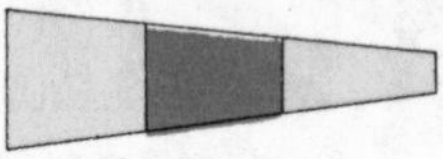

NOTE :- (1) ONLY THOSE LETTERS AND MEANINGS MARKED ✳ MAY BE INDICATED BY THE MORSE CODE. EITHER BY SOUND OR BY FLASHING
(2) OTHER FLAGS, OF THE NAVAL CODE ONLY, ARE GIVEN IN VOLUME II.

Fig. 240

ROYAL STANDARD AND DISTINGUISHING FLAGS

ROYAL STANDARD

GOVERNORS GENERAL
OF COMMONWEALTHS

OTHER GOVERNORS GENERAL,
GOVERNORS AND HIGH COMMISSIONERS
LIEUTENANT GOVERNORS AND OTHER
OFFICERS ADMINISTERING A GOVERNMENT

H.M. DIPLOMATIC SERVANTS
e.g. AMBASSADORS,
MINISTERS PLENIPOTENTIARY,
AND CHARGÉS D' AFFAIRES

CONSULS GENERAL,
CONSULS, AND
CONSULAR AGENTS

ARMY COUNCIL

GENERAL OFFICERS
COMMANDING STATIONS

Fig. 241

ENSIGNS

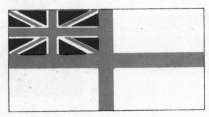

WHITE ENSIGN

SOUTH AFRICAN NAVAL SERVICE

ROYAL FLEET AUXILIARIES

BLUE ENSIGN

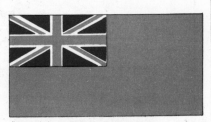

RED ENSIGN

ROYAL AIR FORCE ENSIGN

CIVIL AIR ENSIGN

Fig. 242

DISTINGUISHING AND SPECIAL FLAGS

FLAG OF QUEEN'S HARBOUR MASTER

ENSIGN OF H.M. CUSTOMS

Commandant-General

Lieutenant-or Major-General

Brigadier — General

SENIOR ROYAL MARINE OFFICERS

TRINITY HOUSE ENSIGN

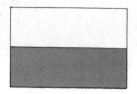

PILOT FLAG

ROYAL MAIL PENDANT

NORTH SEA
FISHERY FLAG

Fig. 243

NATIONAL FLAGS OF THE BRITISH COMMONWEALTHS

UNION FLAG

CANADA

AUSTRALIA

NEW ZEALAND

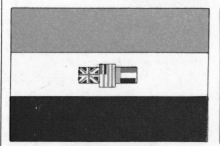

SOUTH AFRICA

INDIA

PAKISTAN

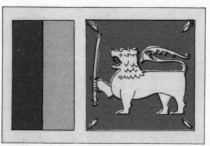

CEYLON

Fig. 244

DISTINGUISHING FLAGS OF THE ROYAL NAVY

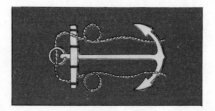

ADMIRALTY FLAG

ADMIRAL'S FLAG

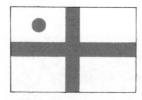

VICE ADMIRAL'S FLAG

REAR ADMIRAL'S FLAG

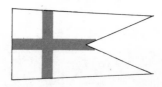

BROAD PENDANT OF COMMODORE 1ST CLASS

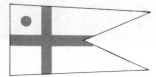

BROAD PENDANT OF COMMODORE 2ND. CLASS

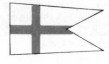

SENIOR OFFICER'S PENDANT

MASTHEAD PENDANT

Fig. 245

CHAPTER XIV

Naval Ceremonial

FLAGS AND THEIR WEARING

Types of Flags

A *Standard* is a flag which depicts the armorial bearings of the person entitled to wear it. The Sovereign and certain members of the Royal Family have personal standards, which are flown to denote their actual presence in any ship or place, whether in residence or on a visit.

Colours is a general term describing any flag which is flown to denote the nationality of a ship, of a body of people, or of a place. Examples of colours are the ensigns and jacks worn by ships, the Union Flag of the United Kingdom and the colours of regiments. Except in the normal course of routine colours are only lowered to denote respect, courtesy, mourning or surrender.

Distinguishing flags are flags of special designs which are authorised by the Sovereign to be worn by individuals to denote their rank, command, office, or authority, and their display is governed by special rules. They are flown only during the period of office of the individual and denote the presence of the person in a ship or place.

The naval authorities authorised to wear distinguishing flags are : the Board of Admiralty, the Naval Boards of the Commonwealth, Flag Officers, and certain Commodores.

Other authorities authorised to wear distinguishing flags include Governors-General, Governors, High Commissioners, Lieutenant-Governors and certain other officers who administer a government, H.M. Diplomatic Servants, the Army and Air Councils, General and Air Officers who command stations, Consuls General, Consuls and Consular Agents.

Signal flags are specially designed in colour and shape to be distinguishable from each other at a distance. They are hoisted, singly or in greater numbers, to indicate orders or messages which are interpreted by means of signal codes.

Special flags or pennants such as the Fishery Flag and the Royal Mail Pennant, may be flown in ships to indicate the duties on which they are engaged.

> *Note : Colours, standards, and distinguishing flags are said to be " worn " by ships and by individuals, and they may also be said to be " flown " in a ship or at a place. Other types of flag are only described as being " flown," never as " worn."*

The Union Flag

The original national flag of England and Wales was the banner of St. George (which is embodied in the White Ensign). By Royal Proclamation dated 12th April, 1606, when the three countries were united under one Sovereign, the banner of St. Andrew, representing Scotland, was united with the banner of St. George. By Royal Proclamation dated 1st January, 1801, the St. Patrick's Cross, representing Ireland, was incorporated with the Union Flag which thus represented the union of the four countries, and from this date the Union Flag has been the national emblem of the United Kingdom. It is always flown with the broader diagonal band of white uppermost in the hoist and the narrower diagonal band of white uppermost in the fly.

The Union Flag is generally flown on shore to indicate the British nationality of a subject or place, or to celebrate an event ; it is also flown at the headquarters of army units, and in certain specific circumstances, *e.g.* at the House of Commons when Parliament is sitting.

Afloat the wearing of the Union Flag on the jackstaff denotes a ship of the Royal Navy, and it is not allowed to be worn by any other ships. When the Sovereign is embarked the Union Flag is also worn at the masthead, together with the Royal Standard and Admiralty Flag. The Union Flag is also worn at the main masthead by an Admiral of the Fleet, and is flown at the peak (or at the yard arm if there is no gaff) to denote that a Court Martial is being held.

Ensigns

Ensigns are colours which are worn chiefly by ships. Naval ensigns are only worn on shore by naval establishments, and by certain marine establishments belonging to public offices, and certain recognised marine societies and yacht clubs, when expressly authorised to do so under warrant issued by the Admiralty. Such authority is issued in respect of the vessel, society or club, and not of the owner, representative, or member of any such vessel, society or club, and therefore no person has the right to wear a naval ensign ashore or anywhere except in the actual vessel or place authorised by the warrant ; neither are naval ensigns allowed to be borne in processions or parades without the express permission of the Admiralty or, if abroad, of the local naval Commander-in-Chief.

The three ensigns authorised to be worn by British ships are the Red, White and Blue Ensigns, and it is both interesting and instructive to trace the origin of the regulations governing their wearing.

Up to and including the Tudor period the national colour for English ships was the St. George's Cross. The Red Ensign as the national colour for British ships other than warships appears to have been introduced about 1700, and thereafter was commonly worn by them.

From early in the 17th century the fleets of the Royal Navy were divided into Red, White and Blue Squadrons, and by the middle of that century the ships of each of these squadrons were distinguished by wearing, respectively, the Red, White and Blue Ensigns.

In 1864 this system was discontinued, and by Acts of Parliament of 1864 and 1865, the White Ensign was authorised to be worn by all ships of the Royal Navy, the Red Ensign by merchant ships, and the Blue Ensign by ships belonging to public offices and by ships of the colonial navies. From that time this general allocation of ensigns has remained in force, but has been altered in detail from time to time by subsequent Acts of Parliament.

The reasons for the choice of this allocation are obscure. In the Royal Navy the seniority of the commanders of the three squadrons was in the order Red, White and Blue. The senior or Red Ensign was probably allotted to the Merchant Navy as it had been their colours since 1700.

The White Ensign was probably allotted to the Royal Navy because it had been the colours under which they sailed in battle since 1800, including the battle of Trafalgar. The reason for wearing the White Ensign in battle in preference to the Red or Blue was to avoid the risk of confusion of the two latter with the French " tricolour." A similar confusion, between the White Ensign and the German Ensign arose in the First World War (1914–1918), and so H.M. ships then sometimes wore as their colours the Union Flag, Blue Ensign or Red Ensign, in addition to the White Ensign.

The White Ensign

All H.M. ships in commission wear the White Ensign. It is worn at the ensign staff when in harbour ; it is also worn at the ensign staff at sea whenever possible, but in bad weather, or when cleared for action, or during war, it is worn at the peak of the gaff on the mainmast, or on a suitable staff mounted in the after part of the ship. In action, ships wear at least two ensigns in a conspicuous position. All shore establishments commanded by a commissioned officer wear a White Ensign at the peak of their flagstaff. It is also flown in H.M. ships on the occasion of their launching.

Vessels of the Royal Yacht Squadron are allowed by Admiralty warrant to wear the White Ensign as their colours, and Trinity House vessels may wear the White Ensign at the masthead when H.M. ships are dressed overall.

Ships of the South African Naval Service wear an ensign which is a dark green cross (shaped like the St. George's Cross) on a white background with the Union National flag in the upper canton next to the hoist.

Ships of the Indian Naval Service wear a white ensign embodying the St. George's Cross, and having the national colour of India in the upper canton next the hoist.

The Blue Ensign

By Admiralty warrant British merchant ships may wear the Blue Ensign, plain and undefaced, if they are commanded by a retired officer of the Royal Navy, or by an officer of any of the Naval Reserves provided that the crew includes a certain number of officers and men of any of the Naval Reserves.

Royal Fleet Auxiliaries and ships under charter to the Admiralty wear a Blue Ensign bearing a yellow anchor in the fly, and ships of certain public offices of the United Kingdom, H.M. Customs and H.M. Post Office for example, wear a Blue Ensign bearing in the fly the badge of their office.

Ships belonging to, or under charter to, the Colonial Governments wear a Blue Ensign bearing in the fly the badge of their colony.

The national flag of the Commonwealth of Australia, and of the Commonwealth of New Zealand, is a Blue Ensign embodying the emblems of their respective Commonwealths.

Vessels of certain approved yacht clubs are allowed by Admiralty warrant to wear a Blue Ensign defaced by the badge of their club. A list of such approved yacht clubs is published in the Navy List.

THE RED ENSIGN

With the exception of H.M. ships and ships allowed by warrant to wear a special ensign, all ships of the United Kingdom wear a Red Ensign plain and undefaced as their colours.

The national flag of the Commonwealth of Canada is a Red Ensign bearing in the fly the shield of the coat of arms of Canada, and, with the exception of H.M. Canadian ships and ships allowed by warrant to wear a special ensign, all Canadian ships wear the national flag of Canada as their colours.

Australian and New Zealand ships (other than H.M. Australian and New Zealand ships and ships allowed to wear a special ensign) wear as their colours a Red Ensign embodying the emblems of their respective Commonwealths.

Vessels of certain yacht clubs of the United Kingdom are authorised by Admiralty warrant to wear a Red Ensign embodying the badge of their club. A list of such yacht clubs appears in the Navy List.

It is emphasised that when an ensign is authorised to be worn by warrant it may be worn only by the vessel named in the warrant, and if the officer holding the warrant is in command at the time.

Jacks

Jack is the name given to the colours worn on a staff at the stem or on the bowsprit by ships or vessels at anchor in a harbour. It is a smaller flag than the corresponding ensign and can be square or rectangular in shape.

For ships of the Royal Navy the jack is the Union Flag.

For ships of the Royal Canadian Navy the jack is a Blue Ensign bearing in the fly the shield of the coat of arms of Canada.

Ships of the Royal Navies of Australia, New Zealand, Pakistan and Ceylon, and ships of the South African and Indian Naval Services, wear their national colours as their jack.

Merchant ships usually fly their " house flag " (see page 258) as their jack.

There is an historical reason for allocating the Union Flag as a jack to ships of the Royal Navy. In the days when a warship and a merchant vessel looked very alike and both wore the same ensign it was essential that the one should be distinguished from the other to prevent any masquerading under false colours for purposes of piracy, unlawful aggression, or improper aggrandisement ; and so the Union Flag was ordered to be worn only by H.M. ships of war.

In later days, though the difference in appearance between warships and merchant ships was more obvious, the need in the interests of both the Royal and Merchant Navies for preventing any attempts at masquerading was as necessary as ever, particularly in the less frequented seas and ports of the world. The wearing of the Union Flag is therefore still reserved exclusively for H.M. ships, although its use is confined to wearing it as a jack, and then in harbour only.

Commissioning or Masthead Pennant

This pennant, which is flown at the main masthead, is hoisted on the day when a warship commissions, and, except when the ship is wearing a Royal Standard or a naval distinguishing flag, it is never struck until the day on which the ship pays off. H.M. ships not in commission do not wear any colours, except that when undergoing trials before acceptance into H.M. Service they fly the Red Ensign.

Certain ships which are authorised by warrant to wear a Blue Ensign may be specially authorised to wear a blue masthead pennant. Such ships are usually those which are commanded by an officer of one of the Royal Naval reserves of the United Kingdom, or of one of its Commonwealths. Otherwise no British ships other than H.M. ships are allowed to wear masthead pennants.

The Queen's Colour

The Queen's Colour is a special White Ensign embodying the Royal Cypher, presented by the Sovereign to the Home ports and to commands afloat or abroad. It is never paraded on board ship or on foreign territory, and is paraded on shore only on the following ceremonial occasions :—

(a) by a guard of honour mounted for the Sovereign or a member of the Royal Family, or for the head of a foreign state ;

(b) at parades held to celebrate the birthday of the Sovereign ;

(c) on important ceremonial occasions abroad as ordered by the Admiralty or by Commanders-in-Chief.

The Queen's Colour is lowered only to royalty or heads of foreign states, or to their representatives.

When the Queen's Colour is carried uncased it is received with the highest marks of respect, *i.e.* with arms presented, officers saluting, and bands playing the National Anthem.

At the discretion of the Commander-in-Chief, or the Senior Naval Officer present, the White Ensign may be paraded abroad on important ceremonial occasions at which the parading of the Queen's Colour is not authorised.

Distinguishing Flags

A distinguishing flag may be worn by a person so entitled to denote his presence in a ship, boat, vehicle, place or establishment.

THE ADMIRALTY FLAG

This was the flag of the Lord High Admiral, but as there is no such person nowadays it is now the flag of the " Commissioners for executing the Office of the Lord High Admiral," known generally as the Board of Admiralty. It is flown day and night over the Admiralty in London, and at the main masthead of the Admiralty yacht when the Board is embarked in her (at least two Lords Commissioners of whom one must be a naval officer, and in addition a secretary, may constitute a " Board "). It is also flown in H.M. ships on the occasion of their launching.

When the Sovereign is embarked the Admiralty Flag is worn at the fore masthead, or in some other suitable position, to denote that the Sovereign is the source from which are derived the powers of the Board of Admiralty. At the same time the Royal Standard is worn at the main masthead, and the Union Flag at the mizzen masthead or other suitable position.

FLAG OFFICERS' FLAG

A Flag Officer is an admiral who is entitled to wear a flag of rank and command by virtue of the nature of his appointment, and his appropriate flag is worn by a ship or shore establishment by day and night throughout the period of his command. When his flag is shifted from one ship to another, or to a shore establishment, it is hoisted to its new position simultaneously with being hauled down from its former position.

COMMODORE'S BROAD PENNANT

When a Commodore is entitled by virtue of his appointment to wear a broad pennant it is worn in the same way as is the flag of a Flag Officer.

SENIOR OFFICER'S PENNANT

If there is more than one commissioned ship in port and no Flag Officer or Commodore is in company, this pennant is hoisted by the senior captain. It is worn at the starboard fore-topsail yard-arm, or the modern equivalent of this position.

Other Special Flags and Pennants

PAYING-OFF PENNANT

Since before the Napoleonic wars it has been the custom for H.M. ships to fly a " paying-off pennant " at the main truck when they leave their fleet to return to their home port to pay off. Custom ordains that the length of the pennant should equal the length of the ship if she leaves her station at the end of a normal period of foreign service. If, however, a commission has been extended, the length of the pennant is increased in proportion to the extra length of service (e.g. for a commission of 2 years extended to 2 years and 2 months the length of the pennant would be the length of the ship plus 1/12th). It is similar to, and flown in place of, the masthead pennant, and is displayed by a ship from a foreign station when entering or leaving harbours during her passage home, and by a ship of the Home Fleet on leaving for and arriving at her home port. It is also the custom on all stations for a ship to fly this pennant on the Sunday preceding her departure, or, if already in her paying-off port, on the Sunday preceding the day on which she pays off.

BLUE PETER

This flag is commonly flown by merchant ships to denote that they are about to sail, and it is the general recall for any passengers or crew who may be out of the ship. If used as the recall by H.M. ships attention is sometimes called to this signal by the firing of a gun.

HOUSE FLAGS

These flags are flown by merchant ships, usually at the main masthead, to denote the ownership of the vessel. Their general use dates from about 1840. They bear the device of the individual or company owning the ship, or to whom the ship is chartered, and they are flown when entering or leaving harbour or on meeting other ships, or as a jack when laying at anchor or alongside.

ROYAL MAIL PENNANT

This is displayed by merchant ships which are under contract to H.M. Post Office and are actually carrying the Royal Mails. It is usually flown at the fore masthead or fore yard-arm when entering or leaving harbour.

Courtesy Flags

It is the custom among many merchant ships when entering a port of foreign nationality and during their stay in that port to fly the colours of that country at the fore masthead, and, when leaving, similarly to fly the colours of the country to which they are immediately bound. Care is taken not to give offence by flying colours which may be exclusively reserved for warships or for special purposes, or by displaying the colours of a country which may be at enmity with the country which the ship is leaving ; for instance, the correct flag for a foreign merchant ship to fly when leaving for, or entering, a British port is the Red Ensign.

Fishery Flag

This flag is worn by H.M. ships engaged in fishery protection duties in the North Sea.

Wearing of Colours

H.M. ships in commission, when at anchor in home ports or roads, hoist their colours (*i.e.* the ensign and jack) at 0800 from 25th March to 20th September inclusive, and at 0900 from 21st September to 24th March inclusive. Abroad colours are hoisted at 0800 or 0900 in accordance with the orders of the Commander-in-Chief of the station. Colours are always lowered at sunset, unless the Senior Officer present directs otherwise.

When one of H.M. ships is at sea or under way in harbour the ensign only is worn ; in war it is worn day and night, but in peace it is worn only when there is sufficient light for it to be seen and may be hauled down when out of sight of land and of other ships. No ceremonial is carried out at the hoisting or lowering of the ensign at sea.

Naval shore establishments wear the ensign only from 0800 or 0900 to sunset.

Ensigns are worn at half mast to indicate a death, usually on the day of the funeral only and from the time the body leaves the ship or place where it has been lying until the time when it is buried.

Boats belonging to H.M. ships or establishments wear ensigns only on certain occasions, which are described in Volume II of this manual.

Hoisting of Colours

When colours are hoisted in harbour, at either 0800 or 0900, a guard and band is paraded 15 minutes before the time of hoisting whenever weather or other circumstances permit. During this period the band plays martial music (a " troop " or a " march ") and the guard is drawn up athwartships, facing the ensign staff. If the ship is in company she takes her time from the Senior Officer's ship, which hoists the " Preparative Flag " five minutes before, and hauls it down at, the appointed time. A signalman, specially detailed for this purpose, then calls out the hour, which is then struck on the ship's bell and immediately followed by the bugler sounding the " Alert," the guard presenting arms, and the band playing the National Anthem. All hands on deck or within sight or sound (except men fallen in, who are called to attention instead) face the ensign and come to the salute on the sounding of the " Alert," and the ensign is then hoisted slowly up the ensign staff so that it is close up as the last note of the National Anthem is played. At the same time the jack is hoisted close up on the jackstaff. After a suitable pause the bugler sounds the " Carry On " and everybody returns from the salute. The guard and band then march off.

During the ceremony, whenever circumstances permit, all work and noise cease. Power boats stop engines, pulling boats toss or lay on their oars, sailing boats let fly sheets, crews come to attention and coxswains salute. The " Carry On " is not sounded until the full ceremony is over, and all hands on deck remain at the salute until the " Carry On " is sounded.

LOWERING OF COLOURS

The full ceremony of lowering the ensign and jack at sunset includes the parading of guards and bands and the beating of the " Tattoo " for 15 minutes before the appointed time, but this is only carried out on special occasions. The normal ceremony is similar to that for hoisting the colours, and the same marks of respect are paid except that guards and bands are not paraded, the signalman calls out " Sunset Sir," at the correct time, and " Sunset " is sounded on the bugle instead of the " General Salute." The Commander-in-Chief may order the sentries of each ship to fire a volley of musketry at the hour of sunset (the origin of this was to ensure that the muskets were in working order).

Dressing Ship and Illuminating Ship

DRESSING SHIP

The flying of flags to celebrate an occasion or an event is one of the oldest customs. At one period our ships on occasions of celebration used to display flags and trophies captured from the enemy. Until 1889, it was left to the junior captain of a fleet or squadron to draw up the order of flags to be worn when ships dressed with flags overall, but now full instructions in regard to dressing ship are laid down in the *VS Equipment Handbook*. Flags and pennants of the signal codes, disposed in as variegated and symmetrical a manner as possible, are used. Except for the masthead ensigns, national flags and ensigns are not included, because the order in which they were flown might possibly give offence.

ILLUMINATING SHIP

This consists of rigging special lighting circuits, with lamps fitted at intervals of a few feet, round the ship at upper and forecastle deck levels, along the water-line, up the masts and in the wake of the dressing lines, so that at night the outline of the ship is picked out by the lamps. Ships are illuminated on special occasions of ceremony or festivity, as ordered by the Senior Officer, and the lighting is usually switched off at midnight unless otherwise ordered.

SALUTES AND MARKS OF RESPECT

Types of Salutes and Marks of Respect

Salutes and marks of respect are accorded in different ways, examples being : the hand salute, blowing of bugles, piping the side, parading of guards and bands, playing of national enthems and other musical salutes, lowering or dipping of colours, and the firing of guns.

The Hand Salute. The hand salute is the personal salute of officers and men.

Salutes by the Bugle

The General Salute is a personal salute paid to rank. It is only sounded when no band is available to play the appropriate anthems or musical salutes.

The Alert sounded on the bugle is a mark of respect paid to the occasion or to rank, and, with certain exceptions, it is only accorded to persons who are specifically entitled to it. When a bugle is not available the " Still " is piped on the boatswain's call, or blown on a whistle instead of sounding the " Alert." The " Alert " is sounded on the following occasions :—

(*a*) at the hoisting and hauling down of colours ;

(*b*) between the times of hoisting the colours and sunset, on the arrival or departure of Royalty, or of certain other persons specifically entitled to it ;

(*c*) between the times of sunrise and sunset, in a warship not under way, when a boat or tender passes which is wearing a standard of Royalty or the flags or emblems of other persons entitled to it ;

(*d*) between the times of sunrise and sunset, when a warship in harbour or in an anchorage is passing or being passed by a flagship or a foreign man-of-war, provided that one of the ships is at anchor.

Note : Whenever the " Alert " is sounded all hands on deck stand to attention and face outboard until the " Carry On " is sounded (except at the hoisting and lowering of colours, when all hands on deck or nearby stand to attention, face the colours and salute, remaining at the salute until the " Carry On " is sounded).

Sunset is the salute sounded when the colours are hauled down at the end of the day.

First Post and *Last Post* originate from the days when the " tattoo " was beaten ashore and afloat at the time of curfew, and sentries were posted for the night. On board H.M. ships nowadays the " First Post " is sounded at 2040 and the " Last Post " at 2100, but if sunset occurs after 2040 neither is usually sounded. The " Last Post " is also sounded at military funerals over the body in its last resting place, as a farewell salute to the deceased.

Gun Salutes

The firing of salutes in honour of a royal or other personage, or of a country, is a very old custom. In gun salutes an odd number of rounds are always fired, the firing of even numbers of rounds in former days being reserved for occasions of mourning. A salute is referred to as, for example, " a salute of 21 guns," or a " 21-gun salute," though nowadays only 3 or 4 guns may actually fire the 21 rounds.

It used to be the custom to fire salutes with the guns shotted, and when news of the declaration of King Charles II reached the Fleet which was then anchored in the Downs, Mr. Pepys recounted that : " The General began to fire his guns, which he did, all that he had in the ship, and so did the rest of the Commanders, which was very gallant, and to hear the bullets go hissing over our heads as we were in the boat ! " The Admiralty prohibition against firing salutes above Gravesend is said to date from an occasion when a shot fired during a salute by a man-of-war lying off Greenwich went unpleasantly close to Greenwich Palace, where Queen Elizabeth was then residing.

11

The interval between the successive rounds in a salute is 5 seconds. Before stop watches were invented the interval was timed by the repetition, by the Gunner, of the couplet " If I wasn't a Gunner I wouldn't be here, number (two, three, etc.) gun, fire ! " spoken deliberately.

Salutes Between Ships

When one warship passes another in harbour they exchange salutes. The nature of the salute depends upon the nationality of the ships, and upon the relative ranks or seniorities of their respective Flag Officers or Captains or any important personages in them ; it may be made by parading guards and bands, sounding the " Alert " on the bugle, or piping the " Still." Warships do not usually exchange salutes at sea.

When a merchant ship passes close to a warship, either at sea or in harbour, she dips her ensign as an act of courtesy and recognition, and the warship acknowledges it also by dipping her ensign. On no other occasion (except when they are half-masted) are the colours of H.M. ships lowered out of routine times. H.M. ships do not dip their ensigns to each other or to foreign warships.

Reception of Officers

When, in H.M. ships, accommodation ladders are rigged on both sides officers of lieutenant's rank and above enter and leave the ship by the starboard gangway, and all other officers use the port gangway. In flagships three accommodation ladders may be rigged, one on each side aft and one amidships ; the starboard after gangway is then reserved for Flag Officers, officers of Captain's rank, and Commanding Officers when flying their pendants.

All officers are saluted by the gangway staff, both on arrival and departure, and the Officer of the Watch salutes all officers of and above his own rank and acknowledges the salutes of his juniors. The rank or status of an officer arriving by boat in daylight hours may be indicated by a flag, pennant, or plate, flown or displayed prominently in the boat ; these should be identified in sufficient time for the necessary marks of respect to be paid to the officer on his arrival.

Piping the Side

Piping the side is a mark of respect, which, in the Royal Navy, is reserved exclusively for the Sovereign, for a member of the Royal Family of the rank of Captain and above when in naval uniform, for Flag Officers, Captains of H.M. ships, and certain other naval officers of the executive branch in naval uniform, and for all foreign naval officers of all branches in uniform.

This mark of respect owes its origin to the days when captains used to visit other ships when at sea. On such occasions the visiting captain was hoisted aboard from his boat in a chair slung on a whip rove from the lower yard arm, to the accompaniment of the pipes of the boatswains as they passed their orders to the men manning the whip.

SOME NAVAL CUSTOMS AND CEREMONIES

Official Visits

On the arrival of one of H.M. ships in a British or foreign port a series of official visits is exchanged between the Flag or Commanding Officer of the ship and the various governmental, naval, military, or civil authorities in the port. The extent of, and rules for, such visits are laid down in the *Queen's Regulations and Admiralty Instructions*, and sometimes they may occupy several days.

Entering Harbour

When one of H.M. ships enters harbour all harbour gear is provided and prepared beforehand ; lower booms are rigged and stowed ready for getting out, accommodation ladders are shipped and prepared for lowering, awnings are provided and prepared for spreading, and boats are prepared for hoisting out ; but such preparations should not mar the shipshape appearance of the ship. All hands remain fallen in at their stations for entering harbour until the last practicable moment, when the " Extend " is sounded on the bugle, or piped. At this order only those hands required for the various evolutions fall out and run to their appropriate stations, to the lower booms, ladders, boats, and awnings, etc. The " G " blown on the bugle, or the " Hoist Away " piped on the boatswain's call, is the executive order for getting out lower booms, lowering accommodation ladders, hoisting out the boats, spreading awnings, etc. The speed and efficiency with which these operations are carried out is an indication of the smartness of the ship concerned. The " G " is sounded as the anchor is let go when coming to single anchor, as the second anchor is let go when mooring, and as the picking-up rope is brought to the capstan when coming to a buoy.

Officer of the Guard

On the arrival in a British port of a foreign man-of-war, a merchantman, or a yacht, it is customary for the Senior Officer to send the Officer of the Guard (as detailed by the Guard Ship) to visit her and offer her the usual courtesies and facilities of the port. On his return the Officer of the Guard writes out a report of the details of his visit.

Man and Cheer Ship

Manning and cheering ship as a collective mark of respect in honour of a person or of another ship is a very old custom. In the days of sail the yards and shrouds were manned as well as the decks, but nowadays only the decks are manned. Some examples of occasions on which this mark of honour is paid are :—visits of the Sovereign to the Fleet ; the entry into port of ships which have shared in a victory ; the final departure of a ship from a foreign station on her way home to pay-off.

Ceremony Ashore

On all ceremonial occasions the Royal Navy, as the senior service of the armed forces of the Crown is accorded the position of honour, *i.e.* on the right of the line in review order, and in the van in marching order. The naval marches are " Heart of Oak " for the march past, and " Nancy Lee " for the advance in review order.

Badges, Trophies

The badge of the Royal Navy is the naval crown, which consists of a circlet surmounted by the sterns of four men-of-war, each with three poop lanterns, and four square sails each spread on a mast and yard and fully filled and sheeted home ; the ships and sails being positioned alternately. This badge or the Royal Crown is often displayed on the trucks of the ensign and jack staffs.

Each ship has her own badge or crest, with a motto, which is allotted to her on commissioning, by permission of the Board of Admiralty, from the College of Heralds. This badge is displayed prominently on board and also on the bows of her boats.

Ships display their " battle honours," and those of their predecessors of the same name, in some prominent position on board.

Any trophies of war, presentation cups or plate, etc., belonging to the ship and her predecessors are displayed between decks. All such trophies ·or presentation plate are the property of the ship and are recorded in the Ship's Book. Whenever a ship is paid off or broken up the trophies are returned to the manning port of the ship, where they are kept until the ship re-commissions or a new ship of the same name is commissioned. In war the trophies may be landed for safe custody.

The ship's bell always bears the name of the ship and the date of her launching. Unless it is damaged the bell remains with the ship until she is sold or broken up, when it is either presented to some public body, or offered for sale, preference being given to anyone who served in her.

Launching Ceremony

The custom of breaking a bottle of wine over the stem of a ship when being launched originates from the old practice of toasting prosperity to the ship in a silver goblet of wine, which was then cast into the sea in order to prevent a toast of ill intent being drunk from the same cup. This practice proved too expensive and so was replaced in 1690 by the breaking of a bottle of wine over the stem. Another old custom which is still observed, is to pray for Divine blessing on the ship and her company throughout her life.

Until 1811 the ceremony for H.M. ships was always performed by a Royal Personage or a Royal Dockyard Commissioner, but in that year the Prince Regent introduced the custom of allowing ladies to perform it. It is interesting to note that on one subsequent occasion a certain lady missed her aim with the bottle, which struck and injured a spectator who sued the Admiralty for damages, and this resulted in the Admiralty directing that in future the bottle should be secured to the ship by a lanyard.

Traditional Customs

New Year's Day. It is the custom for the youngest member of the ship's company (officer, man or boy) to " ring out the Old Year and ring in the New " by striking 16 bells at midnight on New Year's Eve.

Splicing the Main Brace. The order " Splice the main brace " may be given by the Sovereign, or by members of the Royal Family on occasions of inspections of, or visits to, H.M. ships or establishments ; or it may be ordered by the Admiralty on special occasions of celebration or national rejoicing.

This order authorises the issue of a tot of rum to all officers over the age of 20, and an extra tot to all men over the age of 20, with which to toast the Sovereign and the occasion. Those who prefer it, and all who are under 20 years of age, may be issued instead with a ration of lemonade. The term " splicing the main brace," which was well known in 1756, appears to owe its origin to the custom of issuing an extra ration of spirit on occasions of particularly arduous service or exposure, such as might be experienced in the days of sail when repairing or replacing the main brace, which was a very important and heavy part of the running rigging.

Crossing the Line. The unofficial ceremonies of " initiating novices into the brotherhood of the seas and as subjects of His Oceanic Majesty, King Neptune," are held in many ships when circumstances allow as they cross the equator. The ship is usually placed out of routine for the day and officers and men share impartially in the proceedings, which are made the occasion for much good-natured skylarking.

Garlands. When a member of the crew of a ship is married in the port in which the ship is lying it is the custom to hoist a garland of evergreens between the masts on the day of the ceremony.

It is also the custom to decorate the trucks and yard arms with sprigs of holly on Christmas Day.

Whistling. Whistling is prohibited in H.M. ships because the noise is apt to be confused with the piping of orders. It is usually anything but sweet, except in the ears of the perpetrator, and is more often than not a cause of annoyance to his messmates.

Acknowledgment of Orders. The seaman acknowledges an order with the words " Ay Ay, Sir ! " and should then immediately carry it out.

APPENDIX

Questions

The questions in this appendix are intended only to give the candidate for examination a guide to the type of question which he may be asked and a general idea of the knowledge which he is expected to possess ; they are not intended for use as standard or stock questions for examinations. Reference to the text of the relevant chapter will enable the reader to answer every question correctly.

The extent of knowledge required by a candidate in any particular subject will be found in the syllabus for the examination which he is taking ; the syllabuses for all examinations in seamanship held in the Royal Navy are published from time to time in B.R. 1066, *Advancement Regulations*.

CHAPTER I

GENERAL SEA TERMS

1. A ship has two masts, a funnel and a bridge. The funnel is abaft the bridge, but before the after (or main) mast. A man is standing abreast the bridge and looking aft at a boat which is stowed amidships and to starboard between the mainmast and the funnel. Draw a plan of the ship and indicate the positions of these objects.

2. Two ships are steaming abreast of each other. The starboard-hand ship has a lighthouse abeam to starboard of her, while the other has a sailing vessel on her port quarter. Sketch the relative positions of the steam ships, sailing vessel and lighthouse.

3. A ship is steaming on a course of 045 degrees. A lighthouse bears 090 degrees from her. Sketch the relative position of the ship to the lighthouse, and indicate the direction of north.

4. A ship is sighted on a relative bearing of green 70, and a lighthouse bears red 140. Sketch the relative position of the ship to the lighthouse.

5. What points of the compass are opposite to north-east and south-east ?

6. Define the following terms :—lift and launch ; under way ; adrift ; sternway ; ship's head ; weather deck ; lee side ; to fleet.

7. The inclination of a ship on the port quarter is 20 degrees Right. Sketch the relative position and course of each ship to the other.

8. Make a sectional sketch of a ship showing her forecastle, and her upper, main, lower and platform decks.

9. Draw a plan of a ship indicating the positions of her waist, forecastle, quarter deck and boom-boats.

10. Define the terms freeboard, camber, tumble home, sheer line, draught, bilge, chine, and flare.

11. What is the object of the " Plimsoll mark " and " load lines " ?
12. What is the difference between displacement and gross tonnage ?
13. What are the differences between a camber, a dry dock, and a basin ?
14. What are the purposes of a lock, a caisson, a patent slip, and a slipway ?
15. What are a trot, hard, warp, lighter, brow, and pontoon ?
16. How many feet are there in a fathom, and how many yards in a nautical mile ?

CHAPTER II

TYPES OF SHIP

1. What is the distinction between the terms type of ship and class of ship ?
2. Name the various types of warship.
3. Name the various types of merchant ship.
4. What are the main functions of each type of warship ?
5. What are the main functions of each type of merchant vessel ?
6. Do you know the meaning of all the terms explained in this chapter ?
7. Sketch as many rigs of sailing craft as you can remember.

CHAPTER III

DESIGN AND CONSTRUCTION OF WARSHIPS

1. Give the seaman's equivalent for the following civilian terms :—room, ceiling, floor, trap-door, outside wall, inside wall, roof, stairs, up-stairs, down-stairs, cellar, window, ground floor, second floor, third floor, steps, entrance, front door, cupboard, rubbish, dust-bin, table-ware, kitchen, clothing, corridor, bannisters, railings.
2. How are a hatch, a door, and a scuttle made water-tight ?
3. What are a manhole, a dead-light, and a wind-scoop ?
4. What is a remotely controlled valve, and why should it not be used as a clothes peg ?
5. What general precautions are necessary in regard to electrical equipment ?
6. Why should equipment such as electric irons and portable electric drills be repaired only by men of the Electrical Branch ?
7. How may wireless aerials and radar aerials endanger life ?
8. What precaution should you take with regard to wireless and radar before you go aloft ?

9. Make a rough sketch of the longitudinal section of a warship and indicate on it the following :—engine-room, boiler-rooms, magazines and shell-rooms, store-rooms, and living spaces.

10. What is the object of water-tight subdivision in a ship ? Are the decks water-tight ?

11. How is a compartment ventilated ? Why should the forced ventilation system not be tampered with by unauthorised persons ?

12. What is the difference between main machinery and auxiliary machinery ?

13. Why is it necessary to economise in the use of fresh water in a ship ?

14. What is a fire-main ?

15. What are the following : round down, pallisade, safety net, arrester wire, and safety barrier ?

16. What are the following : bilge, strake, butt, and seam ?

17. Describe the following : frame, longitudinal, double bottoms, and main structural bulkhead.

18. What are the functions of beams, and pillars ?

19. What are the following : scuppers, gunwale, flat, stringer, bulwarks, and knees ?

CHAPTER IV

ROUTINE, PASSING ORDERS, AND ORGANISATION

1. What times of the day are indicated by striking " five bells " ?

2. What does the term " silent hours " mean ?

3. What is " little one bell " ?

4. For what purposes, other than marking the time, is the ship's bell used ?

5. What is the " guard and steerage " ?

6. How would you call away (a) the barge, and (b) the first motor boat ?

7. Pipe the following :—" Still," " Hands to dinner," " Hoist away," " Pipe down," " Up spirits."

8. Which pipes require no verbal amplifications ?

9. How are the hands called in the morning ?

10. When is the expression " D'ye hear there ! " used in piping ?

11. When does a bugle call require amplification by pipe ?

12. Recite the phonetic alphabet and numerals.

13. What are the general responsibilities of the Executive Officer of a ship ?

14. What is the Executive Officer of a destroyer called ?

15. What is a department in a ship ?

16. Why is a ship's company organised in watches ?

17. What is the difference between the two-watch system and the three-watch system ?

18. Into how many parts is a watch divided and sub-divided ?
19. What is a " part-of-ship ? " Of how many watches is it composed ?
20. What abbreviations are used for forecastle, foretop, maintop and quarter-deck ?
21. What is a division ? What is the main principle of the divisional system?

CHAPTER V

ROPE AND ITS USAGE

1. What are fibres, yarns and strands ? Describe how they form a rope.
2. How does a fibre rope hold together under stress ?
3. What is the lay of a rope and how does it effect the rope's elasticity and strength ?
4. What is the difference between hawser-laid and cable-laid rope ?
5. What are the general characteristics of cordage ?
6. From what materials is cordage made, and how can the different types be distinguished at a glance ?
7. Why should not a neck lanyard be formed with a running Turk's head ?
8. Demonstrate a common whipping on a rope's end.
9. With what, other than a whipping, can a rope's end be finished ?
10. What is the difference between a soft eye, a bollard eye, a thimble eye, and a hawser eye ?
11. Why in the Royal Navy is a rope coiled down right-handed ?
12. Why must the end of a rope be free when coiling it down ?
13. What detail must be observed when coiling down a rope for running ?
14. Describe " thorough-footing." What is a cow-hitch ? What is meant by under-running a rope ?
15. When coiling a rope in the hand, which way should the thumb point ?
16. Describe what is meant by flaking, and by cheesing down.
17. Demonstrate the methods of belaying to a cleat and to a staghorn. Why is it necessary for the first belaying turns to be taken correctly ? How are a small coil and a large coil stowed on a belaying pin or cleat ?
18. What is the most important rule for the care and maintenance of cordage ?
19. How is the size of cordage measured ?
20. What is the rough rule for finding the breaking stress and working load of a fibre rope ?
21. Describe the method of opening up a new coil of fibre rope.
22. How would you cut a length off a 6-inch manila rope ?
23. Describe the construction of wire rope.
24. What is the purpose of the hemp heart ?
25. How is wire rope made flexible ?

11*

26. Describe the difference in construction between S.W.R., F.S.W.R., and E.S.F.S.W.R.

27. How is the size of wire rope expressed ?

28. How are the different types of wire ropes described ?

29. What is the rough rule for finding the breaking stress of a wire rope ?

30. How do you find the working load for wire rope ?

31. What are the main differences between fibre and wire ropes ?

32. How is a kink removed from a wire rope ?

33. What is a " bad nip " ? How is wire rope crippled ? How are kinks avoided when coiling wire rope ?

34. How is a wire rope run out from a coil ? Why should not wire rope be run out from the top of a coil ? What is a " Frenchman " ?

35. Describe the methods of opening up a new coil of wire rope.

36. How is wire rope cut ?

37. Demonstrate the use of " bulldog grips " ; can they be used for joining two wire ropes together ?

38. Make the following knots, bends, and hitches blindfold :—reef knot, clove hitch, round turn and two half hitches, fisherman's bend, double sheet bend, buntline hitch, double Blackwall hitch, bowline, catspaw.

39. State what knots, bends, or hitches you would use for the following purposes and demonstrate each example named :—lashing up a sail or awning ; slinging a bale ; hoisting or towing a spar ; hitching a rope to a guard rail or a spar ; bending a fibre hawser to the ring of an anchor ; making fast a boat's painter to a ringbolt ; making fast a boat's painter to a lizard ; hitching a boat's lazy painter to a Jacob's ladder ; bending a sheet to a sail ; bending a rope to a cringle ; lowering a man over the side ; and bending two fibre hawsers together, (a) which will not be passed round a capstan, and (b) which will be passed round a capstan.

40. Does a knot in a rope reduce its strength ? If so, by how much ?

41. How are wire hawsers joined together ?

42. How can a rope be shortened ?

43. How is the bight of a rope secured to a hook ?

44. What is a mousing ?

45. How are slip knots made ?

46. How is the eye of a rope secured to a spar ?

47. What is parbuckling ?

48. How is a tail jigger clapped on to a fibre rope

49. How is a chain tail secured to a wire rope ?

50. How can the strain be taken off the hauling part of a fall ?

51. What is meant by " choking the luff," and what is its disadvantage ?

52. How are two spars cross-lashed ?

53. What are the following and how is each used ? Selvagee strop ; butt sling ; can hooks.

54. What is the chief point to remember about the use of slings ?

55. How is the tension in the legs of a sling increased or reduced ?

56. What is a span, and how is the tension in a span increased or reduced ?

57. What other whippings are there besides the common whipping, and where would they be used ?

58. How are a wall knot and a crown knot made, and what purposes do they serve ?

59. What are the purposes of a short splice, a long splice, a back splice and an eye splice ?

60. Does a splice reduce the strength of a rope, and if so by how much ?

61. Demonstrate your ability to make a short splice, an eye splice, and a back splice.

62. What is meant by the following orders and terms ? " Avast ! ", " Marry ! ", " Handsomely ! ", " Roundly ! ", " Light to ! ", to snub, to surge, to render, to fleet.

CHAPTER VI

RIGGING

1. What are the differences between the following shackles ? A straight shackle, a bow shackle, a screw shackle, a keyed shackle, and a clenched shackle.

2. Name the parts of a shackle.

3. Describe the different types of thimbles.

4. Name the parts of a hook. Which is the stronger, size for size, a hook or a shackle ?

5. For what are the following hooks used ? A cargo hook, a ram's-horn hook, and a trip hook.

6. In what ways can a hook be moused ?

7. Describe the following :—eye-plate, eye-bolt, deck clench, ring-bolt and union plate.

8. What different types of rigging screw are provided in the Royal Navy ? What is a rigging slip ?

9. Name the parts of a block.

10. How is the size of a wooden block measured ? What size of ordinary wooden block would be required for a $2\frac{1}{2}$-inch rope ?

11. What is the relation between the size of a metal block and the rope it is designed to take. How can you tell the size of a metal block ?

12. What is the difference between an I.B. block, a gin block, a common block, and a fiddle block ?

13. What is a clump block and what is a snatch block ? What are the strengths of these blocks in comparison with an I.B. block ?

14. What different means of attachment are fitted to blocks? What is the jaw of a block?

15. How is a block described?

16. Name the parts of a tackle?

17. What is meant by the terms " mechanical advantage " and " velocity ratio " when applied to a tackle?

18. What is meant by the terms " reeving to advantage " and " reeving to disadvantage " ?

19. When hoisting a given weight how can the load on the standing block be reduced?

20. Describe the following whips and tackles and state the mechanical advantage of each :—double whip ; guntackle rove to advantage ; luff rove to disadvantage ; jigger ; handy billy ; two two-fold purchases, each rove to advantage and rigged luff upon luff.

21. Describe a Dutchman's purchase. When is it used?

22. What is the practical rule for finding the loss in the mechanical advantage of a tackle due to friction? What is the loss due to friction in a two-fold tackle when used to hoist a weight of 1,000 lb. ?

23. Name the parts of a mast.

24. What are the following? Tabernacle, mast-coat, mast partners, stayband, truck, trunnion hoop, spur, Samson post, and trestle-trees.

25. Describe how a topmast is fitted. What are the terms used for lowering a topmast (a) for a short distance, and (b) down to the deck?

26. What are the advantages of a tripod mast and a lattice mast over a polemast?

27. Describe how a merchant ship's lowermast and topmast are stayed.

28. What are the following? Sheerpole, gaiters, and ratlines.

29. What are the following? Hammock gantlines, dressing lines, and Inglefield clips. What is the name of the dressing line which is rigged between the masts?

30. Name the parts of a yard.

31. Describe how a slung yard is rigged.

32. Describe how a standing gaff is rigged.

33. Describe how a screen derrick is fitted and rigged.

34. Is any mechanical advantage gained by a winch? What is the purpose of the pawl and ratchet on a winch?

35. What is a warping drum? How would you use a warping drum?

36. With what boat-booms is a large warship equipped? Describe how a lower boom is fitted and rigged.

37. When is a boat-rope rove, and what is its use? How is it rigged?

CHAPTER VII

SHIPS' BOATS

1. What different methods do you know of propelling a rowing boat? Why are rowing boats called pulling boats in the Royal Navy?

2. How are different types of sailing boat described?

3. What are the two main classes of power boats?

4. Name and describe the different methods of boat construction in general use. What materials are used in boat building?

5. Where, in a boat, are the following situated and what is the purpose of each? Backboard, benches, breast hook, dickie, floor, gudgeon and pintle, hog, keelson board, knee, rubber, stringer, strongback, tabernacle, timber, transom, and wash strake.

6. Where in a boat are the eyes, head sheets, and stern sheets?

7. What is the purpose of each of the following items of a boat's fittings or equipment? Barricoe, horse, lazy painter, running hook, steadying span, sling plate, and stern fast.

8. To what fittings are a boat's slings attached?

9. Before taking away a pulling boat what items of her equipment would you see were in place?

10. What are the contents of a boat's bag, a carpenter's bag, and a boat's distress signal box?

11. What do the following pulling orders mean? " Lay on your oars," " Back port," " Easy starboard," " Stroke together," " Way enough," " Eyes in the boat."

12. Describe the drill in a whaler for getting under way and returning alongside.

13. When going alongside in a cutter how is the order " Way enough " obeyed? On what occasion are a cutter's oars boated without first being tossed?

14. Name the parts of a whaler's mainsail, foresail and mizzen.

15. What are the following? Boltrope, sheet, earring, headsail. What is the difference between a lug sail and a gaff sail?

16. What is the name of the sail set between a gaff and the masthead? What are stormsails?

17. Give an example of a trysail and of a staysail. What is the difference between a foresail and a jib? What is a headsail?

18. What, respectively, are the terms for putting a reef in a sail and taking a reef out of a sail?

19. How is a mast stayed? What is the difference between standing rigging and running rigging?

20. State as many as you can remember of the elementary rules for sailing.

CHAPTER VIII

ANCHORS AND CABLES

1. What are the three principal methods by which a ship can be secured with ground tackle to the bottom ? What are the advantages or disadvantages ot each ?
2. What are the following ? Bridle, buoy pendant, and buoy securing shackle.
3. Name the parts of an anchor.
4. Describe how an anchor holds. Why should the pull on an anchor be horizontal ?
5. With what anchors is a large warship equipped ? Describe the general purposes for which each is used.
6. Sketch roughly the anchor and cable arrangements of a destroyer.
7. For what are the following used : Cable holder, navel pipe, cable locker, capstan, Blake slip, screw slip, riding slip, bonnet, clump cathead, Scotchman, bullring, compressor, windlass, and gypsy.
8. How are the ends of a ship's bower cable attached (a) to the anchor, and (b) to the ship ?
9. How are the capstan and cable holders driven ?

CHAPTER IX

THE MARINER'S COMPASS

1. What are the three methods of graduating a compass card ?
2. What are a cardinal point, a half-cardinal point, and a three-letter point ?
3. Box the compass, omitting the by-points.
4. What are the angular equivalents in degrees of 2 points, 4 points, 6 points, and 8 points ?
5. If an object is said to lie two points before the beam, what is its bearing in degrees relative to the ship's head ?
6. Define the following directions :—ship's head, course, track, and bearing.
7. What is the chief difference between a magnetic and a gyro compass, and in what direction does each point ?
8. What is the lubber's line, and to what does it point ?
9. What is a relative bearing ring, and what is its use ?
10. What is an azimuth circle, and what is its use ?
11. What are gimbals, and what is their purpose ?
12. What precautions are necessary when using a magnetic compass ?

CHAPTER X

CONNING AND STEERING

1. Describe how conning orders are given, repeated and obeyed when the Officer of the Watch or Navigating Officer is conning the ship.

2. What is the difference between a conning and a steering position ?

3. What are the normal limits of the rudder angle ?

4. What care is needed when putting on or taking off wheel ?

5. What is the purpose of the wheel indicator ?

6. What is the meaning of the following orders or reports : " Starboard fifteen " ; " Ship's head " ; " Midships " ; " Steady " ; and " Course."

7. The course ordered is 270 degrees and the ship's head is pointing 268 degrees, which way do you put the wheel to bring the ship back to her proper course ?

8. What is meant by the expression " making good the course " ?

9. What is meant by the term " carrying rudder " ?

10. What information does a helmsman turn over to his relief ?

11. What is the purpose of the combined engine telegraph and revolution transmitter ?

12. What is the correct repeat and report for the engine order " Stop port and centre " ?

13. What is the purpose of the reply gongs ? For a two-shafted warship how many reply gongs are provided at the primary steering position ?

CHAPTER XI

SOUNDING BY LEAD AND LINE

1. What is the difference between a boat's lead and line and a hand lead and line ?

2. Of what is the lead-line made ?

3. What are the markings of a hand lead-line ?

4. How is a hand lead-line made up, marked, and fitted ?

5. What is meant by the term " arming the lead," and what is its purpose ?

6. What is the difference between " marks " and " deeps " ?

7. How would you call the following soundings :—11 fathoms, 17 fathoms, $5\frac{1}{2}$ fathoms, $8\frac{3}{4}$ fathoms ?

8. How can you distinguish the marks in the dark ?

9. What is meant by the term " drift " ?

10. What do you call if you cannot obtain a sounding ?

11. When the ship is under way but not making way, how do you tell whether she is drifting ?

12. What precautions does a leadsman take before entering the chains ?

13. What is meant by the term " benefit of the lead " ?

CHAPTER XII

CHARTS, BUOYAGE AND LIGHTS

1. What is the " chart datum " of a chart ? To what level of the sea are the depths shown on a chart related ?

2. What depth is recorded by a sounding ?

3. How is a depth recorded on a chart ?

4. If a bank or a rock is uncovered at low water how is it indicated on a chart ? Explain this indication.

5. If the height of a rock or a lighthouse is shown on a chart, what does the height indicate ?

6. Why is it important to know the nature of the bottom ? How is this indicated on a chart ? Give some examples.

7. What constitutes " good holding ground " ?

8. On a chart, from what level are the indicated heights of features on land calculated ?

9. On what sides are the starboard and port hands of a channel ?

10. Which sides of a channel are indicated by starboard and port hand buoys ?

11. If no land is visible how would you tell on which side to pass a port-hand buoy ?

12. When leaving harbour on which side do you pass a starboard-hand buoy ?

13. What is the purpose of a middle-ground buoy ? Sketch the various types of middle-ground buoys with their topmarks.

14. What is the purpose of a mid-channel buoy ? On which hand should it be left ? Sketch one.

15. What is the purpose of a landfall buoy ? Sketch one.

16. How are wrecks marked, and how is the side indicated on which they may be passed ?

17. Name four other types of buoys or landmarks.

18. What is meant by the " characteristic " of a light ?

19. Describe, with the aid of sketches, the four main light characteristics.

20. Describe with the aid of sketches the following lights :—F. Fl. ; Gp. Fl. (3) ; F. R.; Fl. R. and G. ; Gp. Occ. (2) ; and Int. Qk. Fl.

21. What does the symbol (U) indicate ?

22. Where are details to be found of lighthouses, lightships, wreck-marking vessels, and buoys ?

CHAPTER XIII

NAVAL COMMUNICATIONS

1. What was the name of Nelson's signal officer ?
2. What is the origin of the name " Telegraph Hill " ?
3. Name the various communication systems used in the Royal Navy.
4. What do the following abbreviations mean ? LT, TP, W/T, PG.
5. What methods of signalling are included under the term " visual signalling " ?
6. What is " sound signalling " ?
7. What is a " hand message," and where is it usually delivered ?
8. What is the difference between the terms " precedence " and " security " ?
9. Name the various precedence and security classifications.
10. What groups of flags and pennants are used in Naval signalling ?
11. Of what may a flag signal consist ?
12. Describe the colours and shapes of the following alphabetical flags :— R, O, Y, A, L, N, A, V, and Y. What is the name given to each of these letters ?
13. Describe the colours of the following numbered pennants :—3, θ, 7, and 5.
14. What is the colour and shape of the " Third Substitute " ?
15. Write your name and number, and below each letter and figure mark the equivalent symbol of the Morse code.
16. What are the Morse code symbols for the following special signs ? All Ship Call, Long Break, Ending, and Receipt.
17. When are the following signs used :—

    $\bullet\ \bullet\ \text{—}\ \text{—}\ \bullet\ \bullet\ \ ,\ \ \text{—}\ \bullet\ \bullet\ \text{—}\ \ ,\ \ \bullet\ \text{—}\ \bullet\ \text{—}\ \bullet\ \text{—}\ ?$

18. How is a period written in plain language ?
19. Make the following letters and numerals by the Semaphore code :— S, E, A, M, A, N, S, H, I, P, 5, 2, 9, 6.
20. How can you tell which way the sender of a Semaphore signal is facing ?

CHAPTER XIV

NAVAL CEREMONIAL

1. What general distinctions are there between standards, colours, distinguishing flags and signal flags ?
2. What constitutes a " suit of colours " of one of H.M. ships in commission ?
3. When and by whom is the Union Flag worn afloat ?
4. Which ships wear the White Ensign, and which wear the Blue, and the Red Ensigns ?

5. When is the Jack worn by H.M. ships ?

6. When do H.M. ships wear a masthead pennant ?

7. What is the Queen's Colour ?

8. What distinguishing flag is worn by (*a*) a Vice-Admiral ? and (*b*) a Commodore, 2nd Class ?

9. For what purpose are the following flags flown ? Paying-off pennant, house flag, courtesy flag.

10. Between what times are colours worn by H.M. ships in harbour ?

11. Describe the ceremonies attending the hoisting and lowering of colours in harbour.

12. When is the ensign worn at sea ?

13. When are ensigns half-masted ?

14. What is meant by (*a*) dressing ship, and (*b*) illuminating ship ?

15. What are the following, and in what circumstances are they used ? " Alert," " Still," " Last Post," " Sunset."

16. Is the number of rounds fired in a gun salute odd or even ? Give the reason for your answer.

17. How does one warship salute another ?

18. In what manner may a merchant ship salute a warship ? How does the warship return this salute ?

19. If a warship has an accommodation ladder rigged on each side, by which ladder should a midshipman go aboard ?

20. Who should be piped over the side ?

21. State what you know about the following customs :—" manning and cheering ship," " splicing the main brace," " sounding the hour of midnight on New Year's Eve."

22. Why is whistling discouraged on board a warship ?

INDEX

Printed in Great Britain under the authority of Her Majesty's Stationery Office by
McCorquodale, London, S.E.1

Wt. 4579   K 200   S.O. Code No. 20–87–1–57*